MAN AND HIS PHYSICAL UNIVERSE

An Integrated Course
in Physical Science

MAN AND HIS

An Integrated

Drawings by RUDOLPH E. FINK

RICHARD WISTAR

Associate Professor of Chemistry, Mills College

PHYSICAL UNIVERSE

Course in Physical Science

New York: JOHN WILEY & SONS, INC.

London: CHAPMAN & HALL, LTD.

Library of Congress Catalog Card Number: 53–6321

PRINTED IN THE UNITED STATES OF AMERICA

Preface

Courses in general physical science are planned and taught from many different points of view. The usual practice is to present a digested or condensed version of the four principal physical sciences: astronomy, geology, physics, and chemistry. Many writers put special emphasis on such recent scientific advances as plastics, vitamins, radar, and atomic energy. The writer of this book has found that it is difficult enough to present in one full year the material which is usually considered the minimum basic background for any one of the physical sciences. As a result of this experience, he has attempted an approach which differs from the usual one in several important respects.

Many recent articles about courses in general physical science emphasize the point that these courses present a unique opportunity because they are terminal courses. There is no need to build up an elaborate vocabulary in any science. Such a vocabulary is essential for further work in that subject, but the student who does not continue to use it forgets it in a matter of days, after the final examination. The time saved here can be spent profitably in telling the student more about how each subject has been affected by contemporary forces, how the scientists went about solving their problems, and how the abstract developments have been applied to present-day problems. In this type of course, science can come to life.

Few of the students who take courses in general physical science will earn their living as practicing scientists, but all of them will be citizens in a world where scientific problems are constantly confronting the general public. As this is being written, the outstanding example of such a problem is the question of our national policy toward atomic energy. On a different level, but no less real, are the questions of local water supply and sanitation, soil conservation, air pollution, modern techniques of house construction, etc. This book does not attempt to give

v

the answers to these problems, but it does show how scientists have solved problems, and it shows that an objective search for facts can be more fruitful than an emotional approach, or one that seeks to vindicate preconceived ideas. It shows that science, in order to grow, must have stimulation from many directions.

With the realization that the four physical sciences cannot be treated adequately as such, a new basis for organization had to be found. The central problems around which this book is organized are those which are important in the fields of the physical sciences and, at the same time, are related to experiences of continuing interest to the student. There is a twofold purpose in this plan. In the first place, the student's life after he leaves college will be richer for his having gained more understanding of what goes on around him; in the second place, he will probably retain more of any subject that he learns around a framework of everyday experience. The subjects are treated broadly. There are many gaps in the field, but the teacher must remember that if he does his job well the student will not stop learning when classes are over. Those subjects which have been picked for treatment have been presented carefully and rigorously.

The usual order of treatment is to begin with facts of everyday experience, then to go on to facts which can be presented by demonstration, then to present additional factual material in the text, and, from all this, to develop the models and theories which are currently accepted as the best representations of the nature of the physical world. To the extent that it is possible, the functioning of modern scientific developments is explained in terms of these models and theories. Problems are put in their historical and cultural setting.

There has been no attempt to segregate the subject matter of the different branches of physical science. Chemistry and physics are scattered throughout all the units. Astronomy is mostly confined to the unit on the solar system, and geology to the unit on the geological history of the earth. Photography and weather forecasting, treated broadly, serve to introduce many important scientific subjects. There are many small problems, rather than one central one, covered in the unit on electricity and magnetism, and the subject of atomic structure draws on a wide background.

In one of the several book reports required each year from my students I found the following comment: "This book is written a great deal in the manner of a textbook. It is completely factual with little attempt to bring out any great interest." It is my earnest hope that such a criticism will not be applied to this book. A textbook for physical science should be interesting and exciting. It is also hoped that those students who read this book will gain a new respect for scientists and their contributions to our civilization, and that they will have a developing interest in and understanding of science as they go through life.

RICHARD WISTAR

Oakland, California
March, 1953

Contents

Unit 3 ▶ THE STORY OF THE EARTH

Unit 4 ▶ FORECASTING THE WEATHER

Unit 5 ▶ ELECTRICITY AND MAGNETISM

Unit 6 ▶ ATOMIC STRUCTURE

Unit 1
▼
PHOTOGRAPHY

The Camera and Lens Action

1. THE CAMERA

When you take a good snapshot with your camera you have made use of many important scientific principles. We are going to study these principles carefully, and when we have finished, you will be taking better pictures and you will have a more thorough understanding of light, color, and sound.

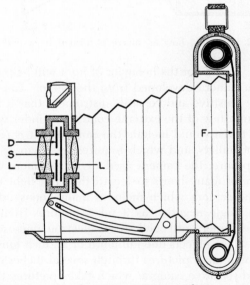

Figure 1-1. Cutaway view of a camera. Between the two compound lenses, L and L, are the diaphragm, D, and the shutter, S.

From the cutaway view of a simple camera (Figure 1-1) you can see the working parts, which consist of the light stop D, the lens L, the shutter S, and the film F. When you are changing the film in your camera next time, take the back off and hold the camera up to the light. Experiment with changing the exposure time and the f opening. Contrast the ordinary camera with an even simpler type, the pinhole camera (Figure 1-2), which has no lens, and in which the light stop can be no larger than 1/250 inch in diameter or the image will appear blurred. An exposure time of many minutes is needed to get a picture on the light-sen-

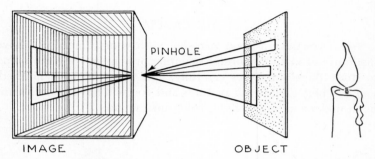

IMAGE   OBJECT

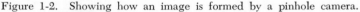

Figure 1-2. Showing how an image is formed by a pinhole camera.

sitive film. A study of the behavior of light will help explain how the modern camera developed from the pinhole camera into the remarkably sensitive and versatile instrument that it is today.

The list of a few of the extreme conditions under which photographs are taken would include the camera that is used to study the flight of bullets, and which requires less than 1/100,000 second for exposure; the camera used by astronomers which needs an exposure of many hours to record the faint light from distant galaxies; the camera which includes many thousands of square miles on a single negative as it takes pictures from high-flying rockets; the camera attached to an electron microscope, which enables us to see objects one millionth of an inch long; the X-ray camera, which takes pictures through several inches of steel; and the infrared-sensitive camera, which takes pictures through several miles of haze.

2. REFLECTION

(a) Law of Reflection

Our experience with mirrors and still pools tells us that smooth surfaces reflect light with little distortion. On an upright mirror place a piece of tape at a height exactly half the distance from the floor to your eyes. No matter how far you stand from the mirror, the tape will cut out the reflection of your feet. This situation is diagrammed in Figure 1-3. The light ray which strikes

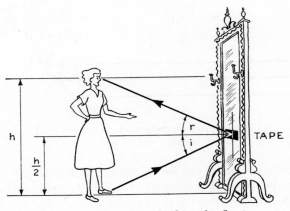

Figure 1-3. Illustrating the law of reflection.

the mirror from your feet is called the incident ray, and the angle it makes with a line perpendicular to the mirror is called the angle of incidence (angle i in Figure 1-3). The angle between this perpendicular and the ray reflected to your eye is called the angle of reflection (angle r in Figure 1-3). In this example, from the similar triangles involved, you can see that the angle of incidence equals the angle of reflection. A number of similar experiments will convince you that this is a general rule. For reflection from a flat surface, the angle of incidence equals the angle of reflection. This law of reflection holds for curved surfaces as well as for flat ones. Here the angles are measured between the path that the light takes and the perpendicular to the line tangent to the curve at the point where the light strikes it. Through the use of properly curved reflectors, all the reflected light from a bulb can be directed into the narrow beam of a searchlight or an automobile headlight (Figure 1-4) or the absurd effects of the hall of

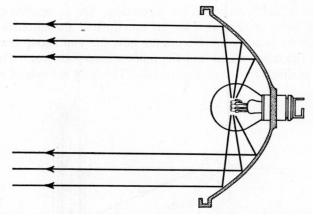

Figure 1-4.   The reflector of an automobile headlight sends out a beam of parallel rays of light.

mirrors in a fun house can be achieved. If a well-defined reflection is to be avoided, a number of small, irregular surfaces will break up the reflection as in the case of velvet cloth and face powder.

(b) Amount of Reflection

The percentage of incident light reflected from even the best mirror is less than is generally supposed, and that reflected from what appears to be a completely transparent pane of window glass is much more than one usually realizes. Eighty per cent reflection is considered good for a mirror. The mirror of the 200-inch telescope at Mt. Palomar has been surfaced with a special aluminum coating to give about 90% reflection. The annoying glare from the windshield of an approaching car when you are driving with the sun at your back is an indication that much of the light falling on a pane of glass is reflected. It is important to bear this in mind when taking pictures indoors by daylight. A snapshot is hard to get under these conditions because much of the outdoor light is reflected and does not pass through the window.

A technique has been developed for treating the surface of glass so that reflection is almost eliminated. Such "coated lenses" transmit the light that would have been reflected. They are useful in cameras, telescopes, binoculars, and meters (Figure 1-5).

Figure 1-5.   The left half of the glass front of this meter has been "coated" to cut down on reflection.   (*General Electric Co.*)

The problem of avoiding glare is a very real one for architects designing storewindows, for museum directors in lighting pictures, etc.

3. REFRACTION

(a) Examples of the Bending of Light

The statement is frequently made that light travels in straight lines. This is true only under the most unusual conditions, and it is doubtful that you have ever seen a ray of light which traveled in a straight line from its source to your eyes. Certainly, as light travels through your eye to the retina, the light is bent, and it is this bending that we are now going to study. You can easily experiment with seeing around a corner by placing a coin in the bottom of a pan, standing far enough away so that the coin is just hidden by the rim of the pan, and having someone fill the pan with water. The coin appears to rise into view. If the water is siphoned out of the pan, the coin will sink out of sight again. Figure 1-6 shows the path that the light takes. A magnifying or

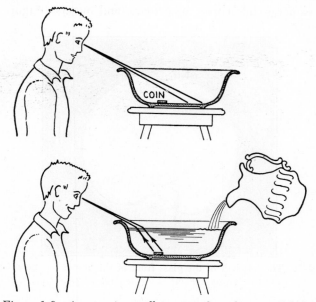

Figure 1-6. An experiment illustrating the refraction of light.

"burning" glass forms a small image of the sun. If a glass 2 inches in diameter is used and a 1-inch circle of black paper is pasted over the center of it, an image will still be formed, and it is obvious that the straight path of the light from the sun to the image has been blocked off.

(b) Law of Refraction

If a narrow beam of light falls on a prism as in Figure 1-7, it will take the path *ABCD*. It will be bent at *B* as it passes from air to glass, and at *C* as it passes from the glass out into the air again. This bending of light as it passes from one substance to another is called refraction. In Figure 1-8, the line *BX* has been drawn perpendicular to the face of the prism at *B*. If the light

had not been bent as it entered the glass it would have gone to
C', but instead, it follows the path BC. Here it is bent toward
the perpendicular, BX. In Figure 1-9, the line Y'CY is perpendicular to the face of the prism at C. In passing from glass to

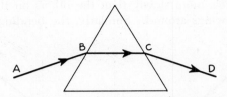

Figure 1-7. The path of a ray of light through a prism.

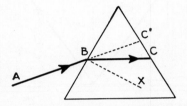

Figure 1-8. Refraction of a beam of light as it passes from air to glass at B.

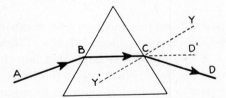

Figure 1-9. Refraction of a beam of light as it passes from glass to air at C.

air, the light does not travel the straight line BCD' but is bent at
C and goes to D. This time it is bent away from the perpendicular. Figure 1-10 shows the path of a beam of light when it enters a tank of water at B, is reflected from a submerged mirror at
P, and leaves the water at C. The beam is bent toward the perpendicular as it enters the water at B, at the mirror the angle of incidence BPP' equals the angle of reflection P'PC, and the beam
is bent away from the perpendicular as it leaves the water at C.

To understand the reason for the change in direction of a beam of light when it passes from one medium into another, consider a car traveling along a paved road which has sandy shoulders. If one of the front wheels goes off the pavement and into the sandy soil, the whole car tends to turn off the road. The one wheel in the sand travels more slowly than the others on the pavement, and the car swings around. Similarly, the bending of the path

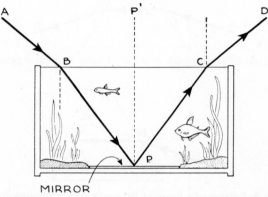

Figure 1-10. Refraction and reflection. The beam of light is refracted at B, reflected at P, and again refracted at C.

of light as it passes from one medium into another is due to its change in speed. Figure 1-11 shows a beam of light traveling in air and water. If you think of it as coming into the water from the air, the part of the beam which strikes the water first is slowed down, and the part in the air continues on its original path until it, too, strikes the water, and then the beam proceeds with its direction altered. In changing direction, the light is bent toward the perpendicular to the air-water surface. If you consider that the beam of light is traveling upward into the air, the line of travel is bent away from the perpendicular to the surface.

The speed with which light travels through a medium (water, for instance) is not affected by the angle at which it enters that medium. For any pair of substances, such as air and water, the ratio of the speed of light in the two is a constant. This is known as Snell's law, and it may be stated

$$\frac{\text{speed of light in air}}{\text{speed of light in water}} = K = \frac{\text{sine of angle of incidence}}{\text{sine of angle of refraction}}$$

When the comparison is made between the speed of light in a vacuum and in some substance, the constant is called the index of refraction for that substance. The speed of light in air is slightly less than it is in a vacuum so the index of refraction of

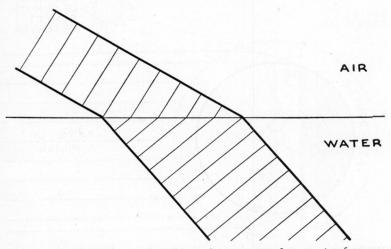

AIR

WATER

Figure 1-11. Refraction explained as a change in speed on passing from one medium into another. The waves travel faster in air than they do in water.

air is slightly greater than one. This results in the light from the sun at sunrise and sunset being bent down over the horizon so that we see the sun before it has actually risen and after it has set (Figure 1-12).

There is no simple way to predict the value of the index of refraction for a substance, but with two samples of the same substance, the one with the greater density will have the greater index of refraction. Density is defined as the mass of a certain volume (usually one cubic centimeter) of a substance. For instance, water has a density of 1, and glass a density of about 2.5 grams per cubic centimeter. The density of air is only a little more than 0.001 gram per cubic centimeter. As we shall see later, this varies considerably with temperature and pressure, so that it is almost impossible to find even two adjoining cubic feet of air that have exactly the same density. As the density of air changes, so does the index of refraction, and light passing through it is constantly zigzagging back and forth. The twinkling of stars and of distant lights serves to illustrate this point.

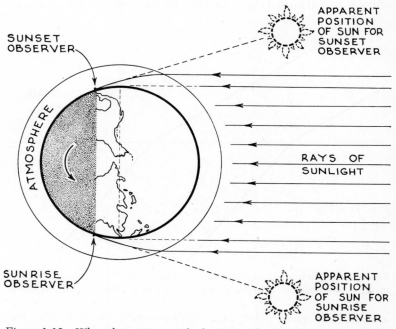

Figure 1-12. When the sun is near the horizon, refraction by the atmosphere makes it appear higher than it really is.

(c) Total Internal Reflection

In Figure 1-9, the angle BCY' is called the angle of incidence and the angle DCY the angle of refraction. When light passes from glass into air, the angle of refraction is always greater than the angle of incidence. Therefore, as both the angle of incidence and the angle of refraction are increased, the angle of refraction will reach a right angle first, and the emerging light will just graze the surface of the prism. If the angle of incidence is made even greater, the light will not get out at all; it will be reflected at the glass-air surface and return into the prism. This situation is called total internal reflection. When the angle of refraction is a right angle, the angle of incidence is called the critical angle. For water, the critical angle is about $48\frac{1}{2}°$. A fish, or a submerged swimmer, as he looks above him, can see out of the water at an angle of $48\frac{1}{2}°$ from the perpendicular. If he looks at a greater angle, he sees the bottom of the pond reflected at the under surface of the water. This total internal reflection is more efficient than the reflection given by a mirror.

4. LENS ACTION

The index of refraction for glass is greater than that for air. Snell's law (page 10) tells us that light slows down when it passes from air into glass, and speeds up when it emerges from glass into air. Instead of one prism, as in Figure 1-7, consider two prisms placed base to base as in Figure 1-13. A beam of light

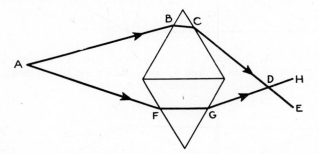

Figure 1-13. The converging action of two prisms.

traveling from A to B would be bent as it enters the prism, and again as it leaves it at C, and would continue toward E. Another beam would follow the path $AFGH$. These cross at D. Instead of two prisms, a continuously curving convex lens is designed so that all the rays of light striking it from any one point are bent, as they pass through the lens, in such a way that they converge at another point on the opposite side. Figure 1-14 shows two rays of light from the point of an arrow as they pass through a lens, converge at C, and diverge beyond it. Figure 1-15 shows the same thing for two rays of light from the tail which converge at J.

Figure 1-16 is a composite of the upper two. All the rays from *A* which strike the lens between *B* and *E* will also pass through *C*,

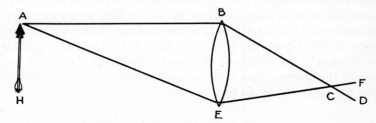

Figure 1-14. The formation of an image by a lens. All the rays from *A* striking the lens between *B* and *E* converge at *C*.

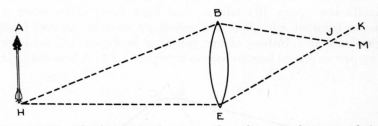

Figure 1-15. The formation of an image by a lens. Looking toward the lens from *J*, all that can be seen is light coming from *H*. An image of *H* is formed at *J*.

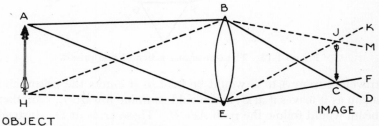

Figure 1-16. The formation of an image by a lens. This drawing is a composite of Figures 1-14 and 1-15.

etc. The rays from any point along the shaft from *A* to *H* will converge at corresponding points along the line *CJ*, and an image of the arrow will be formed. This is the way your camera lens forms an image on the film (Figure 1-17).

If the object (arrow) is placed closer to the lens than at Figure 1-16, the angles of incidence of the rays striking the lens will be greater. The angles of refraction will also be greater, and the rays will converge at a point farther back of the lens (Figure

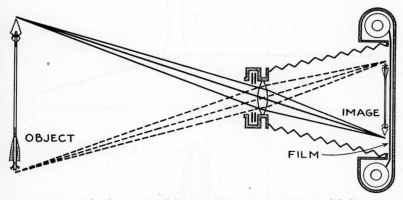

Figure 1-17. The formation of the image in a camera. A simplified camera lens is shown here.

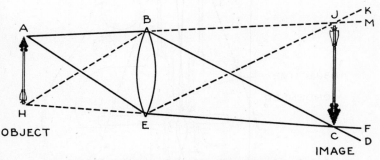

Figure 1-18. With the object and the lens closer together than they are in Figure 1-16, the image is found farther back of the lens.

1-18). If your camera is of the type that can be adjusted for the distance of the object you are photographing, you will notice that the lens moves away from the film for objects that are near.

A lens may be ground so that it is thick at the edges and thin in the middle (concave). This kind of lens diverges the rays that pass through it (Figure 1-19). Many irregular shapes of lenses have been worked out for special purposes.

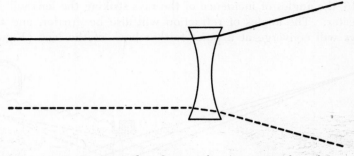

Figure 1-19. A concave lens diverges the rays passing through it.

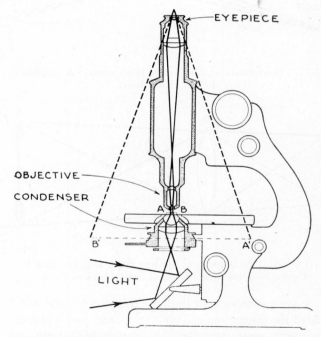

EYEPIECE

OBJECTIVE

CONDENSER

A   B

B'   A'

LIGHT

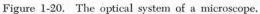

Figure 1-20. The optical system of a microscope.

(a) Applications to Cameras, Telescopes, etc.

By means of suitable combinations of lenses, we can extend our ability to see objects. For those that are very small we use a microscope, and for those that are very faint, a telescope. The lens system of a compound microscope is shown in Figure 1-20. The

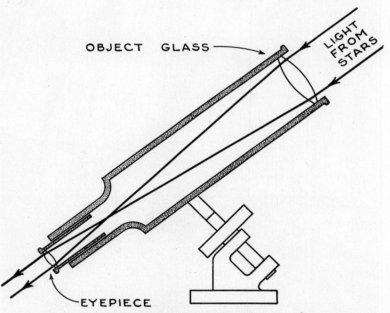

Figure 1-21. The optical system of a refracting telescope.

object, AB, must be illuminated with a strong light so that the large image $B'A'$ will be bright enough to see.

In the astronomical telescope, we are interested in enlarging the image when viewing members of the solar system, but even more important is the gathering of as much light as possible from faint stars. The refracting telescope has a large lens to gather and focus the light, and a small eyepiece to magnify the image (Figure 1-21). The area, and hence the light-gathering power, of the objective of a telescope is proportional to the square of its diameter. The large 40-inch lens of the Yerkes Observatory telescope (Figure 1-22) intercepts about 45,000 times as much light

as the lens of the average human eye. A concave mirror ground
to the shape of a parabola in cross section will bring the parallel

Figure 1-22. Forty-inch refracting telescope at the Yerkes Observatory.
(*Yerkes Observatory.*)

rays of light from a star to focus at a point. By placing a small
reflecting prism in front of the mirror, the light can be turned
aside for study (Figure 1-23). The reflecting telescope is popu-

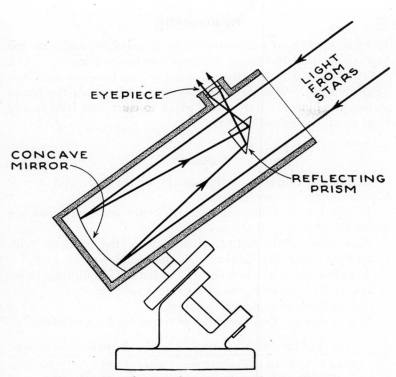

EYEPIECE

CONCAVE
MIRROR

LIGHT
FROM
STARS

REFLECTING
PRISM

Figure 1-23. The optical system of a reflecting telescope.

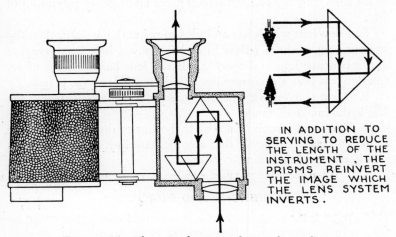

IN ADDITION TO
SERVING TO REDUCE
THE LENGTH OF THE
INSTRUMENT , THE
PRISMS REINVERT
THE IMAGE WHICH
THE LENS SYSTEM
INVERTS .

Figure 1-24. The optical system of prism binoculars.

lar with those who enjoy astronomy as a hobby, and it is the type used in all the larger telescopes in observatories.

Prism binoculars use two reflecting prisms between each lens (Figure 1-24). This shortens the distance between the lenses so that the binoculars are much easier to carry and hold steady than an old-fashioned spyglass.

SUMMARY

1. The working parts of the camera are the lens, light stop or iris diaphragm, shutter, and film.

2. The law of reflection states that the angle of incidence equals the angle of reflection.

3. A good mirror reflects about 80% of the incident light. Much light is lost by reflection from glass windows.

4. Refraction is the bending of the path of an oblique beam of light as it passes from one medium into another.

5. Density is mass per unit volume.

6. Law of refraction: the index of refraction for a substance =

$$K = \frac{\text{speed of light in a vacuum}}{\text{speed of light in the substance}} = \frac{\text{sine of angle of incidence}}{\text{sine of angle of refraction}}$$

7. The critical angle for a substance is the angle of incidence of an emerging ray of light which gives an angle of refraction of 90°.

8. For a lens which has an index of refraction greater than the surrounding medium (glass in air), a convex lens is converging and a concave lens is diverging. If the lens has an index of refraction less than the surrounding medium, the reverse is true.

9. For a converging lens, the greater the object distance, the less is the image distance.

10. The focal length of a lens is the image distance when the object distance is so great that any increase in it makes no measurable change in the image distance.

QUESTIONS AND EXERCISES

1. What is the minimum length of a vertical mirror that would be needed by a person 5 feet 10 inches tall to see himself from head to toe?

2. Examine the difference between the construction of velvet and satin and show how this explains the fact that one is dull and the other is shiny.

3. Explain how a spherical fish bowl filled with water can start a fire.

4. Look outside through a pane of window glass and move your head back and forth. Notice how the scene is distorted. What causes this?

5. The index of refraction for water is less than that for glass and greater than that for air. Would the focal length of a convex glass lens be greater in air or in water?

6. Why does a microscope need a particularly bright source of illumination?

7. What are some of the advantages of a reflecting over a refracting type of telescope?

8. If 80% transmission is obtained each time light passes from air into glass and from glass into air, what per cent of the light which strikes the prism binoculars (Figure 1-24) would finally reach the observer's eyes?

9. As you look at a stone on the bottom of a stream, does it appear closer or farther away than it actually is? Make a sketch of the situation which explains your answer.

10. A block measures 8 x 12 x 9 centimeter and weighs 2160 grams. What material was this block probably made of?

2

Light Intensity

1. MEASURING INTENSITY

In taking a picture, you must consider the brightness of the light on the subject. The same setting of your camera will not give a satisfactory picture of both a brightly lighted beach scene and a family group on the porch with an overcast sky. When you are using a reading light, it is not only the brightness of the bulb but also its distance from your book that is important.

The common unit for measuring intensity of illumination is the foot-candle. It represents the intensity of the light 1 foot from a standard candle. This is one of the few primitive units of measurement still in use in the physical sciences. Our modern incandescent bulbs give off an amount of light that is roughly proportional to the power consumed (a 100-watt bulb is about four times as bright as a 25-watt bulb), and so rating by watts rather than by the amount of illumination is satisfactory in this case. This kind of bulb is very inefficient because it wastes a great deal of energy in heating up the filament to incandescence. The newer fluorescent bulbs, which operate at a low temperature, give much more light per watt than the incandescent types.

By carefully defining the composition, method of manufacture, and rate of burning of the standard candle, a reasonably reproducible unit is obtained. If you can picture a standard candle burning at the center of a transparent sphere with a radius of 1 foot, and outside that, another sphere with a radius of 2 feet, then all the light passing through the first sphere will strike the second. Recalling that the area of a sphere is $4\pi r^2$, you can see that the areas of two spheres stand in the ratio of the squares of their radii. The same amount of light is falling on both these spheres, but the larger one has four times the area of the smaller; hence, each square inch of the smaller one has four times as much

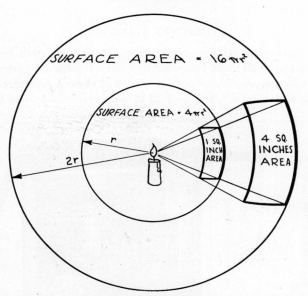

Figure 1-25. The same amount of light that falls on 1 square inch of the sphere with a radius *r* is spread out over 4 square inches of the sphere with a radius 2*r*.

light striking it as does each square inch of the larger (Figure 1-25). This may be generalized as $I \propto 1/d^2$ or $I_1/I_2 = d_2{}^2/d_1{}^2$. The intensity, *I*, is inversely proportional to the square of the distance, *d*. This is illustrated in Figure 1-26.

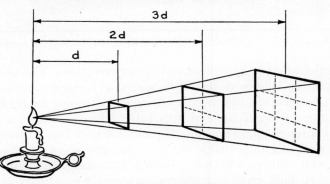

Figure 1-26. An illustration of the law that the intensity of light varies inversely with the square of the distance.

2. LIGHTING STANDARDS

The amount of light necessary for photography will be taken up later (page 28). If you want to survey the lighting conditions in your home, school, or college you will need a lightmeter that reads in foot-candles (Figure 1-27). Frequently, one may be bor-

Figure 1-27.   Lightmeter.   (*Weston Electrical Instrument Corp.*)

rowed from your local light and power company. The sensitive face of the lightmeter should be placed at the same level as the work being done, that is, just where a book would be held, etc., and the readings compared with Table 1-1.

As a rough approximation, 60- and 100-watt frosted tungsten-filament bulbs (the kind in ordinary use) give about 1 foot-candle per watt without reflectors. With a light-colored lampshade, a 100-watt bulb gives a satisfactory intensity for ordinary reading (20 to 50 foot-candles in Table 1-1) at a distance of 3 feet.

TABLE 1-1.[1] CONSERVATIVE FOOT-CANDLE RECOMMENDA-
TIONS ON A NATIONAL BASIS OF CHARACTERISTICS OF THE
VISUAL TASK AND REQUIREMENTS OF PERFORMANCE

100 foot-candles or more. For very severe and prolonged tasks such as
fine needlework, fine engraving, fine penwork, fine assembly, sewing on
dark goods, and discrimination of fine details of low contrast, as in
inspection.

50 to 100 foot-candles. For severe and prolonged tasks, such as proof-
reading, drafting, difficult reading, watch repairing, fine machine work,
and average sewing and other needlework.

20 to 50 foot-candles. For moderately critical and prolonged tasks, such
as clerical work, ordinary reading, common benchwork, and average
sewing and other needlework on light goods.

10 to 20 foot-candles. For moderate and prolonged tasks of office and
factory and, when not prolonged, ordinary reading and sewing on light
goods.

5 to 10 foot-candles. For visually controlled work in which seeing is
important, but more or less interrupted or casual and does not involve
discrimination of fine details of low contrasts.

0 to 5 foot-candles. The danger zone for severe visual tasks, and for
quick and certain seeing. Satisfactory for perceiving larger objects
and for casual seeing.

[1] Luckiesh and Moss, *The Science of Seeing*, p. 345, Table LVIII. New
York, D. Van Nostrand Co., 1937.

3. f VALUE OF LENSES

The f-value adjustment of a camera regulates the size of the
opening (aperture) near the lens. By using a large opening on
a dull day and a small one on a bright day you can have the
same amount of light falling on the film in each case. The f value
is defined as the distance from the lens to the film divided by the
diameter of the aperture. As the distance from the lens to the
film does not usually change appreciably, the f value is inversely
proportional to the diameter of the aperture. The larger the f
value the smaller the opening. If the lens opening, or light stop,
is $\frac{1}{2}$ inch across and the lens is 4 inches from the film, the f value
$= 4 \div \frac{1}{2} = 8$. If the stop is cut down to $\frac{1}{4}$ inch, the f value
$= 4 \div \frac{1}{4} = 16$.

The light stop is a circular opening, and the areas of two
circles vary as the squares of their diameters, so the $\frac{1}{2}$-inch
opening lets through four times as much light as the $\frac{1}{4}$-inch one.

If you want to figure out what f value corresponds to $\frac{1}{2}$ as much light as $f8$, you multiply 8, not by 2, but by the square root of 2, which is 1.4. This gives $8 \times 1.4 = 11.2$. Fortunately, the f-value scale on cameras has been standardized into a set of numbers, each one of which represents approximately half as much light as the next smaller one. It is convenient to memorize this scale for rapid work, once an exposure meter reading has been made. The scale runs like this: 2, 2.8, 4, 5.6, 8, 11, 16, 22, 32, 45. Very few cameras cover the full range, but you can memorize the part of the sequence that is available on yours. If your camera were set for a regular snapshot under fairly good lighting conditions, such as 1/25 second and $f16$, and you suddenly had occasion to take an action picture, you would want to change the shutter speed to 1/100 second. To get a proper exposure the light stop would have to be opened up to let in four times as much light as $f16$. If you have the f-value scale well in mind, it is easy to go to the second number smaller than $f16$, which is $f8$.

4. CHANGING APERTURE AND DEPTH OF FOCUS

Referring to Figure 1-16, you can see that, as the rays of light from any one point on the arrow converge at C and then diverge again, they form two cone-shaped bundles with their points together at C. If you cut across these cones parallel to the lens you will have a circular image except at C, where it is a point. If a camera is not focused correctly, so that the film is either in front of or behind point C, then the image on the film will be a conglomeration of overlapping circular images. This circle over which the image is spread is called the "circle of confusion." If the diameter of the circle of confusion is less than 0.1 mm, we are not able to distinguish it from a point, and the picture appears to be in focus. If it is any larger than that, the picture looks fuzzy. This is the reason for the statement that the opening of a pinhole camera should be no larger than 1/250 inch (page 4) (1/250 inch = 0.1 mm).

Remembering that objects at different distances form images at different distances back of the lens, it is clear that the object at only one distance from the lens can be in perfect focus on the film of your camera. The circle of confusion for objects immediately in front of and behind the one you are focusing on will be so small that they will appear to be in focus. The smaller the light stop you are using, the narrower will be this cone of con-

Figure 1-28. Picture taken with small aperture (*f*32). Notice that the sign in the foreground and the one in the middle distance as well as the distant church steeple are all in sharp focus. (*R. R. Frame and Co.*)

verging images, and the greater will be the range of objects that appear to be in focus. The distance from the nearest object which seems to be in clear focus to the farthest one which is also in good focus is called the depth of focus. You get a good depth of focus with small *f* openings like *f*16, 22, and 32; but with large openings like *f*4 and an object close to the lens, the depth of focus may be only an inch or two (Figures 1-28 and 1-29).

Figure 1-29. Picture taken with large aperture (f4.7). Notice that the
sign in the foreground is in sharp focus but the sign in the middle distance
and everything beyond it are out of focus. (*R. R. Frame and Co.*)

5. EXPOSURE METERS

An exposure meter is practically a necessity if you want to avoid
frequent failures with your camera. The eye adjusts to give satisfactory vision with such a wide variety of light conditions that
your impression of how bright it is may be very inaccurate. An
exposure meter (Figure 1-30) is essentially a sensitive cell which
generates an electric current proportional to the intensity of the
light that strikes it (page 26). A meter measures this current,
and from the reading on the meter you can decide upon the
proper setting for your camera. The exposure meter is adjusted
for the type of film you are using (film-speed information may
be obtained from your photographic supply dealer), and from
the meter reading you make a setting which gives you the proper
choice of shutter speeds and f openings. For example, from a
certain meter reading you will find that you have a choice of

Figure 1-30. Photographic exposure meter. (*Weston Electrical Instrument Corp.*)

*f*5.6 and 1/100 second, *f*8 and 1/50 second, or *f*11 and 1/25 second. They will all allow the same amount of light to fall on the film.

Which one of the above combinations of *f* values and shutter speeds shall you choose? It is generally considered good technique to have as great a depth of focus as possible. To be sure, it is a matter of taste, but in current practice the photographer does not deliberately have part of his picture out of focus. This means that he uses the smallest light stop (the largest *f* number) that the conditions will permit. He therefore chooses the slowest shutter speed that will stop the action in his picture and then uses the f opening that is appropriate. For ordinary snapshots, a shutter speed of 1/25 second is about right. For pictures of children or of anything in motion, 1/100 second is needed, and for some rapidly moving subjects an even faster shutter speed may be necessary.

SUMMARY

1. A foot-candle is the intensity of the light one foot from a standard candle.

2. Variation of light intensity with distance:

$$I \propto 1/d^2 \qquad \text{or} \qquad I_1/I_2 = d_2{}^2/d_1{}^2$$

3. f Value of lenses:

$$f \text{ value} = \frac{\text{distance from lens to image}}{\text{diameter of lens opening}}$$

4. The circle of confusion is the circular area on the image screen covered by the image of any one point on the object.

5. The depth of focus is the distance from the nearest object which appears to be in good focus in a picture to the farthest one which also appears to be in good focus.

QUESTIONS AND EXERCISES

1. A lightmeter shows that a certain light, which is 10 feet away, is giving an illumination of 10 foot-candles. At what distance should the light be placed to give 30 foot-candles?

2. Calculate the f value of a camera lens which has an aperture of ⅜ inch and which is 4 inches from the film.

3. What size aperture for the lens in problem 2 would have an f value of 8?

4. Does an f opening of 5.6 let through more or less light than one of $f16$? How much?

5. What exposure time should be used with $f5.6$ if $f16$ takes 1/25 second?

6. Make a survey of the lighting conditions in your home or college and see how they compare with the recommendations presented.

7. If the illumination 3 feet from a bulb is 20 foot-candles, what would it be 10 feet from the same bulb?

8. There are two lights 10 feet apart, and one light is twice as

bright as the other. At what point between them would the illumination from the two be equal?

9. If $f8$ and $1/100$ second give the correct exposure, what f value is correct for $1/25$ second?

10. By actual measurement check the f value of your camera. Be careful not to scratch the lens.

CHAPTER

The Eye and Waves

1. PHYSICS OF THE EYE

(a) Structure of the Eye

There are many striking similarities between the structure of the eye and that of the camera. This is not too surprising, since they have similar functions. The principal parts of the human eye are shown in Figure 1-31. Light passes through the cornea, C, and the pupil, P, which is the dark circular opening inside the iris, I. The lens, L, converges the rays so that they come to a focus on the retina, R, at the back of the eye. The light energy striking the retina sends a nerve impulse along the optic nerve, O, to the brain, where the image is interpreted. The space A is filled with a watery fluid, and V with a gelatin-like material that helps the eyeball maintain its shape.

The light stop of a camera is called an iris diaphragm because it looks and acts like the iris of the eye. It is an interesting experience to look carefully at your iris in a mirror as you shine a flashlight directly into your eye. As the iris can only contract and expand enough to change the area of the opening about 10 times, it is not particularly effective as a light-intensity regulator.

The normal human lens is plastic, in contrast to the rigid glass lens of a camera. The camera focuses by changing the distance between the lens and the film. The eye can accommodate to a slight extent this way, but it does so principally by changing the shape of the lens. A thin lens of slight curvature is used for seeing at a distance; the shape changes to a thick, more nearly spherical one for seeing objects close up.

The retina is covered with light-sensitive rods and cones which change the light energy into nerve impulses. The chemical changes brought about by light on a film (latent image) last indefinitely, but on the retina they disappear after about 0.1 second. The rods enable us to judge light intensity, and they are sensitive over an extremely wide range. The cones give us color vision,

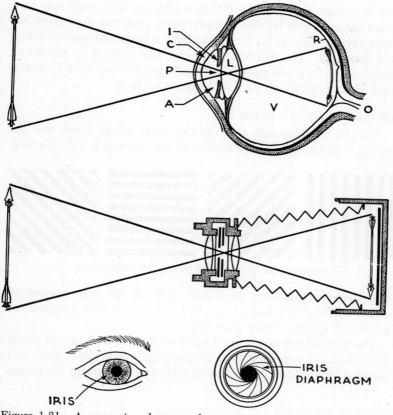

Figure 1-31. A comparison between the eye and the camera. (*Redrawn from Scientific American.*)

and they do not respond to low intensities. This is why we cannot distinguish colors by moonlight.

(b) Binocular Vision

There are two simple experiments you can perform to illustrate the way you judge distances by binocular vision. Hold a paper match-cover edge on at arm's length, and observe that you can see one side of it with your right eye and the other side with your left eye. Then have a friend focus on his finger as he moves it from arm's length up to his nose, and see how his two eyes move. To the extent that you see different pictures with each eye, and from the muscular tension of converging your two eyes more on near objects than on far ones, you have a binocular way of judging distances. You can test how much you depend on binocular vision by closing one eye and trying to put the cap on a fountain pen when it is held about a foot from your face.

(c) Optical Defects of the Eye

We can consider only a few of the many things which may go wrong with the eye. If the surface of your cornea is not spherical

Figure 1-32. A chart for testing for astigmatism.

you have astigmatism. In Figure 1-32 all the lines appear of equal intensity to a normal eye, but to a person with astigmatism some will appear darker than others.

The normal eye reads print most easily at a distance of about 10 inches. If you need to hold the page much closer than this you are nearsighted. The lens of your eye is focusing the image

Figure 1-33. The shape of concave lens used in eyeglasses.

Figure 1-34. The shape of convex lens in eyeglasses.

in front of your retina. This fault is corrected by using a lens which is diverging—thick at the edges and thin in the center (Figure 1-33). If your most comfortable reading distance is much greater than 10 inches you are farsighted, the image is falling back of the retina, and you need converging lenses in your glasses (Figure 1-34).

(d) Visual Illusions

You should not forget that in the seeing process the brain plays as important a part as the eye. Your eye may be entirely normal

Figure 1-35. An optical illusion due to perspective. The three trees are the same height.

and yet you may be fooled by what you see. This subject is far too large to cover here, but a few illustrations may be well worth while.

Figure 1-36. An optical illusion consisting of a series of concentric circles. (*After Luckiesch.*)

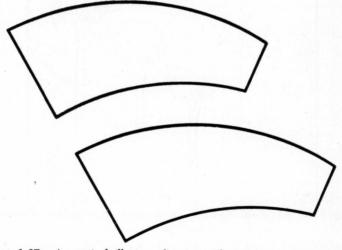

Figure 1-37. An optical illusion of areas. The two areas are the same size and shape.

In Figure 1-35, the trees are actually the same size, but the one to the right appears to be much larger. In Figure 1-36, what appears to be a spiral is made up of a number of concentric circles. The two areas in Figure 1-37 are the same; in fact, one may be exactly superimposed on the other. The apparent difference in size of the full moon near the horizon and high in the sky has been shown by photography to be entirely an illusion. Figures 1-38 and 1-39 show how stubbornly your brain insists that the room is normal when the appearance of the two individuals shows that the ceiling must be farther from the floor on the right than on the left.

2. BEHAVIOR OF WAVES

(a) Characteristics of Waves

The question, "What is light?" is frequently asked and is almost as frequently answered. To a scientist, such a question is meaningless. Scientists have made the progress that can be credited to them by rephrasing the above question to read, "How does light behave?" They study such completely abstract things as waves and such real things as water waves; and when they find a certain amount of similarity between the behavior of light and of the water waves they can say that, to a certain extent, light has the characteristics of a wave motion. There are many ways in which light has a wave-like behavior, and many in which it behaves very differently, and so it would be most misleading to say that light "is" a wave or a wave-like phenomenon. Gertrude Stein uttered a profound philosophical truth when she wrote, "A rose is a rose is a rose." A wave is a wave is a wave, and light is light is light. Light is not a wave, although the two do have some properties in common. We shall find it profitable to study waves in general and sound waves in particular before examining the wave-like behavior of light.

Certain terms that are used in describing waves are illustrated in Figure 1-40. Representing a wave by the familiar sine curve, the high points are called crests, and the low points troughs. The distance from one crest to the next is called the wavelength, and

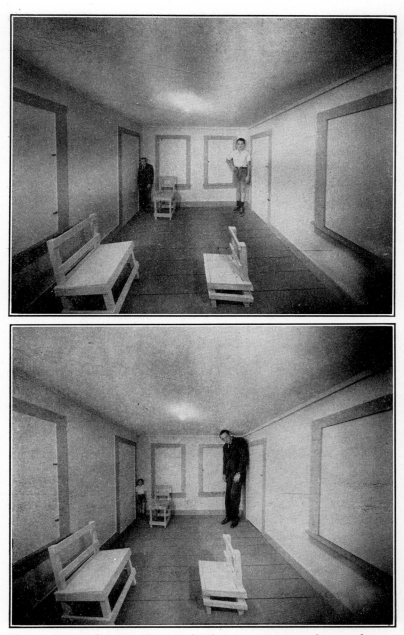

Figures 1-38 and 1-39. Two views of a room constructed to produce a visual illusion. The room obviously cannot be rectangular at the back end but our eyes refuse to believe this. (*Courtesy Life* © *Time.*)

half the difference in height between the crest and the trough is called the amplitude.

In talking about how waves travel, it is easier if you think in terms of something tangible, like a water wave. If you drop a stone into quiet water you see the waves traveling out from the spot where the stone struck. Waves have a speed, and, as they strike the shore, a certain number hit every minute. The number of waves arriving per unit of time is called their frequency. The

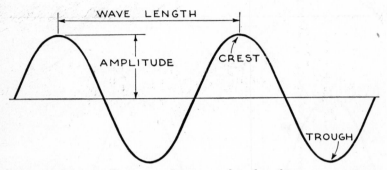

Figure 1-40. An illustration of terms used in describing wave motion.

length of time between the arrival of one crest and the next is called the period. If 5 crests strike the shore in 1 minute, the frequency is 5 per minute and the period is $\frac{1}{5}$ minute. Or, stated as an equation, Period = 1/Frequency.

As you watch the water wave roll toward the shore, you know that the water disturbed by the stone is not traveling from it to the shore; only the wave motion travels, while the water remains pretty much where it was. Or, better still, when you wiggle one end of a clothesline, whose other end is tied to a post, the waves travel along the line as the line moves up and down. You get the impression that the stripes on a rotating barber pole are moving up. In order to set up a wave motion you must have some sort of a vibrating source and something, a medium of some kind, to pass the vibrations along. If the particles of the medium move back and forth in the direction the wave is traveling, the wave motion is called longitudinal. If the particles of the medium move perpendicular to the direction of the wave, the wave motion is called transverse. Very seldom is an actual wave purely one or the other. Any one drop of water will rise with the crest of the wave and travel forward with it, then drop down into the trough and move back to meet the next crest, so that it follows a roughly circular path.

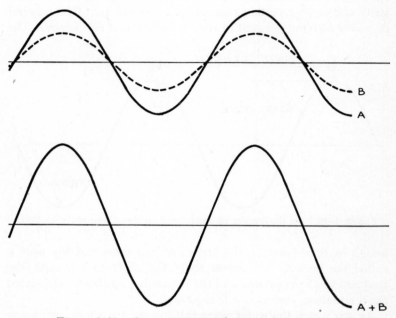

Figure 1-41. Constructive interference of two waves.

When two waves arrive at the same place at the same time, their interaction is called interference. When a crest of one meets a crest of the other, and a trough meets a trough, the result is that the two add together to make a high crest and a deep trough (Figure 1-41). This situation is called constructive interference or reinforcement. When a crest combines with a trough, they add together to produce a very small wave (Figure 1-42). This combining is referred to as destructive interference; when the crest and trough are the same size they exactly cancel each other so that two waves combine to give no wave at all (Figure 1-43).

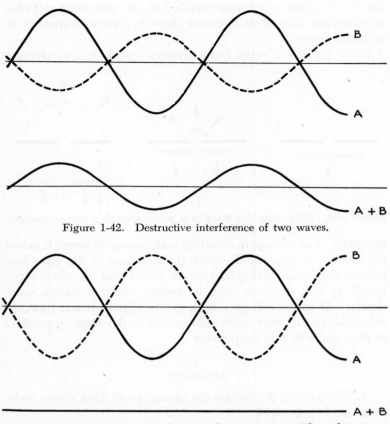

Figure 1-42. Destructive interference of two waves.

Figure 1-43. Destructive interference of two waves. When the waves have the same wavelength and amplitude and are exactly out of phase, the result is that no wave motion is observed.

(b) Reflection, Diffraction, and Refraction of Waves

The reflection of waves of all kinds is such a familiar phenomenon that we do not need to spend time on that, but diffraction may need some explaining. When a wave passes through a narrow opening, the opening behaves like the source of a new wave, which proceeds outward in a semicircle. Figure 1-44 shows a wave front as it approaches and passes through a narrow opening. Diffraction is the name applied to this spreading out of a wave motion as part of it passes through a narrow opening or around a corner.

When part of a wave front changes speed, it also changes

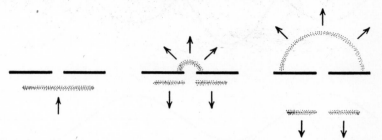

Figure 1-44. Diffraction of a wave as it passes through a narrow opening.

direction. This change in direction with change in speed is called refraction. As you would expect, the slow part of the wave lags behind, the faster-moving part speeds ahead, and the whole wave bends, so that it moves into the region where it travels more slowly. As waves roll up onto a gently sloping beach they are refracted, so that they approach parallel to the shore, regardless of their angle to it in deep water.

SUMMARY

1. The parts of the eye are the cornea, pupil, lens, retina, rods, cones, and optic nerve.

2. Binocular vision helps us judge distances by the tension of the eye muscles and the differences in the images seen by the two eyes.

3. Optical defects of the eye include astigmatism, nearsightedness, and farsightedness.

4. Beware of visual illusions; don't believe all you see. What you see clearly may be misinterpreted by your mind.

5. A wavelength is the distance from one crest of a wave to the next one.

6. Amplitude is half the difference in height between a crest and an adjacent trough.

7. Frequency is the number of waves passing a given point per unit time.

8. The period is the interval of time between the passage of two successive crests of a series of waves.

9. A longitudinal wave is a wave motion back and forth in the direction of travel of the wave.

10. A transverse wave is a wave motion perpendicular to the direction of travel of the wave.

11. Interference is the interaction of two or more waves.

12. Constructive interference, or reinforcement, is interference of waves which are at least partly in phase.

13. Destructive interference is interference of waves which are at least partly out of phase.

14. Diffraction is the spreading out of a wave motion as it passes through a narrow opening or around a corner.

QUESTIONS AND EXERCISES

1. Name the parts of the eye which have a counterpart in the camera.

2. What is the difference in areas of apertures of a camera which has a range from $f5.6$ to $f22$?

3. Examine carefully a pair of pictures which are to be used together in a stereoscope. Describe the differences between them.

4. Using a piece of graph paper, draw: (a) a series of sine waves with a wavelength of 2 inches and an amplitude of ½ inch; (b) a series of sine waves with a wavelength of 3 inches and an amplitude of ½ inch; (c) the wave that would result from the interference of (a) and (b).

5. Since waves tend to line up parallel with the shore line as they approach it, do water waves travel faster in deep or in shallow water?

6. If waves roll up on the shore once every 12 seconds, what is their frequency? their period?

7. Bring to class examples of optical illusions not mentioned in the text.

8. Which one of the optical defects of the eye would probably result from a slight imperfection in the curvature of the cornea?

9. What type of wave motion is illustrated by a rotating barber pole? by a column of marching soldiers?

10. Point out one difference between the phenomena of reflection and refraction and one similarity.

4

CHAPTER

Sound

Sound as a Wave Motion

Strike a tuning fork, and then suspend a pith ball so that it barely touches one of the tines (Figure 1-45). This experiment will convince you that the fork is vibrating even though it is mov-

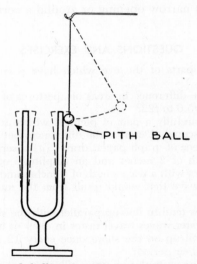

—PITH BALL

Figure 1-45. A pith ball used to detect the vibration of a tuning fork.

ing so rapidly that you cannot see the motion. Sound always has a vibrating source. This vibrating source may be a bell that has been struck by the clapper, a string that has been bowed, plucked, or struck, a column of air in an organ pipe, a reed in a clarinet, etc.

There must be a medium to carry the vibrations. If a noisy

alarm clock or a ringing bell is suspended in a bell jar which can be evacuated, the sound will grow fainter and fainter as the air is pumped out. The medium can just as well be a liquid or a solid. Try holding your head under water while someone holding two stones under the water hits them together. The "clicking" sound will be surprisingly loud. The childhood "telephone" made from two empty tin cans with a wire stretched tightly between them shows how effectively a solid will carry sound.

Sound takes time to travel, as you know well enough from hearing echoes. It is clear by now that sound has several of the properties of a wave motion, and we shall explore several more. The previous paragraphs illustrate a technique that has been very fruitful in the hands of scientists. The mathematically trained scientist notices many similarities between the properties of waves as an abstract mathematical study and those of the real waves in water. The field of mathematics developed more rapidly than the experimental sciences, so that much more was known about abstract waves than about water waves. The mathematicians could suggest things to look for in any phenomena that were suspected of having the properties of a wave motion. And so, by observing that sound has certain properties of waves, we can draw on the extensive knowledge of waves to help us study sound.

When a tuning fork is vibrating, the tines move out, knocking the air molecules away, then move back together, giving the air molecules a chance to bounce back toward the fork (Figure 1-46). The back-and-forth motion of the air particles is transmitted outward from the source in a longitudinal type of wave motion.

The range of frequencies that the human ear can hear runs from about 16 per second to 20,000 per second or somewhat higher. Vibrations above the range that can be heard by human ears are called supersonic. Many animals, such as bats, dogs, and insects, can hear sounds well above 20,000 per second. Extremely high frequencies of several hundred thousand per second have curious and damaging effects. They churn up oil-and-water mixtures into a stable emulsion, and they may kill bacteria, for instance.

When an ordinary calling card is made to vibrate by being held against a rotating toothed wheel, a clear musical note is heard. If the wheel is speeded up, the note is of a higher pitch. A difference in pitch involves a difference in frequency of vibration. When an orchestra is tuning up, the note usually sounded is A above middle C. This note has a frequency of 440 vibrations per second, and middle C is 261.6.

The velocity of sound in air varies with the temperature, but it is close to 1100 feet per second (750 miles per hour) under normal conditions. The velocity is less at lower temperatures and

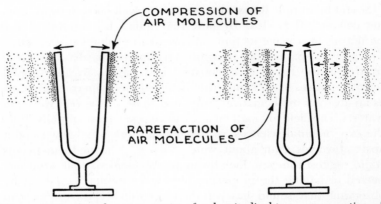

Figure 1-46. Sound waves consist of a longitudinal-type wave motion of air molecules.

pressures (for example, at higher altitudes). The speed of sound in air represents the speed at which the air molecules can pass on a disturbance to their neighbors. As the speed of an airplane approaches the speed of sound, the air molecules tend more and more to pile up in front of the leading edge of the wing instead of flowing smoothly around it. At this speed the propeller is no longer able to knock the air molecules aside fast enough to give the plane a forward velocity. Another use of the word "supersonic" refers to speeds greater than the speed of sound. For nearsonic and supersonic speeds a new wing design is necessary and a different type of propulsion (jet or rocket, etc.) is required. Ernst Mach, the Austrian physicist, worked out the theoretical implications of this situation, and we now use the term Mach number to represent the ratio of a plane's speed to the speed of sound. Only recently have planes exceeded a speed of Mach 1.

Since feet/seconds $\times$ seconds = feet, the wavelength can be obtained by multiplying the velocity by the period, or by dividing the velocity by the frequency.

$$\text{wavelength} = \text{velocity} \times \text{period}$$

$$\text{wavelength} = \text{velocity}/\text{frequency}$$

$$\text{velocity} = \text{wavelength} \times \text{frequency}$$

The third of these equations may be the easiest one to "see." If a string is vibrating 20 times per second, and if the first crest travels so fast that it is 55 feet away when the second one starts out, then the first crest will be 1100 feet away after 20 vibrations. It will have traveled 1100 feet in 1 second, which is one way of expressing the velocity. The lowest note on a standard piano keyboard has a wavelength of about 49 feet. A above middle C has a wavelength of $1100 \dfrac{\text{feet}}{\text{seconds}} \times \dfrac{1}{440/\text{seconds}} = 2.5$ feet. The A which is three octaves above the standard A has a frequency of 3520 per second, and its wavelength is therefore 0.312 foot = $3\frac{3}{4}$ inches.

Echoes not only show us that sound takes time to travel but also that it can be reflected. There are many famous whispering galleries where reflection concentrates sound waves so that a whisper can be heard at a great distance. When an architect designs an auditorium or a radio studio he must be careful to avoid large, flat, hard surfaces that will focus the sound waves or let them bounce back and forth (reverberate) for a long time. A reverberation time of about 1 second is considered the most desirable. Soft drapes and acoustical tile, which has many small holes to break up the sound waves, are effective in controlling echoes.

A very successful method for measuring the depth of the ocean depends on sending out sound impulses and timing the return of the echo from the bottom. A continuous record can be kept which is of great aid in navigation and which has revealed interesting facts about mountain ranges reaching nearly to the surface in the middle of the Atlantic Ocean. Sonic depth finding is used by petroleum geologists to locate strata which might contain oil (Figure 1-47).

A blind person will tap a cane and listen for the echo to warn him of obstacles in his path. An extremely refined version of this technique of navigation (echolocation) is used by bats. While

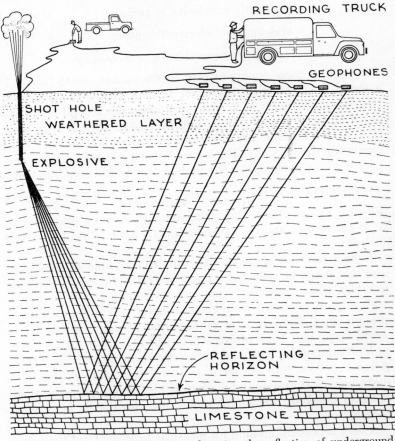

Figure 1-47. Exploring for oil by observing the reflection of underground sound waves.

flying, they send out high-pitched squeaks which start at a frequency of 80,000 and drop to 40,000 vibrations per second, and which last for 0.001 second. The echo from an object as close as 12 inches gives them sufficient warning, so that they fly very successfully in pitch-dark caves.

In sound waves a change of amplitude is heard as a change in loudness. Our unit for measuring sound intensity is the decibel. The scale of decibels is set up so that 0 represents the threshold of hearing, 120 the threshold of feeling, and a sound that differs by 10 decibels from another is 1 power of 10 times louder or fainter. In Table 1-2 the noise from an average radio (70 decibels) is 10 times as loud as that from a noisy office (60 decibels), and it is 100 times as loud as the average restaurant (50 decibels).

TABLE 1-2 [1]

Sound	Level, db
Threshold of hearing	0
Whisper	15
Rustle of leaves in gentle breeze	20
Purring cat	25
Turning page of newspaper	30
Quiet home or private office	40
Average restaurant	50
Noisy office or store	60
Average radio	70
Street noise, large city	75
Truck, unmuffled	80
Noisy factory	85
Newspaper pressroom	90
Noisiest spot at Niagara Falls	95
Inside subway car	100
Loud thunder	110
Threshold of feeling	120

[1] L. W. Taylor, *Physics, The Pioneer Science*, Houghton Mifflin Co., New York, 1941.

The whole range of hearing varies by 120 decibels, which is a difference in loudness of 10^{12}, or a million million. The ear has the greatest range of sensitivity of any of our sense organs.

Interference of sound waves is responsible for the effect of beats. If you listen to the sound from two tuning forks which have exactly the same frequency, you will hear a steady tone; but if one fork is vibrating a little faster than the other, the two sets of waves will get out of step at regular intervals. While they are in step, crests and troughs from each arrive at your ear together. When they get exactly out of step, a crest (a compression) from one and a trough (a rarefaction) from the other arrive

together and cancel each other (Figure 1-48), so that the sound
dies out momentarily. This rising and falling of the intensity of
the note is called beats. Each note on a piano is sounded by
three strings, and on a mandolin by two. These strings must be
very well tuned or the beats will spoil the tone.

The fact that you can "hear around a corner" is largely due to

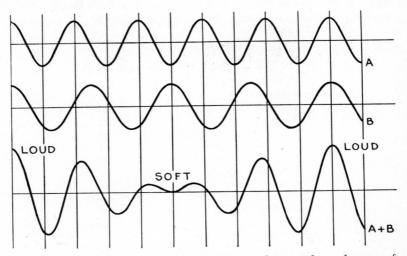

Figure 1-48. The formation of beats by the interference of sound waves of
nearly the same wavelength.

diffraction (Figure 1-49). Otherwise, diffraction is not of much
importance in the study of sound, and refraction is not commonly
observed. The familiar fact that sound carries unusually well
over water is partly due to refraction. With a layer of cool air
close to the water and a warmer one above it, some of the sound
energy is refracted by the warm air and comes back to the surface
(Figure 1-50).

Doppler Effect

The abrupt change in pitch of the note from a passing automobile horn or locomotive whistle is known as the Doppler effect.
Another example is observed when you are riding in a train and
you whip past the warning bell at a railroad crossing. Just as

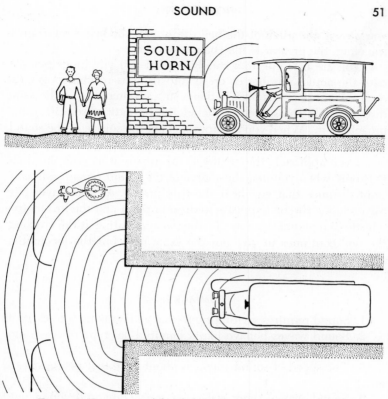

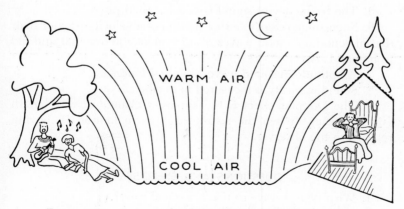

Figure 1-49. An example of the diffraction of sound waves.

Figure 1-50. An example of the refraction of sound waves.

you pass it, the pitch of the bell drops, and the faster the train is traveling, the greater is the change in pitch.

If you are listening to a steady note of 500 vibrations per second, the actual number of crests and troughs reaching your ear each second depends on whether you are remaining at the same distance from the source of the sound, retreating from it, or approaching it. When you are approaching the source of the sound, more than 500 vibrations reach your ear each second, and the faster you approach, the greater is the apparent increase in pitch. It is only when you and the source of the sound remain at a constant distance that you hear the true pitch. As you travel past the crossing, the bell appears to drop in pitch and the locomotive whistle to remain constant. To the person waiting at the crossing, the bell continues to give out the same note but the locomotive whistle drops in pitch as it goes by.

SUMMARY

1. Sound requires a vibrating source and a medium to carry it.

2. Sound waves behave like a longitudinal type of wave motion.

3. The speed of sound waves is about 1100 feet per second in air.

4. Sound waves show reflection, refraction, diffraction, and interference.

5. The frequency of sound waves is called pitch.

6. Supersonic refers to either motion of a velocity greater than that of sound, or sound waves of a frequency above that audible to human ears.

7. Amplitude in sound waves is called loudness.

8. Sound intensity is measured in decibels.

9. The Doppler effect is the apparent change in wavelength (or frequency) when the source of a wave motion is moving relative to the observer.

QUESTIONS AND EXERCISES

1. What type of wave motion is a sound wave?

2. Calculate the wavelength of middle C.

3. Calculate the frequency of the lowest note on the piano.

4. How far would you have to stand from a cliff for the echo of your shout to take 1 second to reach you?

5. An unmuffled truck is how many times noisier than a quiet home?

6. How fast would you have to approach the source of a steady sound to have it appear to be twice the frequency that it really is?

7. A man fires a bullet (speed = ½ mile per second) and hits a metal target ¼ mile away. How long after firing the shot does he hear the hit?

8. Using two tuning forks that give out the same note, listen to them sounding together. Then wrap a rubber band several times around one tine and sound them together again. Notice the beats.

9. How does an increase in temperature affect the speed of sound in air?

10. What is the advantage to the bat of having the pitch of its squeak change in frequency from start to finish?

5

The Physical Basis of Music

Fundamentals and Overtones

We have considered such properties of sound waves as amplitude, frequency, and wavelength, but none of these explains how it is that you can tell the difference between middle C when played on a saxophone and on a violin. The amplitude and frequency can be the same, but there is no question as to which you are listening to. The difference must be in the shape of the wave between one crest and the next.

Experiments with vibrating strings show that, other characteristics being the same, the shorter the vibrating section of the string, the higher is the frequency. The vibrations of a string are not only a simple swinging up and down of the middle section with the ends at rest, but the middle may be stationary with each half vibrating, or the string may vibrate in three, four, or several segments (Figures 1-51 and 1-52). The string on a musical instrument goes through a complicated combination of all these possibilities and consequently gives out a number of different notes. The simple vibration of the whole string determines what we call the "note" that is being played, middle C, for instance. This is called the fundamental. The other notes that accompany it are called overtones. The overtones have frequencies which are 2, 3, 4, etc., times that of the fundamental. The relative loudness of these different overtones determines the quality or timbre of the tone coming from the instrument. Not only string instruments, but also wind and percussion instruments, have combinations of overtones that characterize them. Figure 1-53 shows a graphical representation of notes from various instruments. The tuning fork is the only one that gives a pure fundamental without overtones.

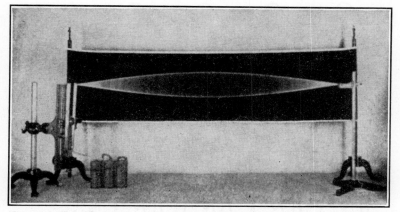

Figure 1-51. Photograph of a string vibrating as a whole. (*Photograph by Professor D. C. Miller.*)

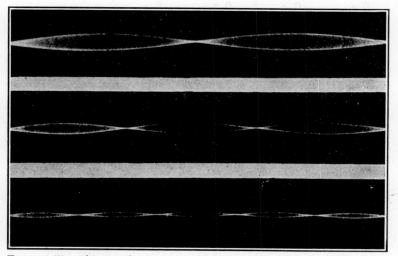

Figure 1-52. Photograph of a string vibrating in two, three, and five parts. (*Photograph by Professor D. C. Miller.*)

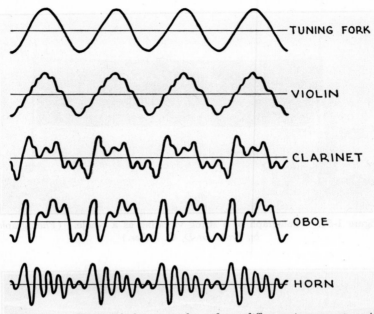

Figure 1-53. Shape of the wave form from different instruments. All these have the same wavelength. The tuning fork is the only one without overtones. (*From Classical and Modern Physics by E. H. White, D. Van Nostrand and Co.*)

Intervals

The earliest music probably consisted of singing in a monotone, with changes in tempo and loudness to give variety. As soon as two different notes were used, the problem of harmony and discord was introduced. The ratio of the frequencies of two notes is known as the interval between them. For A_3 ($f = 220$) and A_4 ($f = 440$), the interval is $440/220 = 2/1$. It is customary to write the fraction so that it is greater than 1. The only limit to the number of intervals possible is the ability of the human ear to distinguish tones. From this almost indefinitely large number of possible intervals, only a few have been used. The decision whether to use an interval is an entirely subjective one. There is nothing in the structure of our ears or nervous systems that makes a given pair of notes sound pleasant or unpleasant, but it is undoubtedly true that we prefer some combinations to others, and that the preferred combinations are not the same from one society to another, or from one century to another in the same society.

At this particular time in our society we consider that a harmonious combination is obtained from any two tones whose intervals can be expressed by the numbers up to 6. Less than two centuries ago the intervals 5/4 and 6/5 were felt to be discordant, and so it looks as though it will not be long before we will accept such intervals as 8/7 and 9/8 as pleasant. The notes G and A have an interval of 9/8, for instance.

The Musical Scale

Our present musical scale of twelve notes for each octave is not the only one in use, but it would take us too far afield to study the others. Using the intervals mentioned in the previous section, the musical scale of twelve notes was built up, the notes for the scale in any one key having the following intervals: 9/8, 10/9, 16/15, 9/8, 10/9, 9/8, 16/15. For the octave starting with A = 220, this would work out A = 220, B = 247.5, C$\sharp$ = 275, D = 293.3, E = 300, F$\sharp$ = 366.7, G$\sharp$ = 412.5, A = 440. If you move up a note and start the scale with B = 247.5, the next note is C$\sharp$ = 278.4 (247.5 × 9/8). Already we have two different frequencies for C$\sharp$. Students of music who have taken their scale for granted will be interested to see the variety of frequencies represented by the same note in the following table. This was obtained by starting with A, B, A$\sharp$, and C, and multiplying by the intervals given above.

It is obvious that we have here a chaotic situation in which an instrument tuned to one key could not be played in any other. This was exactly the situation 250 years ago. Numerous ways out of the difficulty were suggested, but the one favored by Bach (1685–1750) was the one finally adopted. He suggested that the frequency of any note should be obtained from the next lower one by multiplying by the factor the twelfth root of 2, or 1.059. This makes all the intervals equal and gives our modern "equal-tempered" scale, which is included in Table 1-3 for comparison. The actual frequency used for every note except A is a compro-

TABLE 1-3

	A = 220	B = 247.5	A♯ = 232	C = 261	Equal-tempered scale
A	220				220
A♯			232		233.1
B	247.5	247.5			246.9
C			261	261	261.6
C♯	275	278.4			277.2
D	293.3		290	293.6	293.7
D♯		309.4	309.3		311.1
E	330	330		326.3	329.6
F			348	348	349.2
F♯	366.7	371.2			370
G			386.7	391.5	392
G♯	412.5	412.5			415.3
A	440		435	435	440
A♯		464	464		466.2
B		495		489.4	493.9

mise, but the differences between the absolute and tempered pitch are so small that most people do not notice them.

SUMMARY

1. A fundamental tone is the note of lowest pitch that any sounding body can emit.

2. Overtones are any tones except the fundamental that a sounding body can emit.

3. Timbre is the quality of the note from a sounding body as determined from the overtones.

4. An interval is the ratio of the frequencies of two notes.

5. The intervals of the notes on the absolute scale are 9/8, 10/9, 16/15, 9/8, 10/9, 9/8, 16/15.

6. The intervals for all the notes on the equal-tempered scale are 1.059.

QUESTIONS AND EXERCISES

1. In the equal-tempered scale, is the interval A/G actually 9/8?

2. Are the overtones of a certain note always higher in pitch than the fundamental?

3. In the equal-tempered scale, all the intervals are equal. Does this mean that it is the differences or the ratios between adjacent notes that are always equal?

4. Start with C♯ = 275, and calculate the frequencies for D♯, F, F♯, G♯, A♯, and C; compare your values with those in Table 1-3.

5. In the key of C, the interval E/C should be 5/4. Using decimal fractions, calculate how close it is to this in the true tone scale (C = 261) and in the equal-tempered scale.

6

CHAPTER

Light as a Wave Motion

Reflection, Diffraction, and Refraction

Having studied certain aspects of the behavior of light, and having explored wave motion even more carefully, let us now see to what extent we can explain the facts about light in terms of its acting like a wave motion. In reflection, the parallel is complete. The angle of incidence equals the angle of reflection in both cases. Waves and light can be focused or diffused by reflection, etc.

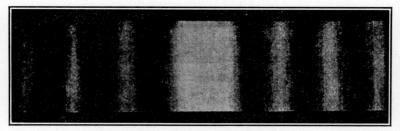

Figure 1-54. Diffraction bands produced by light passing through a narrow slit. The wide central band is directly in front of the slit, the others are off to the sides. (*General College Physics, by Randall, William, and Colby, Harper and Brothers.*)

Figure 1-54 was made by passing a beam of light through a narrow slit. A series of dark and light bands is observed on either side of the central one.

Figure 1-55 is an analysis of what is happening to the beams of light passing through slits *a* and *b*. The distances *ao* and *bo* are equal, but *bp* is longer than *ap* by the distance *bc*. If light behaves like a wave motion, then waves leaving *a* and *b* will travel the same distance to *o* and will always arrive in step; there will be constructive interference (a bright line) at *o*. At some dis-

tance above o there will be a place, p, where the wave from b has
to travel a half wavelength farther than the wave from a, so that
they will arrive out of phase, and there will be destructive interference and a dark line. The distance bc is half the wavelength
of the light under these conditions. Using this type of experiment, Thomas Young, in 1803, demonstrated the wave nature of
light and showed that the different colors of the spectrum have

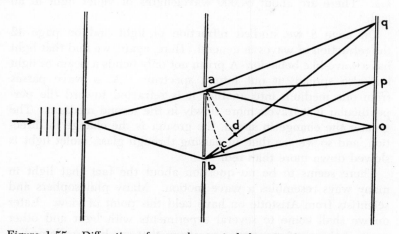

Figure 1-55. Diffraction of monochromatic light. Bright spots appear at
o and q, and a dark spot at p; bc is a half wavelength of the light, and bd
is a whole wavelength.

different wavelengths. You can see in Figure 1-55 that, if bd is 1
wavelength, q will be a bright line. The longer the wavelength,
the greater will be the distance from o, the central bright line, to
q, the nearest bright line on either side of it.

A diffraction grating is made by ruling a number of closely
spaced lines on a piece of glass through which light is transmitted
or from which it is reflected. These gratings have from 1000 to
25,000 lines per inch. Studying the diffraction of a beam of sunlight, we find that we get a spectrum of colors ranging from violet
through blue, green, yellow, and orange, to red. The violet is
nearest the central bright spot, and the red is farthest away (dif-
fracted through the greatest angle). If any small section of this
spectrum is passed through a second grating, it is not broken up

further, and so we see that the white light from the sun is actually
a mixture of all the colors of the spectrum and that they differ
from each other in wavelength. The red has the longest wavelength, the yellow an intermediate one, and the violet the shortest.
These wavelengths are measured in angstrom units (1 AU =
10^{-10} meter) or in millimicrons (1 $m\mu$ = 10^{-9} meter). Visible
light ranges in wavelength from 4000 to 8000 AU, or 400 to 800
$m\mu$. There are about 64,000 wavelengths of violet light in an
inch.

On page 8 we studied refraction of light and on page 42
the refraction of waves in general. Here, again, we find that light
has a wave-like behavior. A prism not only bends a beam of light
but also spreads it out into a spectrum. As a wave passes
from one medium into another it is refracted toward the perpendicular if it travels more slowly in the second medium. The
greater the change in speed, the greater is the change in direction, and so we see that, in passing through glass, violet light is
slowed down more than red.

There seems to be no question about the fact that light in
many ways resembles a wave motion. Many philosophers and
scientists from Aristotle on have held this point of view. Later
on we shall come to several experiments with light and other
parts of the electromagnetic spectrum that are best explained in
terms of light's behaving like a stream of particles. Newton
(1642–1727) considered both theories carefully, and he decided
that rays of light consisted of small bodies, or corpuscles. He
thought that as these corpuscles approached a prism they were
speeded up by attraction, and therefore had their direction
changed. Actually, light is slowed down as it enters glass from
air, but it was not possible, in Newton's day, to measure these
speeds. His point of view was generally accepted until Thomas
Young performed his experiments with diffraction. These
brought the wave theory back into popularity, and only recently
have we come to realize the awkward fact that both ways of
looking at the behavior of light are valid.

The Complete Electromagnetic Spectrum

As we look carefully at the brilliant spectrum from the sun,
we see that at both ends the colors fade rather rapidly, but there

is not a sharp line to mark the end. Could it be that there is "light" coming from the sun that we are unable to see? It is obvious that special methods of trying to detect this type of light will be necessary.

When sunlight is passed through a prism made of quartz, and the resulting spectrum is photographed, we find that the photographic plate is darkened all along the visible spectrum and for a considerable distance beyond the violet. In sunlight there must be rays that have a shorter wavelength than the violet light and that we cannot see. These are called ultraviolet rays. If we place a thermometer beyond the red end of this same spectrum we notice that it shows an increase in temperature, indicating an invisible infrared region in the sun's radiation. The infrared and ultraviolet rays are the same type of radiation as the visible light; they differ from it only in wavelength.

The invisible parts of the spectrum must be detected by many special means; when they are detected, we find an amazingly extensive spectrum of vibrations similar in nature to light.

Curiously enough, the two ends and the middle of the complete spectrum have been the most difficult to work with. Near the end of longest wavelength we have the ordinary amplitude-modulated radio waves with a wavelength of many miles. Special, short-wave radio broadcasting uses wavelengths down to about 100 feet, and also in this range are the wavelengths used for induction heating. Large metal castings can be heat-treated or roasts of beef can be cooked in a few minutes by radiations of these wavelengths. Television and frequency-modulated radios operate on wavelengths of a few feet. Radar detectors send and receive waves a few inches in length, and we are learning to use shorter and shorter waves in this region.

The region around 1 mm, or 10 million angstrom units, has turned out to be exceedingly difficult to work with. From a wavelength of 1,000,000 AU to 10,000 AU is the infrared region, which is used principally for radiant heating and, at the shorter end, for photographing through haze and smoke (Figures 1-56 and 1-57). The visible spectrum lies in the range 8000 to 4000 AU. Between 4000 and 100 AU is the ultraviolet region. Here are the wavelengths that tan the skin, increase the amount of vitamin D in milk, and kill bacteria (Figure 1-58). X-rays have a

Figure 1-56.   Scene photographed by visible light.   (*Eastman Kodak Co.*)

Figure 1-57.   Same scene photographed on film sensitive to infrared light.
(*Eastman Kodak Co.*)

wavelength from 100 AU to 0.1 AU, and are particularly useful because of their penetrating power. Photographs taken through the human body locate broken bones and other internal disor-

Figure 1-58. Blood donations are processed in an atmosphere kept sterile by the long, slender ultraviolet lamps near the ceiling. (*Lamp Division, Westinghouse Electric Corp.*)

ders (Figure 1-59), and industrial products like steel castings and propellers can be examined for hidden flaws (Figure 1-60). Another important use of X-rays is in treating cancer. Overlapping the shorter X-rays and going down to 0.001 AU are the gamma rays, which are the extremely penetrating and damaging radiation from atomic-bomb explosions.

Of even shorter wavelength and greater penetrating power

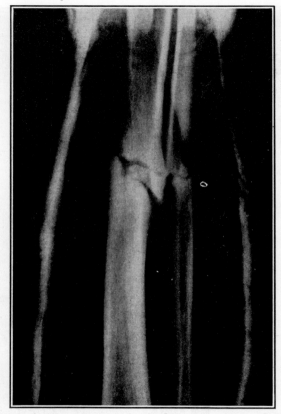

Figure 1-59.   An X-ray picture of a broken arm.   (*General Electric Co. X-ray Department.*)

than gamma rays are cosmic rays. Of their origin or behavior we may say only, on the basis of our present knowledge, that they come from outside the earth, can penetrate many feet of lead, and when they make one of their rare "hits" on a chromosome cell they may bring about a hereditary change that contributes to evolution.

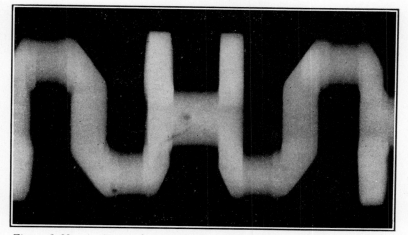

Figure 1-60. An X-ray photograph of an automobile crankshaft, showing a flaw in the casting. (*General Electric Co. X-ray Department.*)

SUMMARY

1. Light and waves follow the same laws of reflection, diffraction, and refraction.

2. Color is a measure of the wavelength of light.

3. Visible light is only a small part of a long spectrum of vibrations of a similar nature.

4. The complete electromagnetic spectrum includes (starting at the long-wavelength end) radio waves of various kinds, infrared, visible, ultraviolet, X-rays, gamma rays, and cosmic rays.

QUESTIONS AND EXERCISES

1. In what ways does light behave like a wave motion?

2. In Figure 1-55 what other distance is equal to *cp*?

3. What is the approximate wavelength of red light?

4. Which color is bent least by refraction through a prism?

5. What are some of the uses of the part of the electromagnetic spectrum with wavelengths longer than visible light?

6. What are some uses of X-rays other than as an aid in setting broken bones?

7. Why do we get a tan at high altitudes faster than at sea level?

8. What parts of the complete electromagnetic spectrum affect a photographic plate?

9. Hold two fingers close together and look through the crack at a bright light. This is an easy way to observe a diffraction spectrum.

10. Would a narrow band of green light be bent by refraction as it passes through a prism, or by diffraction as it passes through a diffraction grating?

7

Color

Color by Subtraction

Why do leaves look green instead of white? Do they emit a light of their own which is green? Of course not, but how do you know? Try looking at the shiny reflection from the surface of a cobalt-blue glass. The light which merely bounces off the surface cannot have had any colors removed, and these colors all show up in the reflection. The transmitted light, however, is mostly blue. Through such a glass a red book appears to be black.

The color of practically everything we see by daylight is obtained from the color of sunlight after certain wavelengths have been removed or reduced in intensity. When the white light from a projection lamp (or the sun) is passed through a prism it is spread out into a spectrum. When colored filters are placed in the path of the light, various parts of the spectrum are cut out. What you would call the "color" of the filter is actually the sum of all the colors it transmits. By subtracting certain colors and transmitting others the filter appears to be colored. A white surface, or a shiny surface of any color, reflects all the colors evenly. Light penetrates a short distance into a green blotter; the blotter absorbs the red and blue ends of the spectrum and reflects the green part of it. By way of contrast, a magenta dye absorbs the central part of the visible spectrum and transmits the red and blue extremes. Your eye does not analyze colors into their parts the way a prism does. In the experiment with the red book and the blue glass, the dye in the cover of the book absorbs all but the red end of the spectrum, and this is reflected. This red light is absorbed by the blue glass so that no light from the book reaches your eye, and you judge it to be black. When one

filter absorbs exactly that part of the spectrum which is transmitted by another, the colors of the two filters are said to be complementary. By subtraction, complementary colors give black.

Color by Addition

Color by subtraction, as described in the previous section,
can also be thought of as color by addition, in that the color
we see is made up of the sum of several colors. We have a
somewhat altered situation when we use several sources of different-colored lights, as is the custom in stage lighting. Many
different-colored bulbs are used in the battery of footlights to
accent the color of shadows. If you examine the color prints
in a magazine with a magnifying glass, you will see that each
colored area is made up of tiny dots of a few different colors
(probably three), with different proportions of each giving the
over-all impression of several different colors.

The difference between color by subtraction and color by
addition is illustrated by the usual technique in painting of
mixing pigments on the palette, and by that of Seurat, who
placed tiny dots of pigment close together. Look at a Seurat
painting at close range and see the confusing mixture of small
spots of color; then step back several feet and the individual
spots will appear to fuse into areas of solid color that have
an unusual brilliance. When the pigments are mixed on the
palette, each one substracts certain wavelengths, so that the
mixture is duller than any of the colors that went into making
it up.

If two spotlights are focused on the same screen, and filters
of complementary colors are placed in front of them, the whole
spectrum will be present on the lighted spot, and it will appear
white. Complementary colors by addition give white.

Spark Spectra and the Spectroscope

When the light from a neon advertising sign is passed through
a prism or a diffraction grating, we find that the spectrum consists of a number of bright lines with relatively long dark
spaces between them. Such an apparatus, set up to measure the
wavelengths of the different bright lines, is called a spectroscope, or spectrophotometer. An electric spark is used to excite

different elements, and the spectra obtained are peculiar to the element. Sodium has a rather simple spectrum, with two prominent lines close together in the yellow; nitrogen, on the other hand, has many lines spaced across the spectrum. The spectroscope is an important tool of the astronomer, and in the unit on the solar system we shall consider some of the information it gives us about the sun and stars. The colors seen in the northern lights are essentially this same phenomenon. Electrically charged particles from the sun enter the earth's atmosphere near the North Pole and excite a glow in the gases of the upper atmosphere.

Fluorescence

We have found that an object may be colored because it absorbs some of the wavelengths from the light that strikes it and reflects others, or it may be colored because it takes the energy from an electric spark and radiates it as visible light. There are a few substances that can absorb visible or ultraviolet light and radiate it as light of a longer wavelength. This behavior is called fluorescence. The rather startling advertising billboards that seem to glow on an overcast day and the teen-ager socks that can be seen for blocks are examples of fluorescence.

Several important minerals fluoresce with a characteristic color when struck by ultraviolet light or X-rays. This property is used in prospecting. Fluorescent lamps consist of glass tubes coated on the inside with a mixture of fluorescent minerals. A mercury arc in the tube provides the ultraviolet light that makes the coating glow with a visible light. The color of the light given off by these tubes can be varied over a wide range by the use of different minerals, and the decorative possibilities here have barely been touched upon. Fluorescent minerals are finding another use on the screens of television sets.

When a doctor "fluoroscopes" you, he places a fluorescent screen in front of you and an X-ray tube behind you so that he can examine the shadows cast by the bones and organs of your body. Since neither you nor the doctor can stand exposure to X-rays for many minutes, it is more usual to take a picture which can be studied carefully.

Some Applications of Color

There are innumerable situations in which an understanding of color will help you know more about what is going on around you; we can discuss relatively few of them here.

You have certainly observed the changing color of the sun as it sinks toward the horizon. At noon it is a blinding yellow-white; at sunset you can look directly at is and its color has changed to red. The color of the sky during the day is blue, which would suggest that the blue end of the spectrum is scattered out of the sunlight. The nearer the sun gets to the horizon, the more of the earth's atmosphere it must travel through, and the greater is the amount of the blue light that is scattered. The light that survives this long journey through the atmosphere has lost nearly all the short visible wavelengths and consists almost entirely of those in the long (red) end of the spectrum.

A brilliant rainbow is one of the most spectacular sights in nature. Remember that to see a rainbow you must stand with your back to the sun and that colors range through the spectrum from red on the top and outside to violet on the inside of the arc.

As the sunlight enters a raindrop it is refracted, internally reflected at the back, and refracted a second time as it leaves near the bottom (Figure 1-61). Since the violet end of the spectrum is bent through a greater angle than the red in both these refractions, as we look higher we see the red light coming from some drops. The yellow, green, and blue coming from these same drops pass over our heads, and we must look at the drops a little lower to see these colors.

The secondary rainbow is outside the primary one; the colors appear in the reverse order, and it is always fainter than the primary one. By studying Figure 1-62 you can see why this is so.

Since the index of refraction of a certain kind of glass is different for different colors, you would expect that a lens would bring the red and the blue light to a focus at different points. There is always a color fringe around the image formed by a simple lens. This behavior of lenses is called chromatic aberration, and it is usually a nuisance. It can be corrected by making use of the fact that some types of glass give a greater spread (dispersion) to the colors than other types. If a slightly di-

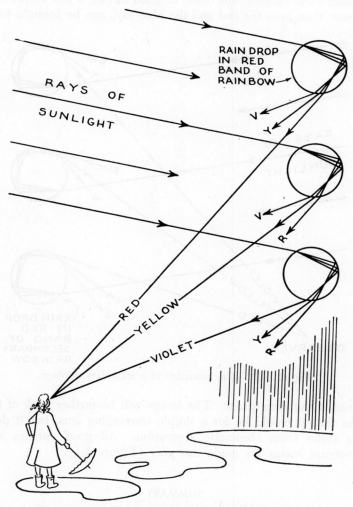

RAIN DROP
IN RED
BAND OF
RAINBOW

RAYS OF SUNLIGHT

RED
YELLOW
VIOLET

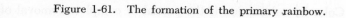

Figure 1-61. The formation of the primary rainbow.

verging lens made of glass with a high dispersing power is placed
behind a converging lens made of glass having a low dispersing
power, then both the red and the blue rays can be brought to a

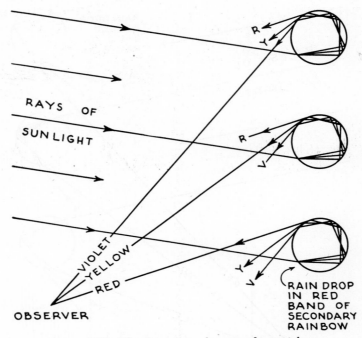

Figure 1-62.   The formation of a secondary rainbow.

focus at the same place. The image will be farther back of the
lens than it would be for a simple converging lens, but it does
not suffer from chromatic aberration. All good camera and
binocular lenses are made this way (Figure 1-1).

SUMMARY

1. Color by subtraction is the partial or complete removal of
certain wavelengths of incident light during reflection or transmission.

2. Color by addition is the adding together of light of two or
more different wavelengths to produce a combination color.

3. A spark spectrum is the light given out by a substance when it receives energy from an electric spark. This type of spectrum consists of a number of narrow lines.

4. Fluorescence is light which is given out by a substance as a result of the absorption of energy or light of a different wavelength. Fluorescence stops immediately after the exciting rays are cut off; in phosphorescence, the glow continues for some time afterward.

5. The particles of the atmosphere scatter the blue end of the spectrum more effectively than the red end.

6. A rainbow is the result of a combination of refraction and internal reflection of sunlight in raindrops.

7. Chromatic aberration occurs when a simple lens focuses the blue light from an object closer to the lens than the red light. A lens corrected for chromatic aberration is said to be achromatic.

QUESTIONS AND EXERCISES

1. What color is the complement to magenta?

2. Are the colors we see around us in life mostly due to color by addition, by subtraction, or a combination of the two?

3. Explain in detail how the use of many different-colored bulbs in theatre footlights produces colored shadows on the stage and, at the same time, the impression of white light on the actors.

4. How could a spectroscope be used to identify the elements present in a mixture of gases?

5. What sources of color have been mentioned which do not have their origin in sunlight?

6. If we had no atmosphere, what would be the color of the sky?

7. Why can't we see the stars in the daytime?

8. Under what conditions could we see a rainbow as a complete circle?

9. Make a sketch showing what an achromatic lens looks like.

10. Suggest two ways of detecting ultraviolet light.

CHAPTER 8

In the Dark Room

Chlorophyll and Photosynthesis

There are many familiar examples of the changes brought about by sunlight. The fading of dyed fabrics, the yellowing of newsprint, the tanning of skin—this short list will bring many more to mind. Plants need light to carry on photosynthesis. They take a number of simple substances like carbon dioxide and water and build them into complex ones like sugar and cellulose. The green coloring matter in leaves, chlorophyll, absorbs certain parts of the sun's spectrum and turns this energy over to the synthetic process going on in the plants.

The energy stored up by photosynthesis is the source of nearly all the energy that we use today. When you burn a piece of wood and change it back into carbon dioxide and water the energy released warms you or cooks your food. When you eat sugar it is burned in your body to carbon dioxide and water and furnishes the energy for you to move around, think, and breathe. Coal, oil, and natural gas are the results of photosyntheses which took place on earth millions of years ago. From the long-range point of view, we are rapidly using up the reserve supply of this stored-up energy, and our industrial civilization will return to the cave-man stage unless we develop a way to use photosynthesis more extensively than we do now. When all the sources of fossil fuel are used up and all the sources of atomic energy have been exhausted, the sun will still be shining. Instead of letting nature take its course, there will be factories consisting of acres of shallow ponds in which chlorophyll will be used to trap the energy in sunlight.

The Latent Image and the Reduction of Silver Bromide

In photography we have the problem of finding a substance that will keep a permanent record of the lights and shadows of the image coming through the lens of our camera. When we move a mirror which has been hanging for a long time in the same place, we notice the unbleached shadowgram on the wall paper. This way of making a picture is unsatisfactory because it takes too long and the image is not permanent. Exposure to sunlight will bleach it.

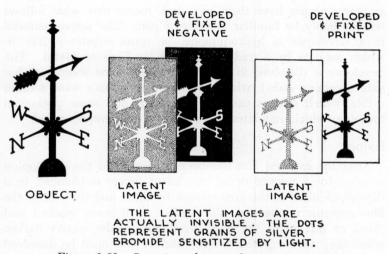

THE LATENT IMAGES ARE ACTUALLY INVISIBLE. THE DOTS REPRESENT GRAINS OF SILVER BROMIDE SENSITIZED BY LIGHT.

Figure 1-63. Steps in making a photographic print.

Certain salts of silver, particularly silver chloride and silver bromide, are changed to metallic silver when exposed to sunlight. This reaction is too slow tȯ be practical, but it was discovered that a crystal of silver bromide that had been struck by light could be changed rapidly to a crystal of silver by the action of a substance called a developer. The developer will not affect an unexposed crystal of silver bromide, nor does a short exposure to light make a visible change in the silver bromide crystal. This invisible image which is formed on the film is called a latent image—latent because, although not apparent, it is capable of being developed (Figure 1-63). In the process of development, a silver bromide grain is either untouched, or it is completely reduced to silver. According to the conception that light is a stream of particles, this would probably mean that those grains that were hit by a light particle (a quantum of light) were rendered susceptible to the action of the developer, and those that were missed were insensitive to its action. It is hard to see how the facts can be explained in terms of the wave theory of light.

A detailed study of the chemistry of photography would require the background of at least two courses in chemistry, but so many people have their own dark rooms that what follows will probably be familiar to most of you. The active material in a developer is hydroquinone, or some substance like it, which may go by a trade name such as Elon or Metol. The developer is dissolved in water containing some sodium carbonate (washing soda), which speeds up its action; some sodium sulfite, which renews used-up developer; and some potassium bromide, which regulates the action to the proper speed.

Fixing

After the exposed film has been immersed in the developing solution for a minute or so, the latent image is changed to a deposit of silver in the areas struck by light, and the rest of the film contains unchanged silver salts. If it were washed and dried at this point the unchanged silver salts would darken when they were exposed to light, and so they must be dissolved away. This next step in the processing of a film is called fixing. The fixing bath contains some acetic acid (the sour substance in vinegar) to stop the action of the developer, and some hypo (sodium thiosulfate) to dissolve the unchanged silver chloride and silver bromide crystals. After the action of the fixing bath, the film is thoroughly washed (Figure 1-63).

Printing

The film at this point carries a black deposit of silver on the parts that received the most light from the original image and is transparent where the image was dark. This reversal of the light values is the reason for calling it a negative. When a picture is taken of the negative the values are again reversed, so that they correspond with those of the original subject. The easiest way to take a picture of the negative is to place it in contact with a sensitive film and let the light shine through it (a contact print). This gets around the need for lenses and focusing. If an enlargement is desired, then the light passing through the negative goes through a lens system that enlarges the image and throws it on a sensitive paper. The print is developed, fixed, and washed in the same manner as the negative (Figure 1-63).

Since the finished negative must be transparent, the crystals of silver chloride and silver bromide are spread out in a thin layer of gelatin on a transparent plastic base. Prints, on the other hand, are viewed by reflected light, so their base is a piece of white paper.

Correcting Film for Color

Since the silver salts used are more sensitive to the blue than to the red end of the spectrum, a bright red would look darker than a dark blue in the final print. This is corrected by adding to the film a dye that absorbs the red light and passes the energy on to the silver bromide crystals in much the same way that chlorophyll absorbs parts of the spectrum and passes them on to the photosynthetic reaction in the leaves. Panchromatic film is an example of this type of color correction.

SUMMARY

1. Light energy can bring about chemical changes.

2. Photosynthesis is a chemical synthesis that uses the energy from light. Chlorophyll is the catalyst used in nature.

3. A latent image is an invisible image formed by light, which is capable of being developed into a visible image.

4. Development is the changing of a latent image into a visible image. In photography this is usually the change of salts of silver into metallic silver.

5. A developer contains hydroquinone (or some similar reducing agent), sodium carbonate, sodium sulfite, potassium bromide, and water.

6. Fixing is the process in which the undeveloped silver salts are dissolved.

7. The fixing bath contains acetic acid, hypo, and water.

8. A negative is made on a transparent base; a positive is usually made on an opaque, white base.

9. There are special conditions for processing negatives and prints, which are not covered in this chapter.

10. Silver salts are not equally sensitive to all parts of the visible spectrum. It is possible to treat film to make this color sensitivity more nearly uniform.

QUESTIONS AND EXERCISES

1. Consider any large animal or fish and show how it depends ultimately upon photosynthesis in plants for its food energy.

2. List the substances present in a photographic-developing solution, and state the part played by each.

3. Would a finished photographic print be damaged by water?

4. Explain the fact that a picture of a bright-blue sky with white clouds looks almost completely white.

5. Take a picture which is considerably underexposed and another which is very much overexposed and observe the appearance of the resulting negatives.

9

Motion Pictures and Polarized Light

Camera and Projector

Photography is much more than a hobby; it is one of our most important means of entertainment, an art form, an aid in education and job training, and a scientific tool. Motion pictures are widely used in all these ways. You may have noticed and been puzzled by the appearance of carriage wheels in the movies. Usually they seem to be rolling forward or backward with no relation to the actual motion of the vehicle. An examination of this problem will help you understand how movies are made and projected. A movie camera takes a picture with such a fast shutter speed that there is usually little or no blurring of the image. The film is stationary while the shutter is open. While the shutter is closed a new frame of film moves into place, the motion of the film stops for another picture to be taken, etc.

Moving pictures are normally filmed at a speed of 24 frames per second. After a reel has been exposed, it is developed, fixed, and washed, and contact prints are made. In this case, the positive print is printed on a transparent celluloid base because it is going to be projected and not viewed by reflected light.

A motion-picture projector is constructed much like a camera with a bright light behind the film (Figure 1-64). The film is motionless while the shutter is open; the shutter closes while the frames are being shifted. Of course, there is no motion in any one picture, and the original subject was moving while the shutter of the camera was closed, so what is projected is a series of stills that differ from each other by a slight extent. The image of each picture persists on our retina (page 32) during the brief time the shutter of the projector is closed. We inter-

pret the series of overlapping images as one of smooth motion.
Getting back to the appearance of the carriage wheel, consider one with four spokes for convenience. If the wheel makes

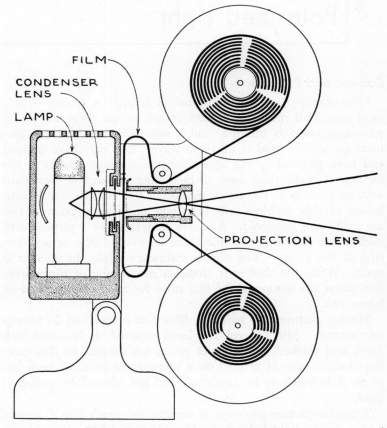

FILM

CONDENSER
LENS

LAMP

PROJECTION LENS

Figure 1-64. A motion-picture projector.

a quarter revolution during the time the shutter is closed, every
picture will show the spokes in the same position and the wheel
will seem to be stationary. If the wheel makes a little less than
a quarter (or a half, etc.) revolution while the camera shutter
is closed, each picture will show it a little behind the position
of the last one, so that it appears to be revolving slowly back-

ward. At other speeds it will look as though it is going slowly forward or moving rapidly.

The Movie Projector as a Time Machine

A movie camera can be used as a time microscope to enlarge an interval of time which is too short to examine carefully; or,

Figure 1-65. Rapid action caught by technique of high-speed photography. (*Harold E. Edgerton.*)

as when binoculars are used wrong end to, a long interval of time can be condensed so that it can be studied more effectively. By running the camera fast, so that it takes 96 pictures a second, and projecting the film at 24 frames per second, action which took place in 15 seconds is slowed down so that it takes a minute to project. Athletic coaches find this "slow-motion" technique very handy. When we want to study the germination of seeds, the growth of a fern, or the opening of a flower, the subject is photographed on a new frame every 5 minutes, or even every half hour, and the resulting film is projected at the normal rate. This compresses the action of many hours into a few minutes and is referred to as "time-lapse" photography. For special industrial problems, lights have been developed that flash brilliantly for a millionth of a second at intervals of one hundred thousandth of a second, the film rolls through the camera continuously, and rapid motion can be studied with precision (Figure 1-65).

Polarized Light

The sciences have been extremely fortunate in that the definitions in these fields are usually operational. In an operational definition a term is defined in words that tell you how to measure or observe it. Contrast the definition of the index of refraction (page 11), which is given in terms of angles that can be measured, with the following one taken from a dictionary: "free. (Political) Having, conferring, or characterized by political liberty; not subject to despotic or arbitrary rule." Just think how that use of that word is open to a variety of interpretations, how many groups of people would disagree about their own and the others' freedom.

In regard to polarized light, we will soon come to a definition that is couched in terms of how it is observed, rather than in terms of what we think is happening. As we learn more about it, our definition will not need changing. If you place a single dot on a piece of paper and look at it through a crystal of Iceland spar, you will see two dots, one of which rotates around the other as the crystal is rotated. If you observe the two dots through a second crystal of Iceland spar, you will find that one or the other dot can be made to disappear by rotating the second crystal in a horizontal plane. The two crystals can be interchanged and the behavior is the same.

It is obvious that the light emerging from the first crystal is different from that entering it. Each of the two dots that you see consists of a beam of light which is said to be polarized.

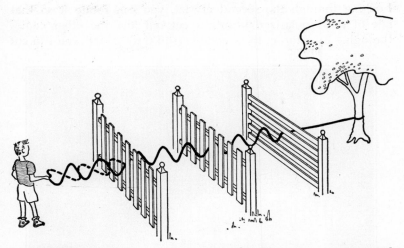

Figure 1-66. An analogy to show why polarized waves are transmitted through a filter held in one position and blocked when the filter is held at right angles to that position. (*After Polaroid Corp.*)

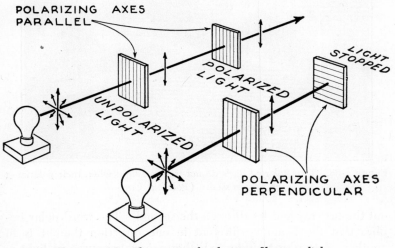

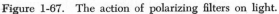

Figure 1-67. The action of polarizing filters on light.

Looking through the second crystal, you can rotate it so that one of these polarized beams is cut out and the other comes through. By rotating the second crystal through 90° you can cut

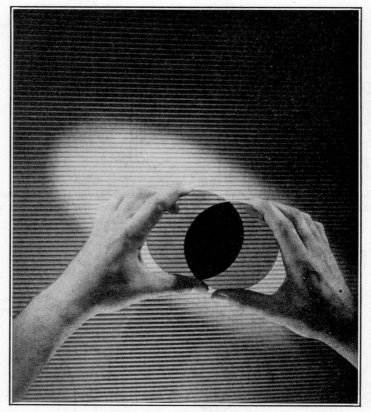

Figure 1-68. Two Polaroid discs do not transmit light when their polarizing axes are crossed. (*Polaroid Corp.*)

out the first ray and let through the second. The word polar implies that the beam is different in one direction than it is in another. In order to judge whether a certain source of light is polarized, you need a crystal of Iceland spar or some material that behaves like it. If this can be rotated in the plane perpendicular to the path of the beam of light to produce a change in intensity of the light, then the light is polarized.

The most suitable explanation for this situation seems to be the conception of light as a wave motion. If we picture a beam of light as consisting of a large number of waves, like waves in a vibrating string, which vibrate in many different planes, and polarized light as consisting of waves which vibrate in only one plane, then this situation makes sense. Imagine a clothesline tied to a tree and passed through three sections of picket fence (Figure 1-66). If the line is vibrated in several different planes, only the waves in a vertical plane will pass through the first fence. The waves approaching the second fence are polarized. The fact that they pass through the second fence does not tell us that they are polarized, but when the third fence stops them we know that they are polarized, and they must have been vertically polarized to have gone through the second fence. Figure 1-67 applies this picture to light. Few human eyes can observe the difference between unpolarized and polarized light.

There are many substances that will polarize light. The only one developed, so far,

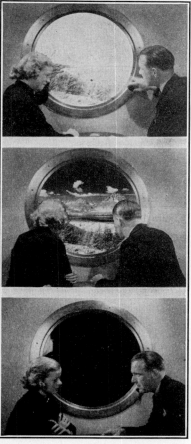

Figure 1-69. By adjusting the angle between the polarizing axes of two Polaroid discs the intensity of the transmitted light can be controlled. (*Polaroid Corp.*)

that can be made in large thin sheets is Polaroid. This was developed by E. H. Land while he was an undergraduate at Harvard University. There are many interesting applications

Figure 1-70. Picture taken without Polaroid filter. Note glare. (*Polaroid Corp.*)

Figure 1-71. Same picture taken with Polaroid filter. Most of the glare has been eliminated. (*Polaroid Corp.*)

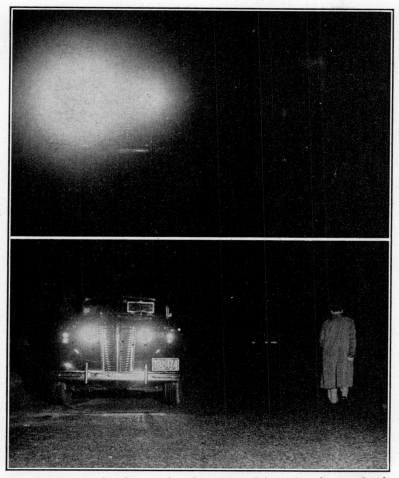

Figure 1-72. Night photographs of an automobile with polarizing head-lights, illuminated by the headlights of another automobile beside the camera, taken without and with suitably oriented polarizing filter over the camera lens. (*Polaroid Corp.*)

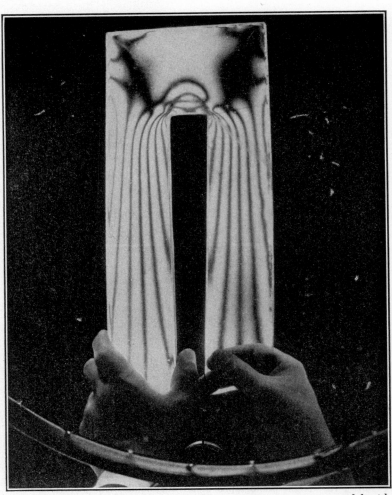

Figure 1-73. Lines of stress revealed by examining transparent model with
polarized light. (*Polaroid Corp.*)

of polarized light that have been opened up by the production of Polaroid. Since a pair of Polaroid discs will not transmit light when their polarizing axes are crossed (Figure 1-68), they can be used to control the intensity of light (Figure 1-69). Reflection partially polarizes light, so that glare can be cut out with Polaroid glasses. These are particularly useful at the beach and for driving. A Polaroid filter placed over a camera lens will cut out the glare from a brightly lighted scene and show more detail (Figures 1-70 and 1-71). If Polaroid filters were used on automobile headlights and a screen were placed on the windshield, the resulting reduction of glare would prevent many accidents (Figure 1-72). A study of transparent plastic models by means of polarized light shows that when the models are under stress the lines of stress are revealed (Figure 1-73). Consequently, it is possible to study various designs to determine which is the strongest for a particular job. Designs for nuts, bolts, gears, and even bridges have been studied this way.

The sunlight scattered by the particles of the earth's atmosphere is partially polarized, the effect being most pronounced in a direction at right angles to the sun. There are a few people who can detect polarized light with the unaided eye. Experiments with bees indicate that they can detect it accurately and that it serves to guide them in their flight.

SUMMARY

1. The ordinary motion-picture camera takes a series of pictures on a long roll of film which moves past the lens in a series of jerks. The shutter is open when the film is stationary and closed when the film is moving.

2. Motion-picture positive film (print) has a transparent base.

3. The motion-picture projector works like the camera, except that there is a light source behind the film.

4. Slow-motion pictures are taken at a faster rate than normal and are projected at the usual rate. This technique is used for studying rapid motion.

5. Time-lapse pictures are taken at long intervals and are projected at the normal rate. This technique is used for studying motion which is too slow to observe otherwise.

6. There are certain transparent substances that will change the intensity of the transmitted light when they are rotated in a plane perpendicular to a beam of a certain type of incident light. When this happens the incident light is said to be polarized.

7. Unpolarized light may be polarized by transmission through a polarizing medium, by reflection, and by other special techniques.

8. A polarizing medium, such as Polaroid, may be used to control light intensity and glare, to study transparent models for strain patterns, and for many other purposes.

QUESTIONS AND EXERCISES

1. What were the two most important factors in determining that motion pictures should be filmed at a speed of 24 frames per second?

2. What valuable metal is recovered from the spent fixing solution of a motion-picture studio?

3. About how long does any one image persist on the retina?

4. In the very highest-speed rapid photography, the film does not stop while a picture is being taken. Why is the image not blurred?

5. Cite an example of an operational definition given previously in the text.

6. By holding a pair of Polaroid sunglasses away from your face and rotating them as you look at some source of light, you can judge whether the light is polarized. Examine light reflected from shiny surfaces, various parts of the sky, the moon, and dots seen through a crystal of Iceland spar.

7. How would the use of a Polaroid filter over your camera lens affect exposure time?

8. List five uses of Polaroid filters.

9. Why would it be necessary to have specific and uniform legislation before the use of Polaroid filters would be practical for controlling headlight glare?

10. In what way would a Polaroid filter help in taking a picture of white clouds and a bright-blue sky?

Unit 2

▼

THE SOLAR SYSTEM
AND BEYOND

Structure of the Solar System

What Goes On in the Sky?

In starting our study of the structure of the solar system it would be well for us to put in order the knowledge of the subject that we have accumulated through everyday experience. Where does the sun rise, and where does it set? Does it always rise in the same place and at the same time? Is there any regularity about these changes? Ask yourself the same series of questions about the moon. How does the moon differ in appearance from time to time? Do we notice the same sort of changes in the sun? Is the Big Dipper always in the same position at ten o'clock at night? How about the Pleiades, Orion, Jupiter, Venus? Any mechanical model that we construct will have to be consistent with the known facts. You probably know that the earth revolves around the sun, but can you point to any fact that is inconsistent with the idea that the sun revolves around the earth? For many hundreds of years the latter was the accepted idea.

Careful observation over several years would be required to answer all the questions asked in the previous paragraph, and people living in different parts of the country would not give the same answer to every question.

Apparent Motion of the Sun

North of the Arctic Circle and south of the Antarctic Circle there are many successive days when the sun never rises above the horizon. As you approach the Poles, the length of this dark period increases to a maximum of 6 months each year, and there is a corresponding period during which the sun never sets below the horizon. As seen from the Equator the sun rises 23.5° north of east on June 21 and sets 23.5° north of west; on

March 21 and September 23 it rises and sets exactly east and west; and on December 21 it rises and sets 23.5° south of east and west. For a house that faces directly north, the sun will shine in the front windows as it rises in the early summer, and in the back windows as it rises in the early winter. We have seen how the length of "day" can vary from zero to 24 hours near the Poles. At the Equator it is slightly over 12 hours long all through the year.

Apparent Motion of the Moon

The moon always rises later than it did the previous time. On the average, it is 50½ minutes later each day. When it rises just about sunset it appears to be round, and we call it a "full" moon. When it is visible in the west at sunset it appears to be a delicate crescent, and we call it a "new" moon. If you start observing the moon when it is new and make a point of looking for it the same time each night for two weeks, you will notice on successive nights that it is farther away from the sun (farther east), and larger. At the end of one week it will be to the south and half full, at the end of the second week it will be rising in the east as a full moon. After that, you will have to wait later and later to see it, and it will be changing back to a half moon. Instead of waiting up until late at night to see it in the east, you can see it in the western sky during the morning. At the end of the third week after the new moon, it will be setting in the west at noon. During the next (fourth) week it will be hard to observe unless you are an early riser. If you have the persistence to get up before sunrise, you will be rewarded by seeing a beautiful crescent old moon floating above the faint glow of dawn in the east. The whole change from new moon to the next new moon takes 29½ days.

Apparent Motion of the Stars

If you are familiar with any bright star, like Sirius, or an easily recognized constellation, like Orion, or the Pleiades, which are prominent in the winter sky, you can observe that they rise about 4 minutes earlier each night. We can make a star map showing the different constellations and their relationships to each other, but the map must be adjusted for the day of the year and the hour of the day to show which groups of stars are above the horizon. The arrangement of the stars in the sky on any one night of the year will be repeated on the same

Figure 2-1.   A time-exposure picture of the stars in the vicinity of the North Star.   The shutter was left open 1 hour.   As the earth rotates on its axis the stars leave arclike trails on the photographic plate.   (*Yerkes Observatory.*)

date of the next year.   Most of the stars rise in a general easterly direction and set in a westerly one; but those near the North Star (the Big Dipper, the Little Dipper, Cassiopea, etc.) swing in a great circle around the North Star and never set below the horizon (Figure 2-1).   To observers in the far north there are many constellations that never set, and as far south as New Orleans the handle of the Big Dipper will be seen to drop below the northern horizon. The sun is to the south of those of us in the United States at noon every day; the moon goes through a complete change of phases approximately every month; and the stars repeat their cycle of motion across the heavens every year.

Apparent Motion of the Planets

In contrast to this regularity of motion of most of the heavenly bodies is the behavior of the five visible planets, Mercury, Venus, Mars, Jupiter, and Saturn. These travel approximately the same path in the sky as the sun and moon. If you watch some of these for several weeks, you will see that they do not appear against the same background of constellations over a long period of time. Sometimes they are farther east and sometimes farther west.

Scale Model of the Solar System

We have now assembled a large number of facts that require an explanation. We should be able to construct some sort of mechanical model that will demonstrate these relationships. It will be less confusing if we study the picture of the solar system that is now believed to be true rather than taking up the various theories in their historical order.

About 1609, Kepler proposed the currently accepted theory of the structure of the solar system (page 154). He said that the earth and the other planets move around the sun in elliptical paths that are nearly circular. To get an idea of the relative sizes involved, imagine the sun as a ball nearly an inch across and at the end of a football field. The earth would be about the size of a pinpoint and at a distance of 7 feet 11 inches. Jupiter, which is the largest planet, would be represented by a pinhead at a distance of 40 feet. Pluto, the outermost planet, would be a pinpoint at the far end of the field (306 feet). The orbits of the planets lie close to a common plane, and all the planets go around the sun in the same direction. On the same scale, the nearest star would be 384 miles away, and the distances to most of them would be many thousands of miles.

If, at the center of the earth, we should draw a line perpendicular to the plane of the earth's orbit, it would form an angle of 23½ degrees with the axis of rotation of the earth. The axis of rotation (the line joining the North and South Poles) points toward the North Star, and so, as the earth travels around the sun, the angle that this axis of rotation makes with a line to the sun changes from 66½ degrees on June 21 to 113½ degrees on

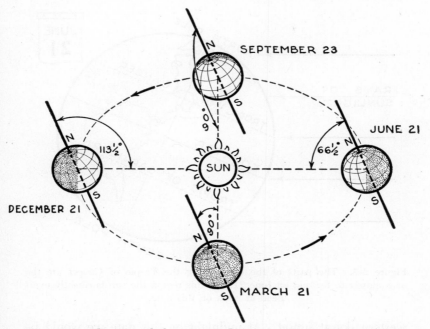

Figure 2-2. The seasonal change in angle between the earth's axis of rotation and the line joining the earth and the sun.

December 21 (Figure 2-2). The parts of the earth closest to the sun on June 21 are those along the Tropic of Cancer (Figure 2-3); on March 21 and September 23, those along the Equator; and on December 21, those along the Tropic of Capricorn.

In the latitudes of the continental United States, the sun is never directly overhead, and at noon it is directly to the south. From one noon to the next is 24 hours by definition. As you look down on the North Pole the rotating earth is turning in a counterclockwise direction. On its trip around the sun the earth rotates on its axis 366¼ times.

Refer to Figure 2-2, and imagine the stars somewhere beyond the limits of the four sides of the page. You can see that those constellations beyond the bottom of the page would appear overhead at midnight on March 21. In April and May they would set earlier and earlier, and by June 21 they would be low in the

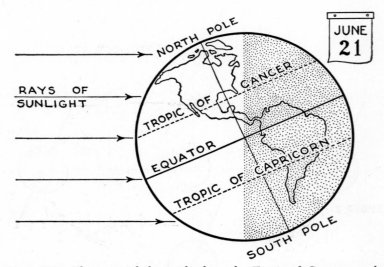

Figure 2-3. The parts of the earth along the Tropic of Cancer are the ones closest to the sun on June 21. In this region the sun is directly overhead at noon on this date.

western sky at sunset. At midnight on this date we would be looking up toward a different quarter of the heavens—the one to the right of the page. At midnight on September 23 we would be looking in exactly the opposite direction from the one we were looking on March 21, and on December 21 we would see those stars in the fourth quarter of the sky, with the ones we had observed in March rising in the east just before dawn. Those stars below the page would not be visible from the United States, and those well above it would be toward the north, and the North Star and some of its immediate neighbors would be visible all year long.

SUMMARY

1. The length of time that the sun is above the horizon varies from 6 continuous months at the Poles in summertime to a little over 12 hours each day at the Equator all through the year.

2. The moon goes through its cycle of phases in 29½ days. It rises on an average of 50½ minutes later each day.

3. The stars rise about 4 minutes earlier each night. They repeat their cycle of motion across the sky once a year.

4. The planets follow an irregular but predictable motion in the sky. Their path of motion is always close to that followed by the sun.

5. On a scale model, with the sun represented by a ball 1 inch in diameter, the planets would all be the size of a pinhead or smaller. This entire model would be slightly over 600 feet in diameter.

QUESTIONS AND EXERCISES

1. At the Equator, why does daylight last a little longer than 12 hours instead of exactly 12 hours?

2. If you were a little north of the Arctic Circle, what path would you observe the sun taking during the 24 hours of June 21?

3. On the Tropic of Cancer (latitude 23.5° north) at noon on June 21, what is the angle between a north-south line (meridian) and a line pointing to the sun?

4. As in Question 3, what would the angle be for a place at 24.5° north latitude? 30° north latitude? 40° north latitude?

5. Express the answer to Question 4 in the form of a general equation.

6. What direction would you have to look to see the constellation Orion in April at about nine P.M.?

7. Take a look some evening and sketch the relative positions of the Big Dipper, Little Dipper, and Cassiopea.

8. What direction from you right now is a constellation which you could see overhead at midnight 6 months ago?

9. What is the greatest number of full moons that could occur in one year?

10. Does a crescent moon ever appear in the eastern sky?

2

The Tools We Use, and a Look at the Sun and Moon

1. TOOLS OF THE ASTRONOMER

(a) Naked-Eye Observation

The first phase of any science is descriptive. The early astronomers concerned themselves with observing where each of the stars was at a certain time and with estimating its relative brightness. Despite the apparent multitude of stars, there are only about two thousand which can be seen at one time from any one place on the earth. The position of a star is described by noting its direction, its angular distance above the horizon, and the time of the observation. Even in the days of Ptolemy some remarkably accurate measurements were made. Tycho Brahe (1546–1601) used a large-scale quadrant similar to the one in Figure 2-4 and also used a mechanical clock.

(b) Modern Tools

When Galileo (1564–1642) invented the telescope, he not only increased the accuracy of this type of measurement but also made it possible to study new problems. Details of structure of the sun, moon, and planets could be observed, and the increased light-gathering power of the instrument revealed stars too faint to be seen by the unaided eye. The optical system of a refracting telescope was shown in Figure 1-21. The Yerkes Observatory of the University of Chicago has the largest instrument of this type, with a 40-inch lens (Figure 1-22). A very large lens absorbs too much of the light that falls upon it and also tends to sag under its own weight, so that the larger telescopes use concave mirrors to gather the light. The optical system of a reflecting telescope is shown in Figure 1-23. The largest telescope of this type, and a real triumph of modern engineering skill, is the 200-inch reflector at Mt. Palomar (Figure 2-5).

Our ability to "see" great distances has been further increased by attaching a camera to the telescope. The effect of light on a

Figure 2-4. An example of the type of large-scale quadrant in use at the time of Tycho Brahe.

photographic plate is cumulative, so that exposures of many hours will reveal details which would be entirely missed by a look through the eyepiece of the same telescope.

Another valuable accessory to the telescope is the spectroscope. When the light collected by the telescope is passed through a prism or diffraction grating, the spectrum can be photographed and analyzed. From this information, we can

Figure 2-5. Reflecting telescope at Mt. Palomar. The mirror is 200 inches in diameter. (*Mt. Wilson and Mt. Palomar Observatories.*)

tell what elements are present in the star, its temperature, and, from any shift in wavelength of prominent lines (Doppler effect), we can tell whether the star is approaching or receding.

2. THE SUN

The sun dominates the solar system in many ways. It is more than 10 times the diameter of the largest planet; its volume is a thousand times greater than that of all the planets combined; all the planets and comets revolve around the sun, and they all shine by light reflected from it. Energy from the sun makes life possible on earth. All but four planets receive so little of this energy that nearly everything on them is frozen solid.

The sun is a great mass of hot gases with a surface temperature of only about 11,000°F, but an interior temperature which may be as high as 40,000,000°F. From time to time whirlpools

TABLE 2-1. DATA ON THE SOLAR SYSTEM

Name	Mean distance from sun in millions of miles	Equatorial diameter in miles	Mass Earth = 1	Period of revolution		Period of rotation		Number of moons
Sun		864,000	332,000			24.7	days	
Moon		2,160	0.012			27.3	days	
Mercury	36	3,100	0.04	88	days	88	days	0
Venus	67	7,700	0.81	225	days	30?	days	0
Earth	93	7,927	1.00	365	days	1	day	1
Mars	142	4,200	0.11	687	days	24h 37m		2
Jupiter	483	88,700	317	11.9	years	9h 55m		12
Saturn	886	71,500	95	29.5	years	10h 14m		9
Uranus	1783	32,000	14.7	84	years	10h 40m		5
Neptune	2794	31,000	17.2	165	years	15h 40m		2
Pluto	3675	7,000?	0.7	248	years	?		?

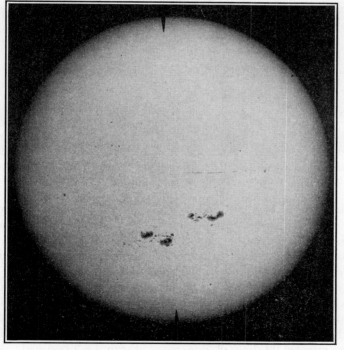

Figure 2-6. Photograph of the sun, showing several large sunspots. (*Mt. Wilson and Mt. Palomar Observatories.*)

of cooler gases appear on the surface of the sun. These may be so large that they can be seen with the naked eye by looking at the sun's reflection in a dish of water. They are called sunspots (Figure 2-6), and by following their progress across the surface of the sun we can observe that the sun rotates on its axis

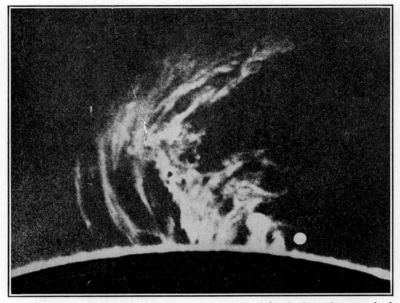

Figure 2-7. A large solar prominence 140,000 miles high. Photographed in light of calcium. (*Mt. Wilson and Mt. Palomar Observatories.*)

with a period of about 25 days. There are regularly recurring times of maximum sunspot activity which have been linked with variations in the weather on earth.

Another type of disturbance on the surface of the sun is called solar prominences. These can best be observed at the edge of the disc of the sun through an instrument called a spectrohelioscope. In one form of this instrument the sun's light is spread into a spectrum by a spectroscope, and a narrow band of that spectrum is viewed through a slit. In this way the light from one bright line of one element can be examined. The picture in Figure 2-7 shows solar prominences photographed by one of the lines from the calcium in the sun. These streamers of hot gases sweep millions of miles out from the sun's surface in a few minutes.

3. THE MOON

The moon, with its diameter of 2160 miles, is greater than one-fourth the size of the earth (Figure 2-8). No other planet

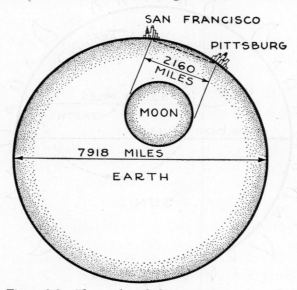

Figure 2-8. The earth and the moon drawn to scale.

has a satellite so near its own size. In revolving around the earth, the moon always keeps the same side toward us. When we send space ships to the moon, mankind will have its first chance to study the far side, which we have not yet seen. In Figure 2-9, the moon's orbit around the earth is drawn to scale inside a circle representing the disc of the sun. Of course, the sun rises and sets on the moon as it does on the earth. There can be no twilight because there is no atmosphere, and at any one spot the sun shines for nearly 2 weeks and then is gone for an equal time.

If the plane of the earth's orbit around the sun is represented by a circle 9 yards in diameter, with a golf ball for the sun at its center, the moon's orbit around the earth would be the size of a nickel. This nickel would tilt slightly as it goes around in the plane of the large circle, making an angle of 5° 8′. As the moon travels between the earth and the sun we can see only a small

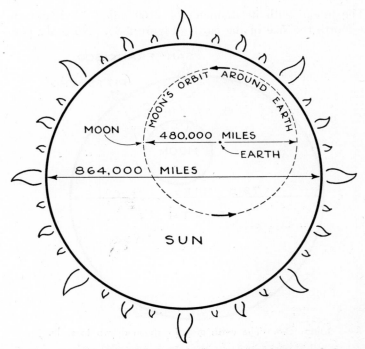

Figure 2-9. A scale drawing showing the moon's orbit around the earth compared with the diameter of the sun.

part of the lighted side, and 2 weeks later it is on the side of the earth opposite the sun, so that we are looking at the whole lighted face.

On the date given in the calendar for a new moon, it is too close to the sun to be seen, but a day or so later it appears briefly in the western sky (Figure 2-10) as a thin crescent, which soon follows the sun below the horizon. The next day, the crescent is thicker, the moon is higher in the sky, and it sets later. At this stage, we frequently notice the rest of the circle of the

moon's face shining with a feeble gray light. The source of
this light is sunlight which has been reflected first from the earth
to the moon and then back again to us. It is understandable

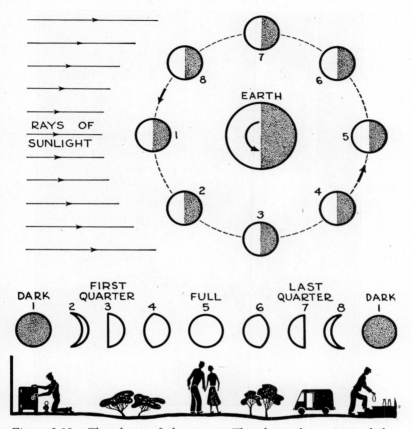

Figure 2-10. The phases of the moon. This shows the position of the
moon in relation to the sun and the earth and its appearance as viewed
from the earth at approximately 3½-day intervals.

that this light is faint, when we realize that both the earth and
the moon reflect only about 7% of the incident light.

Two weeks after the time of the new moon, the moon is rising in the east as the sun sets in the west and we have a full
moon shining all through the night. Since the moon travels

around the earth in the same direction that the earth rotates on its axis, 24 hours later it will have traveled approximately 1/29 of the way around its monthly circle.   The earth will have to

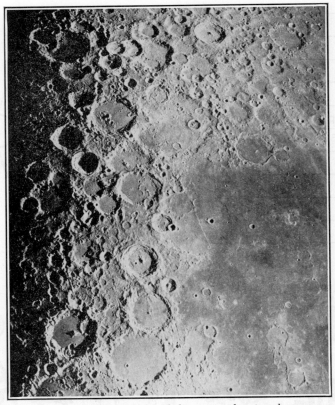

Figure 2-11. A part of the surface of the moon, showing the many craters, some of them overlapping.   (*Mt. Wilson and Mt. Palomar Observatories.*)

keep turning about 45 minutes after the sun has set before we can again see the moon rise in the east.   In Figure 2-10, the sun would be located off to the left of the page.   A week later, the moon will be high in the southern sky at dawn, appearing half full, and will set at noon.   Each following day it will be closer to the sun, until, 29½ days after the previous new moon, it is again between the earth and the sun.

Figure 2-12.   Crater Lake, Oregon.   (*Air Force Photograph.*)

Figure 2-13.   Aerial Photograph of Meteor Crater in Arizona.   (*Photograph by Clyde Fisher, American Museum of Natural History.*)

The surface features of the moon can be examined with a good pair of field glasses, and they have been studied, mapped, and named by amateur and professional astronomers ever since the days of Galileo (Figure 2-11). The most conspicuous features are many crater-like formations, which vary in diameter from a few hundred feet to 140 miles. The lack of any atmosphere on the moon has prevented erosion, and some of these walls stand straight up for thousands of feet. Their origin is a mystery, and the only clue we have is their correspondence to similar features on the earth. If they are extinct volcanoes they should resemble Crater Lake in Oregon (Figure 2-12), and if they were made by meteorites plunging into the surface of the moon they should resemble Meteor Crater in Arizona (Figure 2-13). In nearly every respect the craters on the moon fail to resemble volcanic craters, and they bear a striking similarity to Meteor Crater and to impact craters made experimentally by dropping objects onto a layer of dry powder in the laboratory.

SUMMARY

1. Astronomical observation has proceeded from the use of the unaided eye to the use of the telescope, and then the camera, the spectroscope, and other instruments. Each new instrument has provided us with either more detail or more distant vision, or both.

2. The sun's volume and mass are greater than those of all the other members of the solar system combined. Its surface temperature is about 11,000°F, and its interior may be as hot as 40,000,000°F.

3. Sunspots and solar prominences may be observed on the surface of the sun.

4. The moon always keeps the same side toward the earth as it revolves around it.

5. The moon has no atmosphere.

6. At the time of the new and the old moon, the moon is nearly between the earth and the sun. At the time of the full moon the earth is between the moon and the sun.

7. The surface features of the moon can be studied in detail. The craters were probably made by meteors.

QUESTIONS AND EXERCISES

1. Explain how the Doppler effect can be applied to the problem of a star's motion relative to the earth.

2. What must a star's spectrum be like if it is used to tell us what elements are in the star?

3. Explain, on the basis of the structure of your eye, how you can suffer permanent damage to the retina by looking directly at the sun.

4. The symbol on the flag of Turkey shows a star inside the crescent of the moon. Does this represent an unusual situation or an impossible one?

5. Does the sun ever shine on the side of the moon which is facing away from the earth?

6. What would be the relative positions of the earth, moon, and sun, for the moon to appear as a crescent with the tips pointing down toward the horizon?

7. If the moon sets at midnight, what phase is it in?

8. Would we receive more or less than the normal amount of light energy from the sun during a period of maximum sunspot activity?

9. To get an idea of the vast empty spaces in the solar system, figure the distance from the sun to each of the planets on a scale model of 1 inch equals 1 million miles. This was the one used in the model mentioned on page 107.

10. What is the intensity of the sun's light falling on Mars compared to that on Earth?

The Earth

1. THE SEASONS

Light traveling from the sun at 186,000 miles per second takes 8 minutes 20 seconds to reach the earth. The earth rotates around an axis, which passes between the north and south geographic poles. Anywhere in the middle latitudes of the northern hemisphere this rotation can be timed by observing the shadow cast by an upright pole. When the shadow points directly north it is noon, and the time between successive noons is divided by us into 24 hours, each hour into 60 minutes, and each minute into 60 seconds. The second is the primary unit of time and is defined as the 1/86,400th part of a mean solar day. To get the length of time that it takes the earth to travel around the sun, we note the time that the earth is exactly between the sun and a certain star. When this event occurs again, a sidereal year has passed. A year is very close to 365¼ days.

From Figure 2-2 it can be seen that on March 21 the light from the sun reaches both the North and the South Poles and that the sun is directly overhead at the Equator. This is one of the equinoxes, when the night and day are of equal length all over the earth. A few days later, the sun shines a little beyond the North Pole, so that it does not set during a 24-hour day, and there is a region near the South Pole that receives no sunlight. On June 21 the whole area north of the Arctic Circle gets 24 hours of sunlight, and people on cruises to Spitzenbergen, Norway, stay up to see the "midnight sun" (Figure 2-3). The whole Antarctic region is now in darkness. For those of us in the northern hemisphere, the nights are short and the days are long; the farther north, the greater is the discrepancy. At the Equator, the nights and days are of equal length throughout the year.

Continuing on to September 23 we reach the other equinox and on December 21 the whole Arctic area is in darkness, the rest of the northern hemisphere has its longest nights and shortest days, and the region south of the Antarctic Circle receives sunlight for 24 hours. As we shall see later, our climate would be very different if the axis of rotation of the earth were perpendicular to the plane of the earth's orbit.

2. ECLIPSES

From Figure 2-14 it would seem that the moon would cast its shadow on the earth at every new moon, and that it would pass

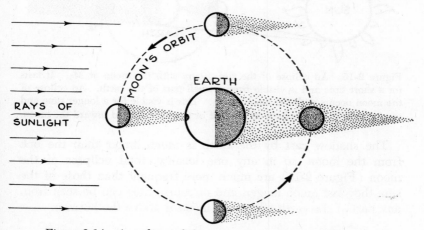

Figure 2-14. An eclipse of the sun and an eclipse of the moon.

through the shadow of the earth at every full moon. However, the plane of the moon's orbit around the earth is tilted slightly with respect to the plane of the earth's orbit around the sun (page 116), and only twice a month does the moon pass through this plane. When it does this at the time of a new moon, the earth passes through the moon's shadow; and if it is at the time of a full moon, the moon passes through the earth's shadow. Most of the time the shadow of the new moon passes above the North Pole or the South Pole, and on the other side of its orbit the moon slips above or below the earth's shadow.

When the moon's shadow falls on the earth we have an eclipse of the sun (Figures 2-15, 2-16, and 2-17). It is only during the few brief minutes of total eclipse that many problems of interest to astronomers can be studied, and so we now have scientific expeditions going to Brazil, South Africa, or Siberia to observe and record an eclipse. Not too many centuries ago the population was thrown into a panic by the superstitious fear that a dragon was eating up the sun.

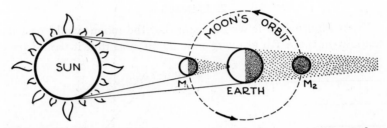

Figure 2-15. An eclipse of the sun occurs with the moon at M_1. It lasts for a short time and is visible from a small part of the earth. An eclipse of the moon occurs with the moon at M_2. This is visible for a longer time and can be seen from anywhere on the half of the earth turned toward the moon.

The shadow cast by the earth is much larger than the one from the moon, so in any one locality, total eclipses of the moon (Figure 2-15) are much more frequent than those of the sun, they last much longer, and of course they can be seen from any part of the earth where the moon is above the horizon.

3. NEWTON'S LAWS OF MOTION

It was in studying the path of the moon around the earth that Sir Isaac Newton (1642–1727) developed his three laws of motion and his law of universal gravitation. These laws are simple, general statements which describe the way matter behaves. They apply to so many situations that the man who discovered them has become one of the most famous of all scientists.

Let us state the four laws and then discuss them individually.

1. A body tends to remain at rest, or in uniform motion in a straight line unless acted on by some force.

2. The force required to accelerate a body is proportional to

both its mass and its acceleration, and the direction of the acceleration will be the same as that of the force.

3. To every action there is an equal and opposite reaction.

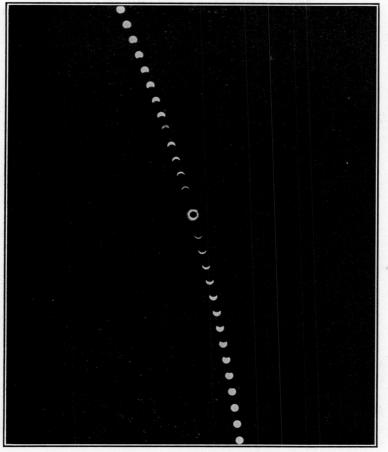

Figure 2-16. A succession of exposures showing the sun before, during,
and after an eclipse. (*National Geographic Society.*)

4. Every particle in the universe attracts every other particle
with a force that is proportional to the product of the masses of
the two particles and inversely proportional to the square of the
distance between them.

The first law describes the property called inertia. When you are sitting "still" you have no feeling of motion, yet you know that the earth is rotating on its axis and traveling around the sun at a speed of several miles per second. When a smoothly running car suddenly stops, you are not "thrown" forward; you tend to keep going forward at the same speed the car was traveling. The sieve-like basket of an automatic washing ma-

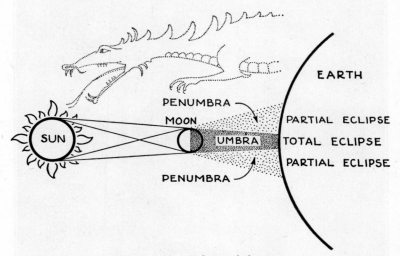

Figure 2-17. Eclipse of the sun.

chine holds the clothes and forces them to travel in circles, but the water can escape through the holes, and it travels, as it and the clothes both tend to do, in straight lines.

The second law can be stated in symbols $f \propto m \times a$. Acceleration is the rate of change of velocity. If the speed of a car changes from 10 miles per hour to 15 miles per hour in 5 seconds, the acceleration is 1 mile per hour per second. The general idea of this second law is obvious from everyday experience, but the precise form of it had to be determined by careful experiment. If you took equally vigorous swings with a golf club at a golf ball and at a 16-pound lead shot, you know which one would receive the greater acceleration. The difference in meaning between the two words "velocity" and "speed" is that velocity includes the ideas both of speed and direction. Thus a change in direction at constant speed would be a change in velocity, just as is a change in speed with no change in direction. It takes a force to make a moving object change its direction of motion, and this change in direction is called an acceleration.

Some applications of the third law are equally obvious, but others require more thought to follow through. If you dive from the back of a rowboat, you travel in one direction and the boat travels in the opposite one. When you stand on the bathroom scales, you are obviously pressing down on them, possibly it is not so obvious that they are pushing up on you just as hard. If the two opposing forces were not exactly equal there would be a net force in some direction, and the first and second laws tell us that you would receive an acceleration in that direction.

When an apple is hanging on a tree, the earth is pulling down on the apple; applying the third law, we know that the apple is pulling up on the earth and that the tree is holding them apart. When the stem finally weakens so that the apple is free to fall toward the earth, the earth is then free to rise toward the apple.

Newton had genius enough to realize that this might be a familiar example of something that had a far more general application. The moon does not travel in a straight line, it circles around the earth, therefore there must be some force acting on it. In Figure 2-18 the moon does not travel from M_1 to M_3, it constantly falls toward the earth as it travels the path M_1 to M_2. By Newton's time, Kepler had shown that all the planets travel around the sun, so that this idea of an invisible force acting between two bodies in space had an entirely general application. Newton stated this in his law of universal gravitation. The attractive force is called gravitation and the law may be stated as

$$F \propto \frac{m_1 \times m_2}{d^2}$$

An interesting deduction which can be made from this law is that, just as the moon falls toward the earth, so should the earth fall toward the moon. With the earth and the apple the two masses are so different that the motion of the earth is too small to detect. The earth is only 83 times heavier than the moon, so the center about which the two bodies revolve should be 240,000

$\times$ 1/84 miles = 2857 miles from the center of the earth. This
would be about 1000 miles below the surface of the earth. Any
such irregularity in the motion of the earth would show up as an
unevenness in the apparent motion of the sun as we watch it
from day to day. To see how this would work, imagine yourself
in the rather improbable situation of riding on a merry-go-round

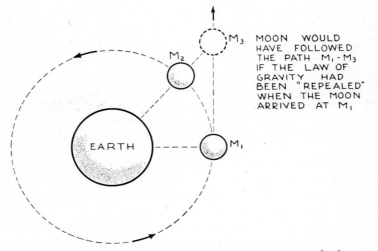

MOON   WOULD
HAVE   FOLLOWED
THE   PATH M_1 - M_3
IF   THE   LAW   OF
GRAVITY   HAD
BEEN   "REPEALED"
WHEN   THE   MOON
ARRIVED   AT M_1

Figure 2-18.   In its orbit around the earth the moon is constantly dropping
away from a straight-line path.

which is located on a moving train. As you go around you would
observe the scenery move by faster when you were facing the
locomotive and slower when your back was to it. The earth is
not traveling evenly around the sun as a train would travel, for
instance. It is traveling in circles around a point 2857 miles from
its own center, and this point is the one that goes around the sun
in a smooth curve. The sun does appear to gain and lose, over
a period of two weeks, just the amount that this calculation shows
that it should. Here, again, is an example where deduction from
a theory led us to new information, and when this was verified
our confidence in the theory was strengthened.

4. TIDES

To one living near the ocean, keeping track of the tides becomes as much second nature as noticing what time it is. From the scheduled time of departure of ocean liners to plans for swimming or digging clams, the tide must be taken into account. There are times when the difference between high and low tide is only a foot or so, and there are places where the difference is sometimes as much as 40 feet (Figures 2-19a and b).

On the average, the time between a high tide and the following low tide is $6\frac{1}{4}$ hours, so that there are usually two high tides and two low tides each day, with corresponding high (and low) tides about an hour later the next day. The difference between the water level at high tide and at low tide passes through a two-week periodic change. When it reaches a maximum (a very high tide followed by a very low tide) we call it a spring tide. A week later, the difference between the two reaches a minimum and we call it a neap tide. After another week, we again have a spring tide. These variations correlate perfectly with the phases of the moon, spring tides coming at the time of the new and full moon, and neap tides when the moon is in the first and third quarter.

Since successive high tides are about $12\frac{1}{2}$ hours apart, there are always two areas of high tides on opposite sides of the earth, with two areas of low tides between them. Let us see how Newton's law of gravitation can be applied to this situation.

Imagine three masses, A, B, and C, suspended on elastic cords with their centers a distance d apart (Figure 2-20). Now add a large mass, M, to one side of this system (Figure 2-21). Masses A, B, and C will be displaced toward M by the force of attraction. C is closest to M and will be displaced more than B, and so C will be pulled away from B and the distance BC will be greater than d. Similarly, B will be pulled away from A, and the distance BA will be greater than d.

In Figure 2-22, the earth is represented by B and the water by A and C. With the attractive force of the moon, M, acting, the water at C is pulled away from the center of the earth and the center of the earth is pulled away from the water at A, so that

Figure 2-19a. The Bay of Fundy at a high tide. (*Geological Survey of Canada.*)

Figure 2-19b. The Bay of Fundy at a low tide, 7 hours later. These two pictures show an extreme example of the differences in tides. (*Geological Survey of Canada.*)

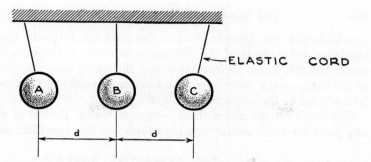

Figure 2-20. An explanation of the formation of tides. The mutual attraction of the masses A, B, and C keeps them at the distances shown.

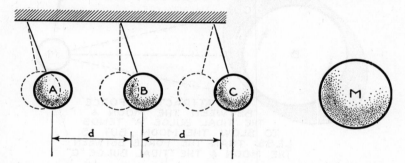

Figure 2-21. The mass M has been added to the system shown in Figure 2-20. C is displaced the most, A the least.

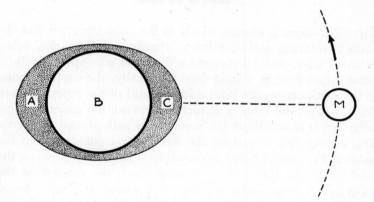

Figure 2-22. As in Figure 2-21, the water at C is drawn away from the earth, B, and the earth is drawn away from the water, A. The water is drawn toward the moon at C and left behind at A.

two high tides on opposite sides of the earth are formed. Since the tides are a result of the difference in distance between the moon and the water on one hand, and the moon and the center of the earth on the other hand, the force is inversely proportional to the cube of the distance: $F \propto 1/d^3$.

The earth rotates under these bulges of water, so that at any one place there are usually two high tides and two low tides each

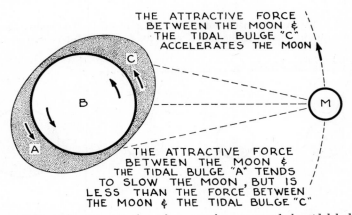

Figure 2-23. The attractive force between the moon and the tidal bulges is accelerating the moon as it revolves around the earth and is slowing the rotation of the earth.

day. The moon is moving slowly in the same direction that the earth is rotating, and so there is a period of about $6\frac{1}{4}$ hours between tides, and on successive days the corresponding tides come approximately 1 hour later. Actually, the rapid rotation of the earth carries the tides a little ahead of the moon (Figure 2-23), so that the force of attraction between the moon and this bulge tends to accelerate the moon in its path around the earth. This acceleration is making the moon spiral outward from the earth at the rate of 5 feet per century. This force between the tidal bulge and the moon is slowing down the rotation of the earth and is lengthening our day by 1 second in 100,000 years. This may seem too small an amount to be of any importance, but the retarding force of the earth on the moon has slowed it down so that it always keeps the same face toward us.

By referring to Table 2-1 you can calculate that the distance from the earth to the sun is 400 times the distance from the earth to the moon, and that the mass of the sun is about 28 million times that of the moon. The tide-raising force of the sun compared with that of the moon is $28,000,000/(400)^3 = 0.44$. Therefore, tides raised by the sun are about 5/11 the height of those

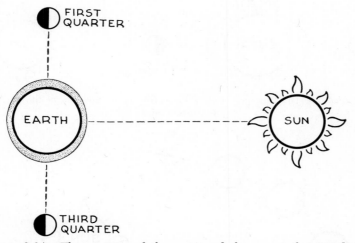

Figure 2-24.   The positions of the moon and the sun at the periods of neap tides.

raised by the moon. When the moon is in the first and third quarter (Figure 2-24), the moon and the sun are competing, so that there is a minimum difference in the tides. When the moon is full or new (Figure 2-25), they are both raising high tides at the same places on the earth and there is a maximum difference in tides. The extremely great differences in tides that are found at certain spots such as the Bay of Fundy and the Bay of Brittany are due principally to the funnel-like shape of the bays.

In the previous discussion the earth was considered as being a rigid sphere. Of course, this is not literally true, and the earth is deformed by tide-raising forces. These earth tides amount to several inches, but they are difficult to observe because we have no fixed point to compare them with.

One plausible theory of the origin of the moon is based on the assumption that soon after the formation of the solar system the earth had a period of rotation of about 6 hours.   The earth is an

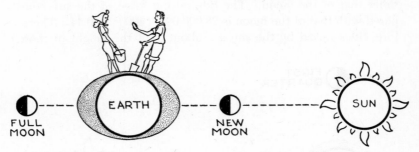

Figure 2-25.   Relative positions of the earth, moon, and sun at the periods of spring tides.

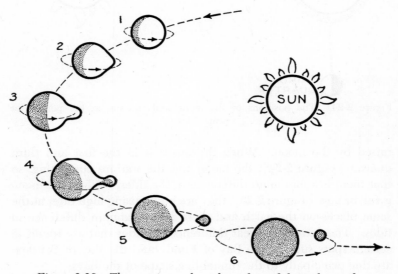

Figure 2-26.   The moon may have been formed from the earth.

elastic body with a natural frequency of vibration which happened to correspond to the period of the earth tides raised by the sun.   Just as properly timed, gentle pushes on a swing will set it swinging through a wide arc, so did these small tidal bulges of the earth grow in size until a chunk broke off. This chunk formed the moon, and it may have been pulled out of the area of the earth which is now the Pacific Ocean basin (Figure 2-26). When the earth lost part of its mass, its natural period of vibration changed and the sun was no longer able to deform it so greatly.

SUMMARY

1. Light travels at a speed of 186,000 miles per second.

2. A second is $1/86,400$ of a mean solar day.

3. A year is close to $365\frac{1}{4}$ solar days.

4. The seasons result from the fact that the axis of rotation of the earth is tilted with respect to the plane of its orbit about the sun.

5. When the moon's shadow falls on the earth we have an eclipse of the sun.

6. When the earth's shadow falls on the moon we have an eclipse of the moon.

7. Newton's laws of motion are: (a) a body tends to remain at rest, or in uniform motion in a straight line, unless acted on by some force; (b) the force required to accelerate a body is proportional both to its mass and to its acceleration, and the direction of the acceleration will be the same as that of the force; and (c) to every action there is an equal and opposite reaction.

8. Newton's law of gravitation states that every particle in the universe attracts every other particle with a force that is proportional to the product of the masses of the two particles and inversely proportional to the square of the distance between them.

9. Acceleration is the rate of change of velocity.

10. The tides are the result of the differential attraction of the moon for the water and for the earth. The tide-raising effect of the sun is $5/11$ that of the moon.

11. Spring tides occur when the sun and the moon are raising tides at the same place. Neap tides occur when the sun and the moon are raising tides at right angles to each other.

QUESTIONS AND EXERCISES

1. A 1-pound rock and a 10-pound rock are resting side by side on a window sill 16 feet above the ground. How do the forces between the earth and each of the rocks compare? How do the forces necessary to give each rock the same acceleration compare? If they were pushed from the window sill simultaneously, would they strike the ground at the same time?

2. The 10-pound rock in Question 1 would take 1 second to reach the ground. What was its average velocity? its final velocity (just before striking)? its acceleration?

3. In Figure 2-18, if the moon travels from M_1 to M_2 in 1 second, what would the distance M_3M_2 be?

4. If the distance between the earth and the moon were increased by 100 miles, would the moon have to travel faster or more slowly than it does now to keep in this new orbit?

5. What and where is the international date line, and why is it needed?

6. If you were watching an eclipse of the moon just beginning, would you see the earth's shadow start to cover the side of the moon on your right or on your left?

7. Which one of Newton's laws of motion is illustrated by: (a) the kicking of a gun when it is fired; (b) the sinking feeling in the pit of your stomach when an elevator starts up suddenly?

8. How frequently would you expect to find a 24-hour day with only three tides instead of four?

9. If we succeeded in harnessing the energy of the tide flowing in and out of a large bay, would it make any difference whatever to the period of rotation of the earth?

10. When an astronomer determines that the earth is exactly between the sun and a certain star which is crossing the meridian, what time is it at the observatory?

The Smaller Inner Planets

1. MERCURY

Mercury is the smallest of the planets and the closest to the sun. It completes its trip around the sun in 88 days, always keeping the same side toward it. Assuming that all the planets rotated on their axes when the solar system was formed, it is to be expected that the powerful tide-raising force of the sun on its nearest neighbor, Mercury, would have braked Mercury to a stop in its rotation. This same argument would lead us to assume that the planets which are relatively far from the sun would be rotating more rapidly than the earth, and this turns out to be the case (Jupiter, Saturn, etc.).

One-half of Mercury's surface is blistered with unceasing sunlight, so that the temperature is over 600°F, whereas the other side is forever dark and cold. Mercury has no atmosphere and no satellites.

2. VENUS

Venus appears brighter to the eye than any other planet or star. Only the sun, the moon, a rare comet, and an even rarer supernova surpass it in brilliance. Its nearness to both the sun and the earth accounts in part for this, and another factor is the mantle of clouds which completely covers the planet. These clouds reflect 59% of the sunlight, in contrast to the 7% reflected from the surface of the moon.

This cover of clouds prevents us from seeing the surface of Venus, so that it is difficult to determine how fast it rotates on its axis. We do not observe any regular motion of the clouds, and so the rotation cannot be as rapid as that of the earth. However, as the temperature on Venus is distributed evenly, some rotation probably occurs. Spectroscopic analysis of the atmosphere of

Venus shows much carbon dioxide and little oxygen. Since photosynthesis uses up carbon dioxide and water and returns oxygen to the atmosphere, it seems probable that there is no vegetable life on Venus. It may very well be at the same stage of evolu-

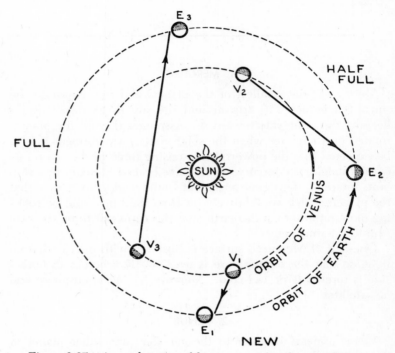

Figure 2-27. An explanation of how we see the phases of Venus.

tion that the earth was a billion years ago, with the first simple forms of life getting started in a warm, fresh-water sea.

Venus always sets and rises within $3\frac{1}{4}$ hours of the sun, and for the month before and after it passes between the earth and the sun it can be seen as a crescent (Figure 2-27).

The earth is nearly the twin of Venus in size. It would be possible for an intelligent observer on another planet to determine that the earth has an atmosphere, that it rotates on its axis, and that it has one satellite.

3. MARS

Mars is quite a bit smaller than the earth, has a length of day about the same as ours, and takes nearly 2 years in its trip around the sun.

Its red color and its brightness make it a familiar object in the sky.   Since its orbit lies outside that of the earth, we never see it as a crescent.   It has two small satellites.   One of these, Phobos, is of interest because of the speed with which it travels around Mars.   Its period of revolution is only 10 hours, so that an observer on Mars would see it rise in the west as a "new moon" and go through all its phases and set in the east all within 4 hours and 20 minutes.   The other satellite, Deimos, revolves nearly as fast as Mars rotates, so that it remains above the horizon for $2\frac{1}{2}$ days and goes through all its phases $2\frac{1}{2}$ times before setting.

Spectroscopic examination of Mars shows that it has an atmosphere that contains less oxygen and water vapor than ours. There are large white areas around the poles that change in size with the seasons as thin caps of polar ice would be expected to do.   There is also a corresponding seasonal change in the appearance of the main part of the planet which suggests a periodic growth and drying up of vegetation.   Since Mars is farther from the sun than the earth is, the Martian temperatures are lower than ours, but they are well within the range that would support life as we know it.

The possibility of life's existing on another planet has intrigued mankind for centuries.   Until interplanetary travel solves the problem the best we can do is to examine the conditions found on our neighbors in the solar system.   There is nothing about Mars that would make life as we know it impossible.   The temperature range and the atmospheric composition and pressure are suitable.   The small amount of water present would present a real problem and a challenge to any intelligent beings.

Ever since Schiaparelli, in 1877, announced the discovery of long straight lines which he called channels, astronomers have studied the surface of Mars, looking for evidence of planned engineering.   W. H. Pickering (1858–1938) and Percival Lowell

(1855–1916) were among the leaders in this effort. It is unfortunate that photography is not as useful as direct visual observation for studying fine detail in surface features. During the long exposure necessary for a picture, the turbulence of our atmosphere blurs the details which can be seen for a few minutes at a time by the eye. The eye, however, is notoriously liable to subjective error, and no two observers agree on the pattern of channels, or canals, which the Martians are supposed to have built to carry water from the melting polar caps to their parched fields. The evidence for a vegetable-like form of life on Mars is almost conclusive, but beyond that we cannot go. When an astronomical observatory is set up on the moon, we shall be able to study this interesting problem more satisfactorily.

4. ASTEROIDS

The asteroids are an unusual group of more than a thousand tiny planetoids traveling in a more or less common orbit between Mars and Jupiter. The largest is 480 miles in diameter, and the smallest located so far is less than a mile across. The reasoning which led to their discovery is an example of the practical value of the scientist's confidence that there is a pattern in nature. When the pattern has been discovered, gaps and irregularities in it suggest something yet to be found.

In 1772 Bode published his "law," which was an approximate description of the distances from the sun to each of the known planets. He showed that the distance from the sun to each planet could be expressed as a multiple of the distance from the sun to the earth, by the following scheme. For the nearest planet, Mercury, the distance is $0.4 + 0 = 0.4$; for the next one, Venus, it is $0.4 + 0.3 = 0.7$; the earth is $0.4 + 2 \times 0.3 = 1.0$; Mars is $0.4 + 2 \times 0.6$; the next one should be $0.4 + 2 \times 1.2 = 2.8$. The number added to 0.4 is always twice the number added for the next-closer planet. Table 2-2 shows the scheme for the planets known by 1800.

With the rather close agreement between the predicted and found values for the known planets, the lack of a planet at the distance 2.8 was not only puzzling, it was irritating. Appropriate portions of the sky were assigned for search to several astron-

TABLE 2-2

	Add	Approxi-mate distance	True distance
Mercury	0.4	0.0	0.4	0.39
Venus	0.4	0.3	0.7	0.72
Earth	0.4	0.6	1.0	1.0
Mars	0.4	1.2	1.6	1.52
?	0.4	2.4	2.8	2.8 (Asteroids)
Jupiter	0.4	4.8	5.2	5.2
Saturn	0.4	9.6	10.0	9.54
Uranus	0.4	19.2	19.6	19.2

omers. In 1801 the largest of the asteroids was discovered and named Ceres. Others were soon spotted, and modern photographic technique turns up more every year. It is surprising that there is a swarm of small fragments circling the sun in the orbit of an anticipated planet, and the reason for this special situation is a complete mystery.

SUMMARY

1. Mercury is the smallest planet and the closest to the sun. It always keeps the same face to the sun.

2. Venus is the brightest planet. It is covered with clouds.

3. There is good evidence that there is plant life on Mars.

4. The asteroids, or planetoids, are a swarm of extremely small bodies traveling in orbits which lie in a general area between Mars and Jupiter. Many hundreds of them have been observed.

QUESTIONS AND EXERCISES

1. How much more strongly does the tide-raising force of the sun act on Mercury than on the earth?

2. As we look at Mercury through a telescope, can we see it go through a series of phases like the moon?

3. If Venus rotated on its axis about as rapidly as the earth, what motion of its clouds would we observe?

4. If Venus always kept the same side toward the sun, what motion of its clouds would we observe?

5. Check the statement that Venus always rises and sets within 3¼ hours of the sun. Draw the two orbits to scale, and measure the

greatest possible angle between the lines joining the earth to Venus and the earth to the sun.

6. How does the speed of Mars in its orbit compare with that of the earth? Figure these speeds in terms of miles per minute.

7. What would be the advantages of an astronomical observatory on the moon?

8. Use Bode's law to calculate the approximate distance to the next planet beyond Uranus.

9. Arrange the four inner planets in decreasing order according to size.

10. Phobos revolves around Mars in the same direction that Mars rotates on its axis (like the moon around the earth). How can it be that it rises in the west and sets in the east?

CHAPTER

The Outer Planets, etc.

1. JUPITER

Jupiter is the planet that requires the most superlatives in its description. It is the largest of the planets; both its volume and its weight are greater than those of all the other planets combined. It rotates on its axis faster than any other planet. With its circumference of 270,000 miles and its period of rotation of just less than 10 hours, a spot on its equator is traveling 27 times

Figure 2-28. Three photographs showing changes in position of the four brightest satellites of Jupiter. (*Yerkes Observatory.*)

as fast as one on the earth's equator. This rapid rotation produces a bulge clearly visible in a telescope. Another "most" for Jupiter is its number of satellites. Twelve have been discovered so far; four of them can be seen with a pair of field glasses. They all rotate in the plane of the equator, forming a system which we see edge on, so that we can observe frequent eclipses (Figure 2-28).

The four largest satellites were the first heavenly bodies discovered by the telescope. Galileo saw them in 1610 (page 156), and their existence supplied important evidence supporting the Copernican theory of the structure of the solar system.

In the seventeenth century, navigators had a difficult time telling their longitude. They could set their chronometers by Greenwich time when they left London, and then, as they traveled across the Atlantic, they could observe the clock time when the sun was directly south of them. If this occurred at 1 P.M. they knew that they had traveled 1/24 of the way around the earth, or 15° west of Greenwich. The best clocks were none too good, and when they were subjected to the rolling and pitching

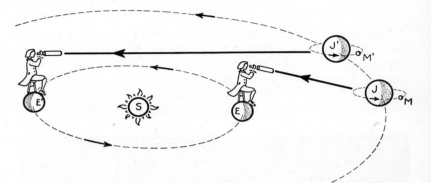

Figure 2-29. Roemer's experiment, which determined the speed of light.

of a small vessel they were decidedly erratic. After a voyage of several weeks they were practically worthless for purposes of navigation. The four moons of Jupiter, with their frequent passages behind and in front of the planet, supplied a set of predictable events that could be used to set mariners' clocks during long voyages.

The astronomers of the Paris Observatory undertook the task of preparing a table showing the eclipses of Jupiter's moons for several years in advance. In 1676, when Roemer checked these calculations with the observed times, he found that they were wrong by as much as 20 minutes at certain times of the year. To a ship's captain this could mean the difference between being a full day's journey from the coast of Brazil or being piled up on the rocks.

Roemer very ingeniously saw that, if the calculations were based on observations made when the earth is at position *E*, Figure 2-29, and Jupiter at *J*, and if they were checked when the earth was at E' and Jupiter at J', then the light from Jupiter had to travel the additional distance EE'. If that took 20 minutes, the discrepancy was explained.

More precise measurement shows that the time for light to travel EE', the diameter of the earth's orbit, is $16\frac{2}{3}$ minutes, and the distance is 186,000,000 miles. This shows that the velocity of light is 186,000,000 miles/1000 seconds = 186,000 miles per second. Because of its extremely high value, previous efforts to measure the speed of light had failed, and some scientists thought that its velocity was infinite. The solving of a problem in navigation led to an important discovery in science.

2. SATURN

Saturn, the most distant of the naked-eye planets, is as bright as most first-magnitude stars. It is next to Jupiter in size, but much lighter. Its density is about that of kiln-dried hardwood. It rotates on its axis only a little less rapidly than Jupiter. The most spectacular thing about Saturn is its breath-taking system of rings. They stand out from the planet like the brim of a golden derby hat, starting 7000 miles from its surface and extending 41,000 miles. As one looks at them through the telescope they appear solid. However, bright stars can be seen through them, and the innermost portions are rotating faster than the outer edge. As Saturn moves around the sun we see the rings edge on (as in 1950) and at a considerable angle (as in 1957). The rings are only about 10 miles thick and are composed of swarms of stony meteorites which are probably the fragments of a moon which was so close to Saturn that the tidal forces disrupted it. Beyond the rings Saturn has nine satellites.

3. URANUS

Uranus is barely visible to the unaided eye, but the fact that it is a planet was not discovered until William Herschel examined it with a telescope in 1781. He thought he noticed a slight disc as he watched it, and after several months of observation it was apparent that Uranus moved among the stars, and its orbit was calculated.

The discovery of Uranus was a well-timed blow at the dangerous practice of arguing by analogy. The great philosopher Hegel had just observed that "just as there are seven openings in the head—the two eyes, two nostrils, two ears, and one mouth —so there must be seven members of the solar system—the sun, Mercury, Venus, Earth, Mars, Jupiter, and Saturn."

Uranus' axis of rotation lies in the plane of its orbit and the four satellites revolve in the plane of its equator. Eclipses, therefore, are possible at only two parts of its orbit.

4. NEPTUNE

Neptune is of interest principally because of the way in which it was discovered. When Uranus was first located, Neptune was about a quarter of a circle ahead of it. For the next 41 years Neptune kept accelerating Uranus, until they passed in 1822, and then it retarded the motion of Uranus. Although the effect was slight, it was well beyond the limits of error of the observations. It was apparent that either Newton's law of gravitation would have to come to the rescue with an explanation of this erratic motion or the law would have to be revised. Newton's law suggested that a planet out beyond Uranus would account for the facts, but calculating its position was no small job when neither its distance from the sun nor its mass was known. Leverrier, in France, and Adams, in England, tackled the problem independently and solved it nearly simultaneously in 1846. Galle, of the Berlin Observatory, received instructions from Leverrier, turned his telescope to the spot selected, and was the first person to observe Neptune. This was slightly more than 200 years after the birth of Newton, and it was a remarkable tribute to him. It is also a rather striking example of the international quality of science.

Neptune is intensely cold, without prominent markings, and it has two satellites, one of which revolves in a retrograde direction.

5. PLUTO

Pluto was discovered in 1930 by the use of a new type of instrument called a blinking comparator. Two different pictures are projected in rapid alternation on a common screen. If they differ at only one point, this point will appear to jump back and forth while everything else remains stationary. This device is ideal for telling whether two documents are identical copies. If pictures of the same section of the heavens are taken on suc-cessive days, any planet in the field will appear to move against the background of the far more distant stars. Clyde Tombaugh, working at the Lowell Observatory, used this technique to search for a suspected trans-Neptunian planet and finally located it.

Instead of being much larger than the earth, as the other distant planets are, Pluto turned out to be smaller. Since it is so small and so distant, and shines by reflected light, it is difficult to see with any but the best telescopes. It travels around the sun in an extremely eccentric orbit which cuts inside the orbit of Neptune at its closest approach to the sun and which is in-clined 17° from the plane of the earth's orbit. No satellite for Pluto has yet been found.

Are there any planets beyond Pluto? Of course, a positive yes or no answer cannot be given to that question. It is highly im-probable that any planets the size of Jupiter could have escaped detection this long, but small ones like Pluto could go undiscov-ered for many years.

6. COMETS AND METEORS

Our detailed study of the members of the solar system con-cludes with a study of comets and meteors. The value of a calm, clearheaded study of natural phenomena is well illustrated by the change in attitude towards comets in the last 400 years. Large ones are so infrequent and so spectacular when they do appear that they used to be viewed with superstitious fear. They were thought to be the cause of war, pestilence, and revolution. Weird rites were performed to neutralize their power. After Kepler worked out the pattern of behavior of the planets, the orbits of several comets were plotted, and it was found that they also travel in elliptical paths around the sun. These ellipses are usually much more elongated than the orbits of the planets, so that a comet may pass between Mercury and the sun at one end of its path and swing beyond Pluto at the other end.

The comets, which have a period of several years, develop a luminous tail as they approach the sun. This seems to be dust and gas which are blown out of the body of the comet by the pressure of light from the sun. As the comet swings around the sun, the tail flies out like a pennant on the lee side (Figure 2-30); this material is never regained by the comet. Comets that have small orbits and visit the sun frequently do not develop tails, or

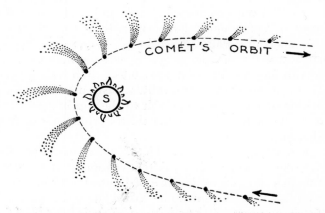

Figure 2-30.   The appearance of the tail of a comet in the part of its orbit near the sun.

they may have lost all the fine-grained material that goes into making one.

The main body of a comet, although brilliant, is nearly transparent and must be made up of a swarm of small particles of assorted sizes—probably pebbles, dust, and even individual molecules. Mutual attraction keeps these together fairly well. Some comets keep their identity for centuries. For example, Halley's comet has been recorded every 75 years since 87 B.C. (Figure 2-31). Others have shown up regularly for a while and have then disappeared.

When the earth passes through the orbit of a "lost" comet, we usually observe a large number of "shooting stars," or meteors. This indicates that the material of the comet has been spread all around its orbit (Figure 2-32), so that there is no longer a concentration which we can see and call a head. Occasionally, one

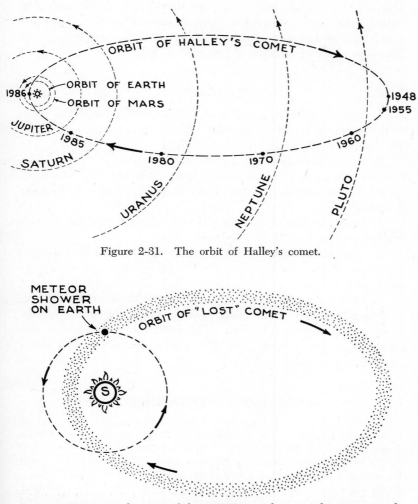

Figure 2-31. The orbit of Halley's comet.

Figure 2-32. An explanation of the appearance of meteor showers on earth at regular intervals.

of these particles is large enough to survive its trip through our atmosphere, and when it is found on the surface of the earth it is called a meteorite. Chemical analysis shows that meteorites are composed of familiar elements; some of them are stony, and some are made of an alloy of iron and nickel.

SUMMARY

1. Jupiter is the largest planet. It has twelve satellites. Our first determination of the speed of light resulted from a study of the moons of Jupiter.

2. Saturn is particularly notable for its system of rings.

3. Uranus was the first planet discovered with the telescope.

4. Neptune was discovered through its gravitational effect on Uranus.

5. Pluto is much smaller than the other outer planets. Of the known planets it is farthest from the sun.

6. Comets are members of the solar system, and have highly elliptical orbits. They consist of a swarm of small particles traveling as a group.

7. Meteorites are particles which survive the trip through the earth's atmosphere from outer space. They are always either stony or an iron-nickel alloy. The frictional resistance of the earth's atmosphere heats them glowing hot, so that we see them as "shooting stars," or meteors.

QUESTIONS AND EXERCISES

1. The longitude of New York City is approximately 75° west of Greenwich, England. On a clock set on Greenwich time, what time would the sun be directly south at New York?

2. Why are the eclipses of the four moons of Jupiter more useful for setting a mariner's clock than those of the moons of Mars?

3. How do we know that Saturn's rings are not solid, like a washer?

4. During an eclipse on Uranus what would be the angle between its axis of rotation and a line joining the planet to the sun?

5. If Jupiter is observed to be on the meridian at 1 A.M. on a certain day, at approximately what time will it be on the meridian at this same station one year later?

6

CHAPTER

Beyond the Solar System

1. THE MILKY WAY AND OUR GALAXY

To anyone but a city-dweller, the Milky Way should be a familiar sight. On a moonless summer evening this gorgeous carpet of star dust stretches from near the North Star to the southern horizon. Hundreds of individual stars can be seen, and in places they are so tiny and so numerous that they look like a glowing stream. The Milky Way seems to be a luminous river flowing across the sky. Why is it that such a large proportion of all the stars are seen in such a small fraction of the whole dome of the sky?

The answer to that question became clear after we found a way to measure the distances to the stars. When the results were analyzed it turned out that our solar system is a part of a vast collection of stars which are organized in a shape resembling a pocket watch. In this arrangement the sun is about where the pivot of the second hand would be (Figure 2-33). In most directions in which we look there are relatively few stars, but we see a concentrated belt of them as we look through the main mass of this system.

Each star shines by its own light, like our sun. Some stars are larger than the sun, some smaller; some are hotter, and some cooler. We may find two or sometimes three stars revolving close together in a common system. In some stars the particles are as scattered as they are in the tail of a comet, and in others the matter is packed together so closely that a cubic inch of it would have a mass of a ton. In fact, our sun is a very ordinary, unspectacular member of the family of stars. It has yet to be determined whether or not other stars are surrounded by systems of planets. The distances are so great that we may never be able to see the planets themselves, but, if such planets should

143

come between us and the star as they circled around it, we might notice a periodic dimming of the light from the star.

The distances to even the nearest stars are so great that we must use a new measuring stick. Light traveling from the sun reaches us in about 8 minutes 20 seconds. It travels on for 4 hours before reaching Pluto. It then travels for more than 4

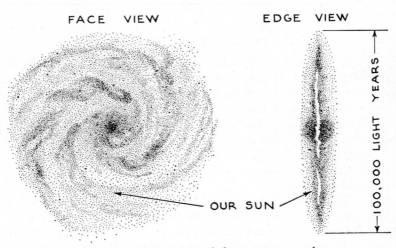

Figure 2-33. The position of the sun in our galaxy.

years before it reaches the nearest star, called Alpha Centauri. The light year, the distance light travels in 1 year at its speed of 186,000 miles per second, is one of the useful measuring rods in astronomy. Even with such a large unit, we find that the system of stars of which our sun is a part is about 100,000 light years in diameter. This system is called a galaxy.

2. EXTRA-GALACTIC NEBULAS

When light from the sun leaves our galaxy it goes through vast regions of nearly empty space for about a million years in every direction, and then it reaches other galaxies much like our own. To a person observing with any but the best telescopes these galaxies look like hazy spots and were first called nebulas (clouds) because of their appearance. When better telescopes were built

and photographic technique improved, it was seen that the nebulas were systems of individual stars like our own galaxy. They
are now called extra-galactic nebulas, or nebulas outside our

Figure 2-34. An extra-galactic nebula. The great spiral nebula in Androm-
eda. (*Mt. Wilson and Mt. Palomar Observatories.*)

galaxy. These are about 100,000 light years in diameter (Figure
2-34), and they are spaced approximately 10 times their own
diameter apart.

When light from these distant nebulas is passed through a
spectroscope, the lines of familiar elements are observed. The

lines from the distant ones are shifted slightly toward the red end of the spectrum. According to the Doppler effect, this would mean that these nebulas are moving away from us. The curious fact that develops is that, the farther the nebula, the faster it is receding.

If this runaway motion is projected backward in space and time, they all seem to have started from about the same place at about the same time—approximately 3 billion years ago. This picture is far from being satisfactorily proved, but it suggests the intriguing possibility that our whole universe was once a gigantic collection of fundamental particles which blew up and collected into stable units as they sped through space.

SUMMARY

1. Our sun is but one of many millions of stars organized in a watch-shaped system called a galaxy. This galaxy is slowly rotating about a point near its center.

2. The stars shine by their own light, like our sun.

3. A light year is the distance that light will travel in 1 year.

4. Our galaxy is but one of thousands of galaxies. They are all approximately the same size, and they are spaced about 1 million light years apart.

5. If the red shift is interpreted as a Doppler effect, the universe seems to be expanding.

QUESTIONS AND EXERCISES

1. Would the constellations with which we are familiar appear about the same, or very different, if viewed from near Alpha Centauri?

2. If you look through even the biggest telescope at an extra-galactic nebula, it appears as a fuzzy spot, but a photograph will reveal its many individual stars. Explain.

3. Would we observe a shift toward the red in light from the stars in our own galaxy?

4. How does our galaxy compare in size with the others?

5. In the following list, which ones shine by reflected light, and which shine by their own light: comets, nebulas, planets, stars?

7

History of the Development of Our Ideas about the Structure of the Universe

1. PRE-GREEK

At any point in the history of civilization the current theory of the structure of the universe is an important part of the culture. Men have gone to prison and have died for daring to challenge the accepted point of view. Any broad philosophy will be influenced by the position that man thinks he has in the general structure of the world around him.

In all the early civilizations the earth was pictured as a flat disc with a dome-shaped sky supported in various ways above it. The stars were lights or holes in the dome, whose revolution accounted for their motion. The sun, moon, and planets moved independently across the dome. By 424 B.C. the Egyptians had determined that the year was 365 days long, and later the Babylonians figured that it was 365 days and 6 hours. The best modern measurement of the length of the year is 365 days, 5 hours, 48 minutes, and 46 seconds.

2. ARISTOTLE AND ERATOSTHENES

The prevailing opinion among the Greek philosophers was that the earth was flat and that the heavenly bodies circled around it. Aristotle (384–322 B.C.) taught that the earth and all the heavenly bodies were spheres and that the earth was the center of the whole system, with the sun, moon, planets, and stars moving around it in circular paths. He reached this conclusion by a method that science has since shown to be untrustworthy. He assumed that circular motion is the most perfect form of

147

motion and that the heavenly bodies were obviously perfect objects, and from that assumption he concluded that they must travel in circular paths.

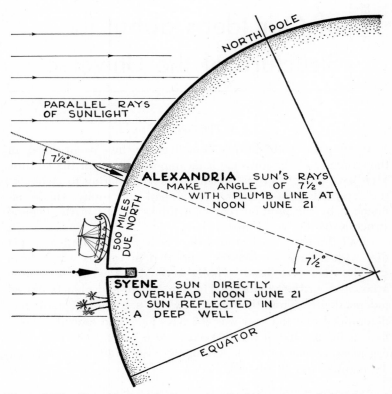

Figure 2-35.   Eratosthenes experiment in which he measured the circumference of the earth.

Somewhat later Aristarchus (fl. ab. 280–264 B.C.) said that the earth, moon, and planets all revolved around the sun and that the stars were located at a great distance from the solar system. About 250 B.C. Eratosthenes used this theory to calculate the circumference of the earth (Figure 2-35). He knew that at Syene (Aswan), in southern Egypt, the sun was directly overhead at noon on June 21. Alexandria is almost directly north of Syene, and at noon on June 21 the edge of a shadow makes an angle of $7\frac{1}{2}°$ with the perpendicular. Since the rays of light from the sun are parallel, a plumb line at Syene would be at an angle of $7\frac{1}{2}°$ with one at Alexandria. Since both lines point to the center of the earth, the distance between Syene and Alexandria must be 7.5/360, or 1/48 of the circumference of the earth. This distance was measured and found to be 500 miles (in modern units), which gives 24,000 miles for the circumference of the earth. This is within 4% of the value accepted now. This experiment demonstrated that the earth cannot be flat, but it did not settle the question of whether the earth revolves around the sun or vice versa.

The authority of Aristotle carried the day, and for over 2000 years the earth was considered to be the center of the universe.

3. PTOLEMY

Claudius Ptolemy, a Greek astronomer working in Alexandria during the second century A.D., elaborated Aristotle's picture of the universe into a scheme which, with slight modifications, was used for 1500 years. Aristotle's assumption that all celestial motion must be circular was the untouchable, unquestionable center, the "sacred cow," of the Ptolemaic system. The motions of the sun, moon, and stars were easy to explain. They all traveled circular paths, with diameters and speeds calculated to agree with experience. The motions of the planets called for a more complicated explanation. They were assumed to travel in circular paths around a point which, in its turn, followed a circular path around the earth (Figure 2-36).

Even though every motion had to be circular, by varying the size of the circle and the speed of revolution, a very complicated apparent motion could be accounted for, and the Ptolemaic system was extremely successful in predicting the behavior of the planets. It was useful for navigation and in making calendars, and it had the psychological advantage of putting mankind at the very center of the universe. The church officially approved, and none questioned the system for many centuries.

In the fifteenth century, it was still not decided whether the earth was flat or spherical. Columbus thought it spherical, and

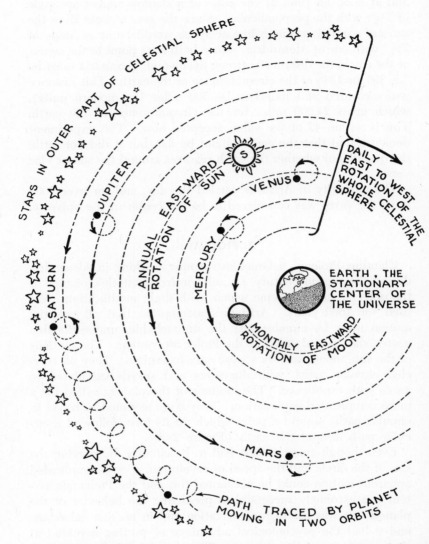

Figure 2-36.   Ptolemy's picture of the structure and relative motions of the
members of the universe.

used for the circumference the value of about 18,000 miles
which had been calculated several centuries before from an experiment like the one of Eratosthenes. Knowing the distance
from Spain to India going eastward by way of Arabia, he figured
that it would be as close and much more convenient to sail westward across the Atlantic. He did this in 1492, and when he discovered land he thought it was India. This is where we get the
names "the West Indies" for the islands and "Indians" for the
natives.

4. COPERNICUS

The original Ptolemaic picture of the universe was not completely perfect; to bring it into line with observation, adjustments
were made, cycles were put on cycles, and by 1500 a bewil-
deringly complex structure had resulted. Nikolaus Copernicus
(1473–1543), a Polish astronomer, was one of those rare intellectual giants who are able to break the bonds of their times and
question the basic assumptions, instead of patching up existing
theories. He came to the conclusion that the behavior of the
planets could be more simply explained if he assumed that the
sun was the center of the rotating system and that the planets,
including the earth, circled around it, with the moon revolving
around the earth. The stars were pictured as being fixed and
very remote in space.

By the use of the model of the solar system that Copernicus
developed it was possible to predict the future positions of the
heavenly bodies with about the same accuracy that had been
achieved with Ptolemy's theory. In other words, it was hard to
decide between them on the experimental evidence available at
the time. The idea of an earth-centered universe was far more
flattering to mankind than one in which the earth was just one
of several satellites revolving around the sun. Copernicus anticipated the antagonism that would be aroused by his theory,
and he delayed publication of his book, *De Revolutionibus Or-
bium Caelestium*, until he was on his deathbed.

There was one critical experiment which would have settled
the question of whether the sun or the earth is the center of
revolution of the solar system. If you hold a pencil at arm's

length and look at the wall beyond it, closing first your right eye
and then your left, you will see a different part of the wall beyond the tip of the pencil each time. Similarly, if the earth
revolves around the sun and we observe the distant stars behind
a near star, they should appear to shift back and forth every 6
months (Figure 2-37). This effect is known as parallax, and its

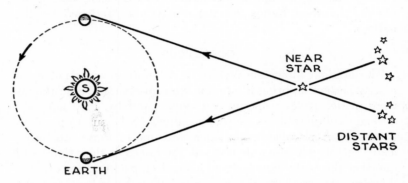

Figure 2-37.   Stellar parallax.   At 6-month intervals we should see different
distant stars behind a near star.

importance for settling this question was realized by Aristarchus.
He explained the failure to observe parallax by assuming that
even the nearest star was so far away, compared to the diameter
of the earth's orbit, that the effect was too small to observe. It
was not until the development of a fairly good telescope that this
crucial test could be applied (1838).

Copernicus had also pointed out that his theory required that
Venus should go through a series of phases—new, half, and full—
like the moon. In his picture of the solar system Venus shone
by light reflected from the sun and revolved in an orbit smaller
than the earth's, so when Venus is between the sun and the earth
we should see only a part of its lighted surface. When the sun
is nearly between us and Venus we should see the lighted side
in full. According to Ptolemy, on the other hand, the sun, moon,
and all the planets revolved around the earth. The moon was the
closest, Mercury and Venus next, with the sun fourth in order.
If this were true, we should never see Venus as a disc. It would

vary between a crescent and a half-full phase, because it never gets very far away from the sun in direction, and it lies between the sun and the earth (Figure 2-38). This test, too, had to wait for the telescope.

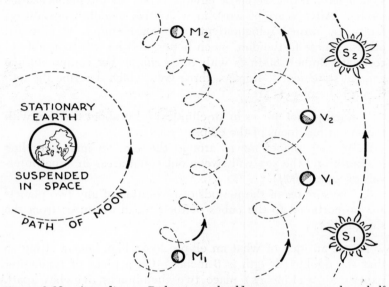

Figure 2-38. According to Ptolemy we should never see as much as half the lighted side of either Mercury or Venus.

5. BRAHE AND KEPLER

Copernicus was followed by two men who, together, combined the qualifications of the ideal scientist. Tycho Brahe (1546–1601) was a painstaking investigator who made many thousands of observations. His patience and accuracy were outstanding, but he did not attempt any generalization from his data. It was indeed fortunate that he had Johannes Kepler (1571–1630) for his assistant. Kepler was an excellent mathematician and he had a consuming passion for demonstrating that the solar system was organized according to a logical, symmetrical pattern. He set up a model of the solar system, from this calculated where the planets should be in relation to each other, and then compared these results with the data accumulated by Brahe. One after another of these models was discarded because it did not agree with the facts. Kepler was under the influence of the Aristo-telian ideas, which were still dominating European thought, and so it is natural that he chose circular orbits for the planets in his model. After years of work in which his models were always faulty, he turned reluctantly to the consideration of elliptical orbits. These fit the data much better, and he was soon able to correlate Brahe's findings with three simple yet comprehensive general statements. Kepler's three laws which describe the motions of the planets are:

1. Each planet moves in an elliptical orbit about the sun, with the sun at one focus of the ellipse (1609).

2. As each planet moves around the sun, an imaginary line joining it and the sun will sweep out equal areas in equal intervals of time (1609).

3. The squares of the periods of revolution of any two planets are proportional to the cubes of their mean distances from the sun (1619).

To get an idea of what an ellipse looks like, knot a string so that the doubled length is 6 inches. On a piece of typewriter paper (8½ x 11 inches) place two thumbtacks 5 inches apart, with the loop around them. Place a pencil in the loop and draw a figure around the tacks (Figure 2-39). This is an ellipse. The sum of the distances from any point on the ellipse to each of the tacks is 7 inches (12 — 5). Move the tacks so that they are 3 inches apart, knot the string so that its doubled length is 5 inches, and again draw an ellipse. As before, the sum of the distances from any point on the figure to the two tacks is 7 inches (10 — 3) but this one is more nearly circular. Each tack is at one focus of the ellipse. The second ellipse is said to be less eccentric than the first. The orbit of the earth is only very slightly eccentric; that of Pluto is much more so; and the orbits of comets are highly eccentric with the sun at one focus.

Kepler's second law is illustrated in Figure 2-40. The eccentricity of this ellipse is much exaggerated to make the point clear. When the earth is closest to the sun, it travels more rapidly than when it is farther away. Referring to Figure 2-31, you

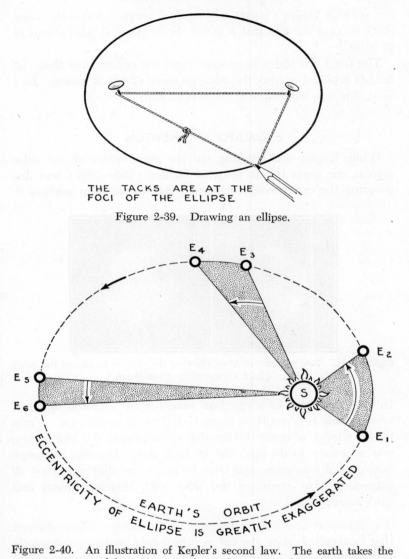

THE TACKS ARE AT THE
FOCI OF THE ELLIPSE

Figure 2-39. Drawing an ellipse.

Figure 2-40. An illustration of Kepler's second law. The earth takes the
same time to travel from E_1 to E_2 that it does to travel from E_3 to E_4 and
from E_5 to E_6. The dotted areas are the same.

can see that Halley's comet takes only 2 years to travel the same distance near the sun that it covers in 30 years at the far end of its orbit.

The third law states in precise terms the general fact that, the farther a planet is from the sun, the more slowly it moves. In a way, this is a repetition of the second law.

6. GALILEO AND NEWTON

While Kepler was working out the architecture of our solar system, the great Italian scientist Galileo (1564–1642) was discovering the experimental evidence that would help confirm it.

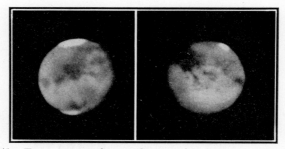

Figure 2-41.   Two pictures of Mars showing the change in size of the polar cap. (*Lick Observatory Photograph.*)

In 1608, he heard of a spyglass, invented by a Dutch optician, which made it possible to magnify objects at a distance.   From his knowledge of optics, he figured out what sort of a lens system was necessary to do this, and he built one.   His first telescope magnified 3 diameters, and later he made one that magnified 30 diameters.   He examined the skies with this instrument and discovered:

1. Sunspots and surface features of the moon.   These showed that heavenly bodies are not so absolutely perfect as Aristotle had claimed.

2. The moons of Jupiter.   This system of moons going around another planet exploded the idea of the earth as the center about which everything revolved.

3. The phases of Venus and Mercury. This showed that the basic idea of Copernicus was correct.

Galileo encountered powerful resistance to his new notions. People denied his facts by saying that his telescope was enchanted. He had an aggressive personality and pushed his ideas whenever possible. He came into conflict with the church, was put into "protective custody," and was forced to recant his heretical views, but it was too late. The work of Galileo and Kepler

Figure 2-42. Two pictures of Saturn taken at an interval of 4 years. (*Lick Observatory Photograph.*)

swept away the old theories, and the sun-centered picture of the solar system gained acceptance. Newton put the capstone on this edifice with his law of gravitation (page 119). This showed the reason for the motion of the planets which Kepler had deduced by trial and error.

SUMMARY

1. In early days, the earth was pictured as flat, with the sky as a dome above it.

2. Some of the Greeks thought that the rest of the solar system revolved about the earth, and some thought that the sun was the center of the solar system.

3. Using the earth as the center of the universe, Ptolemy invented a system of cycles and epicycles for the paths of the

heavenly bodies. This system was tolerably good from a practical point of view.

4. Copernicus invented a system much simpler than Ptolemy's, which was equal to it in predictability. He placed the sun at the center of the universe and had the planets follow circular paths around it.

5. Using Brahe's observations, Kepler was able to work out his laws describing the motions of the planets. They are: (a) Each planet moves in an elliptical orbit about the sun, with the sun at one focus of the ellipse; (b) as each planet moves about the sun, an imaginary line joining it and the sun will sweep out equal areas in equal intervals of time; and (c) the squares of the periods of revolution of any two planets are proportional to the cubes of their mean distances from the sun.

6. Galileo's invention of the telescope provided much evidence in support of the theories of Kepler.

QUESTIONS AND EXERCISES

1. What is the latitude of Syene, Egypt?

2. What was the principal advantage of Copernicus' theory of the structure of the solar system over that of Ptolemy?

3. At what time of the year is the earth traveling fastest around the sun?

4. With the planets and comets traveling in ellipses, what is the changing force that is responsible for their changing speed?

5. What crucial test that would help decide between the ideas of an earth- and a sun-centered solar system was not carried out by Galileo?

6. When Eratosthenes measured the angles of elevation of the sun at two different places: (a) did he have to do it on a certain day of the year? (b) did he have to do it at a certain time of day? (c) could. he have made the measurements at two different dates (be specific)?

7. What is there about the apparent motion of the planets that is different from that of the stars?

8. To what extent can we say that an inaccurate scientific measurement led to the discovery of America?

9. Compare the length of time in which it was generally assumed that the earth was the center of the universe with that in which it has been generally accepted that the earth revolves around the sun.

10. What part of Copernicus' theory of the structure of the solar system was faulty and later corrected?

Unit 3
▼
THE STORY OF THE EARTH

CHAPTER

The Earth as It Is Now

1. EVIDENCE THAT THE SURFACE OF THE EARTH HAS CHANGED

Every landslide, every tree growing from a cracked rock, and every muddy river tell us that the surface of the earth is constantly changing. However, we shall be talking about more extensive changes, such as the appearance and wearing away of mountain ranges, arms of the sea covering millions of square miles of what is now dry land, and the development, dominance, and disappearance of strange types of animals. It may be a good idea to take a preliminary look at the evidence, and to see some of the reasons that compel us to think that such drastic changes have occurred in the past.

In many parts of the United States, particularly in certain limestone and sandstone deposits, there are fossils of marine animals. They are found, for instance, high up in the Rocky mountains. The rocks containing these fossils were undoubtedly formed at the bottom of the sea. Any explanation of this fact requires a considerable stretch of the imagination, but it seems more reasonable to assume that the rocks at the bottom of the sea were lifted up to make the mountains, rather than that the rocks were moved to the mountain tops from the bottom of some distant sea, or that the sea was once deep enough all over the earth to cover mountains as high as the Rockies.

The occurrence of fossils in general is evidence of the changing forms of life on earth. Fossils may be thought of as entombed life. Sometimes only an impression of an organism is left in the rock; sometimes the hard parts, like bones or shells, are preserved; and sometimes the entire organic structure has been petrified (Figures 3-1 and 3-2).

The basic principles which guide the study of fossils are surprisingly simple. The geologists are merely carrying on the same kind of study that has revealed to the archeologist what life was like in ancient Greece, Egypt, Palestine, and among the early cave dwellers in Spain and France. There is a uniformity among the fossils found in any one layer of deposit. There is a

Figure 3-1. Fossil lepidophyte stump. (*Geological Survey of Canada.*)

smooth sequence of changes and an increase in complexity from the lower layers to the upper. It is assumed that the lower layers were deposited before the upper ones, in those situations where the rocks have not been greatly disturbed. Marine-type fossils are found in deposits which are similar to the kinds now found at the bottom of the sea. Fossil land animals and plants are found in deposits like the La Brea tar pits and in rocks formed from the mud of shallow lakes.

Think of the small number of human skeletons that are ever found, compared to the many billions which have been buried since time immemorial. When one considers that most animals die a violent death, and that most dead plants lie on the surface of the ground until they decompose, any fossil remains that we do find must have been preserved by some lucky chance. When a dead plant or animal is exposed to both air and water, it usually decomposes. If either one or both are excluded, a fossil may

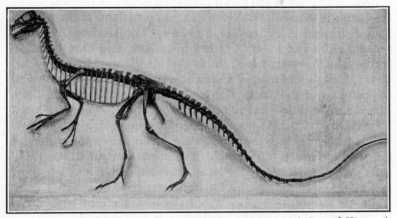

Figure 3-2. Skeleton of theropod. (*American Museum of Natural History.*)

result. These conditions are fulfilled when the remains are covered quickly by mud or tar, or drop to the bottom of the sea. One would expect a particular type of marine animal to be distributed over a large part of the world at the same time, and one would also assume that land animals and plants would have a much more limited range. This is true now, and it is also true of the plants and animals of the past, as recorded in fossils.

The fossil record tells us a story of a time when life was found only in the sea. Then it appeared on dry land in a few forms. These forms became more numerous and complex, and many species developed, flourished, and died out. Specialization increased, and finally man appeared on the scene about a million years ago.

The Colorado River has cut its way through thousands of feet of rock in the Grand Canyon. This river has, in effect, cut the leaves of a book which starts with the granite that underlies all formations. It carries us through ancient layers of rocks that are folded and twisted and carry no fossils, through tilted layers that contain practically no fossils, and, finally, through many horizontal layers of limestone and sandstone. The lowest of these contain only marine fossils; the upper ones are rich in increasingly specialized marine and dry-land remains. This is an unusually complete and extensive record.

Beds of coal containing well-preserved fossils of tropical plants are found in Alaska and Antarctica. Long Island is the type of deposit formed at the end of a glacier. The Hudson River has a channel far out to sea. It has been estimated that the 1950 earthquake in Assam raised the top of Mt. Everest by nearly 200 feet. Many feet of marine sediment were excavated from around the columns of the Temple of Jupiter Serapis in Pozzuoli, Italy. These marble pillars contain holes bored by salt-water molluscs. During the past 2000 years, the ground on which this temple stands has apparently sunk and risen again above the waters of the Mediterranean. You might give some thought to the problems such a situation would create in New York City. All these and many more apparently isolated facts have stimulated us to construct a consistent story about the changes that have taken place on the surface of the earth since it was formed.

We are going to survey very quickly what we know about the structure of the earth as it now is, then study some of the agents that are changing it, and subsequently have a look at the story of the past.

2. PRESENT STRUCTURE OF THE EARTH

(a) Atmosphere

Surrounding the earth is a blanket of air called the atmosphere. This consists of 78% nitrogen and 21% oxygen, the remaining 1% mostly carbon dioxide, water vapor, and rare gases. The higher we go above sea level, the less concentrated are these gases. At 10,000 feet altitude we find ourselves short of breath and high-flying planes use pressurized cabins to avoid discomfort; at 20 miles, 99% of the atmosphere is below us. The atmosphere becomes thinner and thinner with altitude, so we cannot say that it has a certain height. Even at an altitude of 185 miles, the friction of the atmosphere makes falling meteors glowing hot, and the northern lights tell us that there is still some atmosphere 600 miles above the earth.

(b) Surface Features

The ups and downs of the surface of the earth seem considerable when we are climbing a mountain with a 40-pound pack,

Figure 3-3.   Emblem of the United Nations, showing concentration of land masses around the North Pole.

but, when reduced to proper scale on a 12-inch globe, they would be hard to see. The highest mountains are less than 30,000 feet above sea level; the greatest depths in the ocean are slightly greater than this. The extreme difference is about 12 miles, which is only 0.3% of the earth's radius.

As you look at a globe, you should notice that only about $\frac{1}{4}$ of the earth's surface is dry land, and that this is massed close to the North Pole. The emblem of the United Nations takes advantage of this fact (Figure 3-3).

(c) Interior of the Earth

Since our deepest wells go only about 3 miles below the surface, our information about the bulk of the earth must be inferred from indirect observation. We assume that the vast interior of the earth is very hot. Although shallow mines and caves are cool, all deep mines show a steady increase in temperature with depth of about 1°F per 100 feet. We must also assume that the rocks deep in the interior of the earth have a much higher specific gravity than those common on the surface.

The term specific gravity refers to the weight of any volume of a substance compared to the weight of the same volume of water. A cubic foot of quartz weighs about 162 pounds and a cubic foot of water weighs 62.5 pounds, so the specific gravity of quartz is

$$\frac{162 \text{ pounds per cubic foot}}{62.5 \text{ pounds per cubic foot}} = 2.6$$

The units cancel out and specific gravity is only a number, a ratio. The rocks on the surface of the earth have an average specific gravity of about 2.7. The specific gravity of the earth as a whole is 5.5, so the rocks forming the bulk of the interior of the earth must have a specific gravity considerably greater than 5.5. Remember in our study of meteorites that some of them are stony and some are an alloy of iron and nickel. There is reason to believe that the heavy core of the earth is this same iron-nickel alloy, with a specific gravity between 8 and 10. We shall now consider the evidence that indicates this to be true.

Earthquakes will be considered later, but as the study of earthquake waves has given us all our information about the interior of the earth we will also consider them now. The way to study the motion of the earth during an earthquake is to make a record of the relative motion of something that moves with the earth and something that remains stationary during the quake. Figure 3-4 is a drawing of such an instrument, which is called a seismograph. The heavy mass is suspended by a wire and remains fairly quiet, whereas the drum moves with the earth. Most of the time, the light beam marks a straight line as the drum revolves. During a quake, it gives a record such as you see in Figure 3-5. It is observed that three different waves are sent out by an earth-

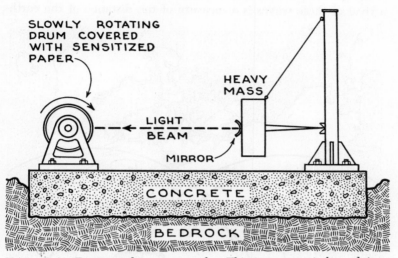

Figure 3-4.   Diagram of a seismograph.   This instrument is housed in a darkroom.

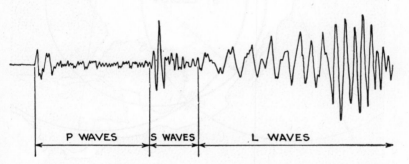

Figure 3-5.   A seismogram.   The record starts at the left with the *p* waves.

quake. They travel at different speeds and are recorded successively on the seismograph. The difference between the time of
arrival of these waves is a measure of the distance of the earth-

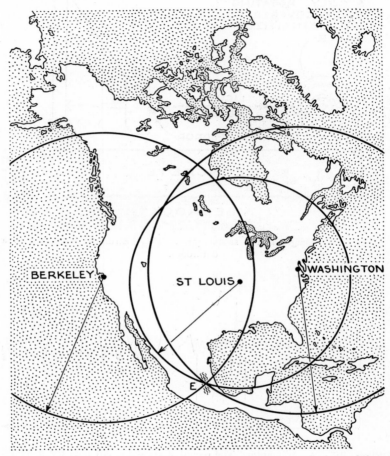

Figure 3-6. Epicenter of earthquake near Mexico City can be located from
observations made at three different stations.

quake from the observing station. If each of three observatories
in different parts of the world draws a circle on the globe showing where the quake could be, these three circles will intersect
at the point (epicenter) above where it was (Figure 3-6).

These three types of waves also give us information about the interior of the earth. The fastest (p in Figure 3-5) is a longitud-inal-type wave (like a sound wave) that can travel through both

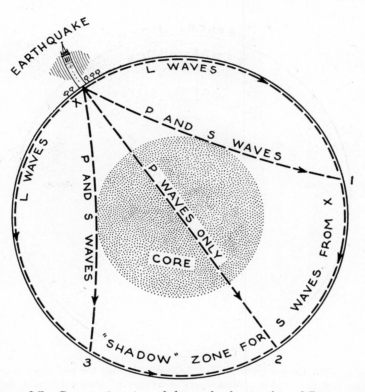

Figure 3-7. Cross-section view of the earth, showing how different types of waves are transmitted.

solids and liquids and is called the primary wave. The second-ary wave, s, is a transverse type which travels more slowly and which is not transmitted through liquids. The slowest is the l wave, which travels around the surface of the earth and is re-sponsible for most of the damage from earthquakes.

Figure 3-7 represents a cross section of the earth, with a severe earthquake at X. The p wave will be observed at all stations, with intensity decreasing with the distance from X. The s wave will be observed at all stations between X and 1 and X and 3, but will be missing on the seismograms of station 2 and all others

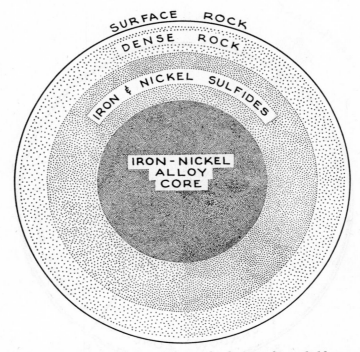

Figure 3-8. Cross-section view of the earth, showing the probable composition and sizes of the various layers as interpreted from earthquake data.

between 1 and 3. The l wave will be registered at all stations. The earth appears to have a central core, C, which transmits s waves very poorly or not at all.

By a study of several examples where the core casts a "shadow" for the s wave, we can get an idea of the size of this core. It has a diameter of about 4000 miles. It is assumed that it is made up of an iron-nickel alloy which is under such extremely high temperature and pressure that it behaves like a liquid. Around this core is a layer of sulfides of iron and nickel (Figure 3-8) surrounded by a 750-mile-thick layer of dense rock on which the surface rocks rest.

Earthquake waves change their speed with changing density of the medium, and hence they are refracted just like sound and light waves.

SUMMARY

1. Fossil remains tell a consistent story of the history of the past.

2. In an undisturbed deposit the lower layers are assumed to have been laid down before the upper ones.

3. There was a long period in the earth's history during which there was no life. Life started in the sea and then moved onto the land. Forms of life became more diverse and more complex as time went on.

4. The atmosphere contains 78% nitrogen, 21% oxygen, and small amounts of carbon dioxide, water vapor, etc.

5. Dry land covers only about one-quarter of the surface of the earth.

6. Specific gravity: the ratio of the density of a substance to the density of water.

7. The specific gravity of the surface rocks is considerably less than that of the earth as a whole, and so the earth must have a core made up of material more dense than the surface rocks.

8. From a study of the refraction of earthquake waves we learn that the earth has a shell-like structure with at least four different layers. The innermost sphere has a diameter of about 4000 miles and is made up of an iron-nickel alloy. The next shell is about 1000 miles thick and consists of sulfides of iron and nickel. The next shell is a 750-mile-thick layer of dense rock with a 50-mile-thick layer of surface rocks.

QUESTIONS AND EXERCISES

1. What are the facts about fossils that make us think that there has been an orderly development in the forms of life through the ages?

2. In what way could a person untrained in geology destroy the value of a fossil that he might find?

3. List some of the facts mentioned which indicate that conditions

in the world many years ago were considerably different from present-day conditions.

4. What is the weight, in pounds per cubic foot, of a substance with a specific gravity of 5.5?

5. Determine, in a rough fashion, the specific gravity of a rock, by weighing it and dropping it in a graduated cylinder containing water. The increase in volume of the water represents the volume of the rock.

6. Why do we assume that the 4000-mile core of the earth behaves like a liquid?

7. What clue do meteors give us to the nature of the interior of the earth?

8. From the shape of the path of earthquake waves (Figure 3-7), do they travel faster near the surface or at greater depths?

9. In a seismograph (Figure 3-4), why must the mass be a heavy one?

10. If the surface temperature is 60°F, what would be the temperature at the bottom of a mine 3 miles deep?

Wrecking and Rebuilding

1. WINDS, CHANGING TEMPERATURE, PLANTS

The earth, like a city, is never finished. Nearly everywhere we look wrecking or building is going on. The floors of oceans and lakes are carpeted with sand from rugged mountain peaks. The present mountains are the beds of ancient seas, which were either pushed up and bent into great ranges or spewed forth from subterranean reservoirs of molten rock. The old material is used and reused, so let us follow this process of tearing down and rebuilding through the ages.

The dust storms of the 1930's are not even an unpleasant memory to the present generation of students, but to the farmers of Oklahoma and Kansas they are a nightmare not soon to be forgotten. That area was turned into a "dust bowl," topsoil was blown as far as the east coast, and many farms were ruined and abandoned (Figures 3-9a and b).

In dry parts of the world, where the surface is not protected by plants, the wind has blown away great quantities of soil. This burden is scattered far and wide, but there are many places where the deposits have built up to a hundred or even to a thousand feet in thickness. These layers of wind-borne soil are called loess deposits (Figure 3-10). As these grains of sand are carried by the wind, they act like a sand blast and take the finish off cars, ruin windshields, and carve rocks into fantastic shapes.

Like nearly all other substances, rocks expand when heated and contract when cooled. As they are rather poor conductors of heat, a large rock in the bright sun will be many degrees warmer on the surface than in the interior. The result of this unequal heating is that the surface layer becomes loosened from the material below and eventually flakes off, leaving a fresh layer to suffer the same fate (Figure 3-11).

Figure 3-9*a*.   The approach of a dust storm.   (*Soil Conservation Service.*)

Figure 3-9*b*.   Wind-borne topsoil has ruined this farm and nearly buried
the buildings.   (*Soil Conservation Service.*)

174

Water has the peculiar property of expanding when it freezes. Broken water pipes and split automobile radiators are indications of the great force of this expansion. Water lodged in the cracks

Figure 3-10. Loess deposits which have been deeply eroded. (*U. S. Geological Survey.*)

of large rocks will similarly split them into smaller parts (Figure 3-12). If soil is in the crack, a seed may take root and the rock can be split wide open by the force of the growing plant (Figure 3-13). All these agents of disintegration attack massive rocks and break them into pieces small enough to be carried away by wind or running water.

Figure 3-11.   Half Dome, Yosemite, showing exfoliation.   (*U. S. Geological Survey.*)

Figure 3-12.   Blocks of granite sprung apart by frost wedging.   Sierra Nevada, California.   (*F. E. Matthes, U. S. Geological Survey.*)

Figure 3-13. Granite rock being split apart by a tree growing through it. (*U. S. Forest Service.*)

2. WATER: RUNNING WATER, WAVES, GLACIERS

Running water is by far the most active agent of erosion. It has been estimated that the Mississippi River carries 1 million tons of sediment each day. This comes from the farms of the Middle West and is dumped into the Gulf of Mexico. In carving out the Grand Canyon, the Colorado River carried away about 2000 cubic miles of dirt, and it is still going strong. Farmland is being denuded of topsoil; reservoirs for irrigation and hydroelectric power are being filled up; ship channels must be kept dredged; giant deltas are being built up—running water is indeed a major factor in our economic life as well as a geological agent which is changing the face of the earth.

Rivers usually carry most of their sediment at one season of the year (spring). Where the river meets a lake or the sea, and the current slackens, the largest particles of dirt drop to the bottom first and the finest ones are carried farthest out. Thus, river-borne deposits are typically graded by size. Between flood seasons these deposits have time to settle into layers. Each year a new layer is added which is distinct from the previous one. The pressure of the layers above consolidates the lower ones, and a typical sedimentary rock is formed.

Waves, and the sand they carry, are constantly eating away at

Figure 3-14.   Remains of the shoreline of old Lake Bonneville in Utah. (*U. S. Geological Survey.*)

cliffs to form beaches at the water line. This is a moderately important factor at present, but the occurrence of wave-cut terraces high above the present water line, or high up on a mountain side, gives us a clue to changing water levels and ancient lakes that have now disappeared (Figure 3-14).

When the summer temperatures of a region are so cool that not all the previous winter's snow melts, the snow accumulates. As the snow deepens year after year, the lower part is compacted into ice, and the pressure from above forces it to flow slowly downhill. This river of ice is called a glacier (Figure 3-15).

Glaciers are common in the high mountainous regions of the world. There are many in the Himalayas, the Alps, the Andes, in Norway, and in Alaska. Greenland is one vast glacier, and so

Figure 3-15. Aerial view of a glacier. (*U. S. Forest Service.*)

Figure 3-16. Glacial cirques. (*U. S. Geological Survey.*)

Figure 3-17. A glaciated valley. Notice U-shaped cross section. (*U. S. Geological Survey.*)

Figure 3-18. The scratches on this rock were made by a glacier pushing other rocks over it. (*U. S. Geological Survey.*)

is the continent of Antarctica. As we shall see later, a large continental glacier spread down from Canada into the northern part of the United States many thousands of years ago.

A solid mass like a glacier moves very slowly; the usual speed is a few feet a day. But even this is sufficient to move rocks, scour out valleys, and make characteristic changes in the land-

Figure 3-19. An exposure of a ground-moraine sheet left by the great glacier of the Ice Age. (*From Elements of Geology, by W. J. Miller, D. Van Nostrand Co., 1939.*)

scape. As the head of a glacier works back into the mountain it wears out a semicircular area called a cirque (Figure 3-16). Since the cutting action is greatest at the bottom and sides, a glacial-cut valley has steep sides and a broad, flat bottom like a U (Figure 3-17). The bottom is marked by deep scratches in the direction of flow of the glacier, where rough rocks have been pushed along (Figure 3-18). These rocks and the soil are carried down to the point where the glacier is melting as fast as it comes down. Here the material is dumped into an unsorted pile called a glacial moraine (Figure 3-19). Since this material is not usually carried very far (in contrast to river sediment), it is still

Figure 3-20. Yosemite Valley before glaciation. (*After Matthes.*)

Figure 3-21. Yosemite Valley after glaciation. (*After Matthes.*)

rough. Hence, a rough, unsorted deposit is readily recognized as glacial till. A careful study of pictures and a geological survey map of Yosemite Valley will reveal many of the characteristics of a region which has been glaciated fairly recently (Figures 3-20 and 3-21).

3. MOUNTAIN BUILDING AND EARTHQUAKES

The eroding effect of wind and water would eventually wear down the continents almost to sea level if it were not for an opposing force which is pushing up the mountain ranges. We are far from having reached a complete understanding of these mountain-building forces, but we do know about some aspects of the process. As you push into a partly filled hot-water bottle at one point, it bulges out at another. As rivers carry sediment down and dump it at coastal regions, the pressure at these points on the earth's crust is increased and the pressure in the mountainous regions is decreased. What readjustment would you predict in this situation if the rocks a few miles under the surface of the earth are subject to plastic flow, somewhat like the flow of a glacier? The coastal region should sink gradually under its increased load, and the mountains should be pushed slowly upward as erosion lightens them. This would keep the downward pressure approximately equal in both places. This explanation for the slow buckling and bulging of the earth's crust is known as the theory of isostasy, and it is illustrated in Figure 3-22.

True equilibrium is never achieved, and the slow downward push where the sediment is being deposited and the slow upward thrust of the mountains will gradually bend and warp the rocks. A downward bend is called a syncline (Figure 3-23); if this is a huge trough extending for many hundreds of miles, it is called a geosyncline. The upward bend is referred to as an anticline (Figure 3-24).

These distorting forces may act so slowly, and the type of rock may be such, that only intense folding results (Figure 3-25). Under other conditions the strain is so great that the rocks break. The line of this break is called a fault (Figure 3-26). The formation of a fault is probably accompanied by an earthquake. Once

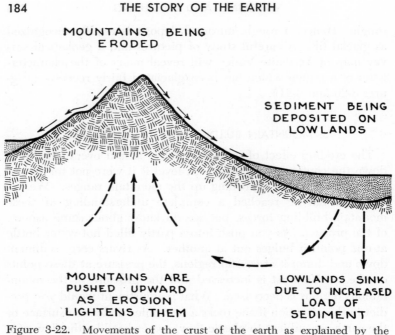

Figure 3-22. Movements of the crust of the earth as explained by the theory of isostasy.

Figure 3-23. A syncline. (*U. S. Geological Survey.*)

Figure 3-24. An anticline. (*U. S. Geological Survey.*)

Figure 3-25. Sedimentary rock which has been folded extensively. (*U. S. Geological Survey.*)

a fault has formed, future tensions tend to be relieved by further movements at the fault line. Many important fault lines have been traced, the most spectacular being the San Andreas fault line in California (Figure 3-27). The earthquake of 1906 involved a sidewise slip of several feet along this line (Figure 3-28).

Figure 3-26.   A vertical fault.   (*U. S. Geological Survey.*)

One would expect to find the greatest stress on the earth's crust in the neighborhood of very high mountains, particularly where mountain ranges are close to the sea. We find these conditions along the shores of both sides of the Pacific Ocean, in India, around the Mediterranean, and in the Caribbean. Compare this with Figures 3-29a and b, which show the regions of the earth where earthquakes are most frequent.

Many earthquakes occur every day, but nearly all of them are so minor that they are only remembered as wiggles on a seismogram. In parts of the world where earthquakes are common, people become worried if several days pass without one, because they know that tensions are being built up that will cause trouble when they finally are relieved.

An earthquake in a heavily populated region can cause serious loss of life and property. On April 18, 1906, there was a hori-

Figure 3-27. Air view along the San Andreas fault zone, at the west base of the Temblor Range, California. The position of the fault is marked by the nearly straight furrow between the hills and the low ground. (*Photograph by M. S. Kennedy from Physical Geology by Longwell, Knopf, and Flint, John Wiley & Sons, 1948.*)

zontal displacement along the San Andreas fault line in California which caused damage to property over an area of hundreds of square miles.   The water pipes in San Francisco were sheared off, and a fire raged out of control.   Millions of dollars of dam-

Figure 3-28.   An example of the horizontal displacement which took place during the earthquake of 1906.   This picture was taken near Pt. Reyes Station, California.   (*U. S. Geological Survey.*)

age was done, and nearly a thousand people were killed.   Where earthquake-resistant construction is practiced even tall buildings can be safe.   During the winter of 1811–1812, three earthquakes centered near New Madrid, Missouri.   They were among the greatest in history.   The region was so thinly settled that there was little loss of life or property, but an area of about 30,000 square miles sank from 5 to 15 feet.   Great swells were seen to roll across the prairie.

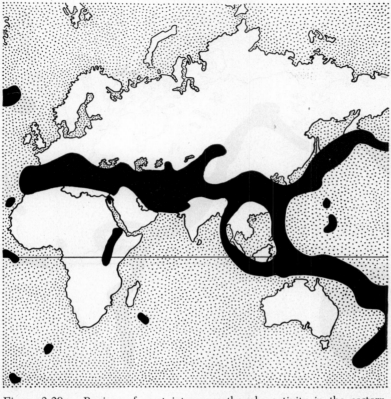

Figure 3-29*a*.   Regions of most intense earthquake activity in the eastern
hemisphere.

4. VOLCANISM

Active volcanoes, geysers, and hot springs are mere surface
features that remind us of the hot, seething condition of the large
core of the earth under the relatively thin, stable crust of surface
rocks. In some parts of the earth, either the crust is particularly
thin or vast cracks permit the molten rock to surge upward. It
is probably more than an interesting coincidence that volcanic
activity is found in the same parts of the world that are subject
to frequent earthquakes.

Below the surface of the earth the heat is so great that the

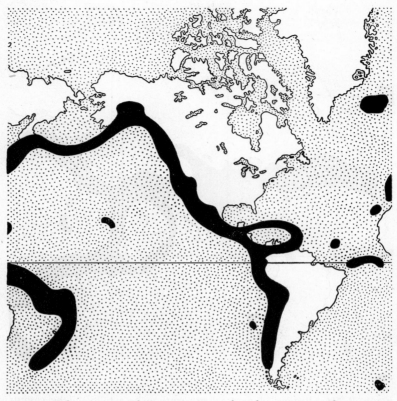

Figure 3-29b. Regions of most intense earthquake activity in the western hemisphere.

rocks melt. They flow out from volcanoes as a viscous liquid called lava. As the lava cools it solidifies into rock. This type of rock is called igneous because of its fiery origin. Granite and basalt are two common types of igneous rocks. Since igneous rock is found below all sedimentary deposits and at the core of all mountain ranges, we suspect that, at one time, the earth was fairly hot and that it has since cooled down. The action of air and water on the original igneous rock dissolved parts of it, and other parts were carried away to be deposited and formed into sedimentary rocks. The further action of heat, pressure, water, and air on the sedimentary rocks and the remaining igneous rocks occasionally changed them so much that we find it convenient to give them a special name—metamorphic rocks. Rocks are thus divided into three broad classifications: igneous, sedimentary, and metamorphic.

Lava may come to the surface in a spectacular eruption, or it may ooze out through a great crack in the earth's surface and

Figure 3-30.   The grand eruption of Lassen Peak, California, May 22, 1915. The volcanic cloud is fully 8 miles high. (*From Elements of Geology, by W. J. Miller, D. Van Nostrand Co., 1939.   Photograph by Myers and Loomis.*)

flow over the ground like cold molasses over a pancake. A lava flow which covered several hundred square miles occurred in Iceland in 1783.

We owe the existence of many beautiful mountains to volcanic activity.   The Hawaiian Islands are the tips of volcanoes which stand on the floor of the Pacific Ocean; Fujiyama, Vesuvius, Pelee, and Ranier are well-known volcanoes.   Mt. Lassen (Figure 3-30), in northern California, should be mentioned as the one most recently active (1917) in the United States (not including Alaska), and Paricutin, in Mexico (Figure 3-31), as the most recent addition to the family (1943).   Katmai, in Alaska, and Krakatoa, near Java, have given us terrifying examples of the

Figure 3-31. Paricutin, the world's youngest volcano, in violent activity.
(From *Physical Geology, by Longwell, Knopf, and Flint, John Wiley &*
Sons, 1948. Photograph by Otto Brehme.)

power of an exploding volcano. When Krakatoa blew up in 1883, the noise was heard 3000 miles away, practically the whole island was thrown into the air as dust, and the so-called tidal wave swept away coastal villages for hundreds of miles. The dust from this explosion colored the sunsets and affected the weather for months afterward. Violent earthquakes and a series of explosions marked the action at Katmai in 1912. Nearly 5 cubic miles of earth were blown into the air.

SUMMARY

1. Rocks are broken up by changing temperature, by the solvent action of water, and by the splitting action of ice and roots.

2. Loess deposits are soil which has been carried to its present position by wind.

3. Running water is the major agent of erosion.

4. The particles of river-borne deposits have rounded edges and are graded by size.

5. Old shore lines can be recognized by their wave-cut terraces.

6. A typical glacial-cut valley has a U-shaped cross section, parallel scratches on the rocks at the bottom, cirques at its head, and a moraine at its mouth.

7. Glacial deposits are rough edged and unsorted.

8. Isostasy is the theory which states that there is a tendency for the downward pressures on different parts of the earth's crust to equalize each other by a slow transverse movement of material under the crust.

9. A syncline is a curved rocky structure in which the center is lower than the sides.

10. An anticline is a curved rocky structure in which the center is higher than the sides.

11. A fault is a break in a rocky structure in which the parts move relative to each other.

12. Earthquakes occur most frequently in the parts of the earth where there are the greatest differences in elevation.

13. Igneous rock is rock that has solidified from the molten state.

14. Sedimentary rock is rock formed by the cementing together of small particles.

15. Metamorphic rock is either igneous or sedimentary rock that has been extensively changed in structure after it was formed.

16. Lava is the melted rocky material that issues from the earth, and the rocks which form from it when it solidifies.

QUESTIONS AND EXERCISES

1. State the different ways in which a large rock may be broken up into small fragments.

2. What are some of the signs that indicate water erosion in the past?

3. If you live in a section of the country where there is a particularly muddy stream, take a glass full of this water and let it stand to see how much sediment settles out.

4. What are the main differences between glacial till and river-borne sediment?

5. Does a wave-cut terrace above the present shore line of the ocean necessarily indicate that the level of the sea has dropped? Explain.

6. How do we explain the fact that the surface of the delta of the Mississippi has remained at about the same level for many centuries?

7. Would you be more likely to find fossils in granite or in sandstone?

8. Would you find particles of igneous rock in a sedimentary deposit? of sedimentary rock in an igneous deposit?

9. How would you explain a situation where igneous rock is found lying on top of a sedimentary deposit?

10. Mention two examples where the level of a part of the earth has changed by thousands of feet.

CHAPTER 3

Progressive Changes in the Landscape

1. SEEING WHAT THERE IS TO SEE ON A TRIP

It may be well to pause at this point to organize somewhat differently the information in the previous section. The succeeding section on the progressive changes in a landscape will hardly need this same treatment. The subject is so large that only the most obvious phases can be mentioned, but even these will be enough to make your trips more meaningful.

The ability to identify rocks and minerals can be developed only by careful study and actual working with the materials. You could no more learn practical geology without laboratory work than you could learn typing without a typewriter. However, Figure 3-32 will give you an idea of what a sedimentary deposit looks like, and Figure 3-33 shows a typical igneous rock. Slate is an example of a metamorphosed shale; marble is a metamorphosed limestone; and gneiss (Figure 3-34) is a metamorphosed granite.

First of all, notice whether the rocks are igneous (granite, basalt, or lava) or sedimentary (sandstone, limestone, layered, gravelly, etc.). Sometimes you will observe sedimentary deposits resting on igneous rock, and occasionally an igneous intrusion breaking through layers of sedimentary rocks (Figure 3-35). Many of the rocks in lava beds are porous and spongy (Figure 3-36). The cones of volcanoes are easy to recognize. From this you can infer something about the origin of the region. It will be practically impossible to date the strata unless you are a trained geologist with a working knowledge of fossils.

Next, observe whether the sedimentary rocks are uniform and sorted (deposited by rivers or marine organisms), or unsorted and angular (deposited by glaciers). A glaciated valley will be characterized by its U-shaped cross section, waterfalls from the

Figure 3-32.   An outcrop of sedimentary rock consisting of shale and sandstone.   Near Oxnard, California.   (*From Elements of Geology, by W. J. Miller, D. Van Nostrand Co., 1939.*)

Figure 3-33.   A specimen of granite.   (*From Elements of Geology, by W. J. Miller, D. Van Nostrand Co., 1939.*)

sides, and cirques at its head. The characteristics of a river-cut valley will be described in the next section. Strata may be traced across a road cut, or even across a valley, and fault lines

Figure 3-34.   Banded gneiss.   (*Geological Survey of Canada.*)

can sometimes be followed for miles. A vein of valuable mineral will usually be broken off at the plane of the fault line, and it then becomes the job of the geologist to figure in which direction to dig to find it again. Grand Canyon National Park offers an unrivaled opportunity to follow the geological history of a single region over hundreds of millions of years.

Figure 3-35. An igneous intrusion (dike) cutting horizontal sedimentary beds at right angles. Alamillo Creek, New Mexico. (*N. H. Darton, U. S. Geological Survey.*)

Figure 3-36. An outcrop of volcanic breccia showing a coarse fragmental texture. Ten miles west of Reno, Nevada. (*From Elements of Geology, by W. J. Miller, D. Van Nostrand Co., 1939.*)

2. THE SEQUENCE OF CHANGES

(a) Mountains and Rivers

We are fortunate to be able to visit, within the limits of the United States, examples of nearly all types of geological formations in all stages of the progressive changes they undergo.   In the Cascade Range of Oregon and Washington we find young mountains still being raised; the Rockies are older; the Appalachians are about 200 million years old; and the Adirondacks of

Figure 3-37.   A very narrow, steep-sided canyon 1500 feet deep.   The Narrows, Zion Canyon, Utah.   (*From Elements of Geology, by W. J. Miller, D. Van Nostrand Co., 1939.*)

northern New York are the stumps of a range raised up about a billion years ago.   Ten thousand years ago a great glacier retreated from the northeastern part of the United States, and we can still see much evidence of its work.   In 1917 Mt. Lassen last erupted, and the trees killed by that action are still standing. As you read these lines, the Great Bear sand dune on the eastern shore of Lake Michigan is engulfing and smothering another grove of trees which are in the path of its relentless march. Among our rivers, the Missouri is old, the Tennessee is middle-aged, and the Columbia is young. Let us now follow through

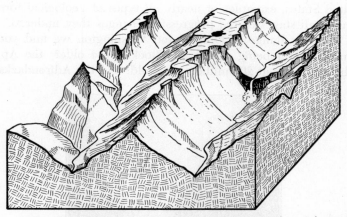

Figure 3-38.   First stage in the development of a landscape, characterized by newly formed mountains and young rivers.

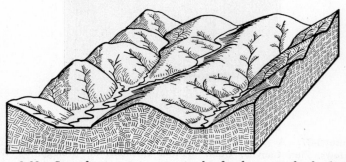

Figure 3-39.   Second, or mature, stage in the development of a landscape.

some of the changes that take place after an extensive mountain-building period.

Young mountains show a lack of the usual signs of erosion. Their peaks are jagged, their ridges sharp. The streams run over waterfalls and cascades and cut deep, steep-sided valleys (Figure 3-37). They run through small lakes and have few tributaries

(Figure 3-38). Since these new streams have a steep gradient, they flow fairly straight and carry their sediment with them. Their burden of abrasive material carried at a high speed enables them to cut downward rapidly.

The downward cutting eventually reduces the gradient of the stream. More and more tributaries are formed. The tributaries are younger and pour a large burden of rocks and sand into the main stream. A point is reached at which the main stream is not able to carry away all the sediment that is brought into it.

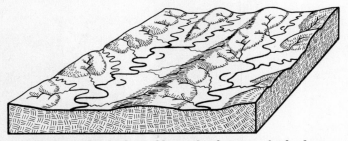

Figure 3-40. The third, or old-age, development of a landscape.

Shoals develop, and the river begins to form a flood plain and meanders (Figure 3-39). By now, most of the lakes and waterfalls have disappeared, the rugged peaks have been worn away, trees, bushes, or grass have covered the soil formed, and the mature stage has been reached. At the mouth of a river, sedimentary layers are laid down for thousands, and possibly millions, of years.

The passage from the mature stage to old age is gradual and poorly marked. The higher ground is subject to the greatest erosion, but it can never be worn down to sea level. The process of washing away becomes slower as the heights are reduced, until a gently rolling peneplain landscape results. Here and there, a particularly resistant mountain root may stand out (Figure 3-41). The flood plain of the river is very wide, with numerous meanders (Figures 3-40 and 3-42). An occasional spring flood may change the course of the river so that one of these meanders is cut off and is left to form a type of lake called an

Figure 3-41. Monadnocks near Moosehead Lake, Maine. (From *Physical Geology*, by Longwell, Knopf, and Flint, John Wiley & Sons, 1948. Photograph by McLaughlin Aerial Surveys.)

oxbow (Figure 3-43). The Yellow River of China has changed
its course by hundreds of miles in a single year.

Not always does the life of a river follow this uninterrupted
course. Mountains grow by fits and starts, so that the river may
have reached the flood-plain stage when a new thrust starts it
flowing more rapidly. It then cuts a new channel down the

Figure 3-42. Meanders of the south Saskatchewan River. (*Royal Canadian
Air Force.*)

center of the flood plain (Figure 3-44). This process is observed
with the Merced River in Yosemite National Park.

As layer upon layer of sediment is deposited at the mouth of
the river (which probably forms a delta), the rocks underneath
are bent under the pressure to form a syncline. For some reason, not yet well understood, a new period of mountain building
begins. This time, the syncline is elevated, either in complex
folds (Figure 3-45) or in great tilted blocks (Figure 3-46). The
former peneplain sinks and is covered by the sea.

The erosion of these new mountains places layers of horizontal
sediment on the irregular outline of the old peneplain to produce
an unconformity (Figure 3-47). An unconformity necessarily

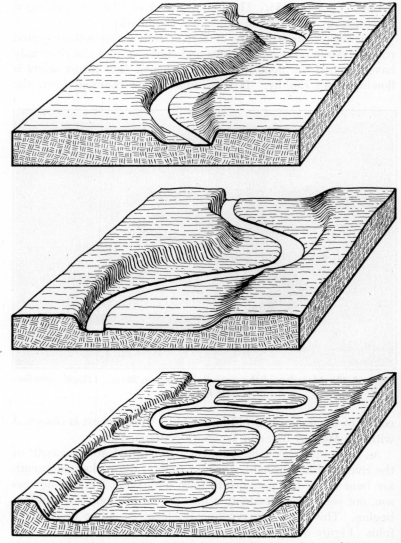

Figure 3-43.   Three steps in the development of a river, showing how it cuts
away its banks and forms oxbows as it matures.

represents a very great difference in age between the lower and the upper layers.

Figure 3-44.   Rejuvenated streams.   From the well-rounded contours of the landscape one would expect to find a mature stream with meanders and a flood plain.   Instead, these streams have steep walls and nearly straight courses.   (*U. S. Geological Survey.*)

(b) Geological Time

It happens that there have been only a few periods of general mountain building throughout the world.   They were comparatively short, in a geological sense, and were followed by long periods of erosion.   A new period of general mountain building followed.   These long, relatively uninterrupted periods of erosion are convenient units for study in geology; they are called eras.   During any one era, changes in climate were less drastic, particular life forms had a chance to develop along several different lines, and many thousands of feet of fossil-bearing strata were laid down.   The period of widespread thrusting up of mountains is called a revolution.   It marks the end of an era, and it is identified by an unconformity. The abrupt change in climate which accompanied a revolution would wipe out many species and speed up the evolution of others.

Before we move into a detailed study of the sequence of changes on the surface of the earth, it will be advisable to see how we put together this jigsaw puzzle of information.

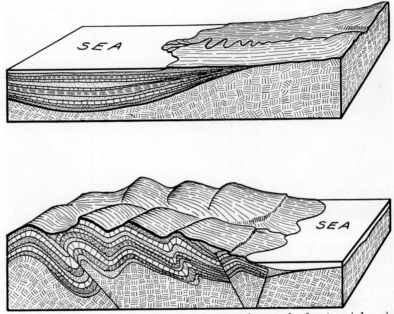

Figure 3-45. Sedimentary layers laid down at the mouth of a river (above) are folded and faulted as they are lifted to form a new mountain range (below).

(c) Dating Strata

The direction in which science is advancing at any one time in history is determined by economic and social pressures to a much greater extent than most people realize. This is nicely illustrated by the combination of circumstances that led to the understanding of how to put geological strata in the correct sequence. Josiah Wedgwood, the eighteenth-century English potter, was having trouble transporting his fragile wares to the

London market from his factory in Staffordshire. He was successful in agitating for a system of canals for inland transportation. One of the surveyors laying out routes for the canals was William Smith. Smith must have been an unusually observant person, because he noticed and studied the surface strata of the

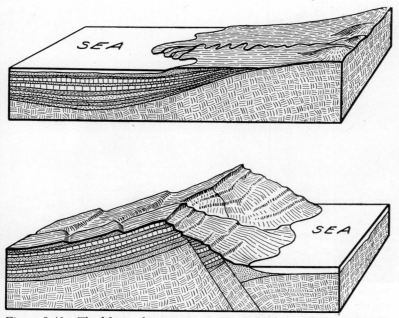

Figure 3-46. The lifting of a new mountain range may result in the breaking of the strata, forming block faults.

country and even the fossils they contained. He found out that each layer contained characteristic fossils and that there was a regular succession of layers that was repeated at widely separated places. Since the order of these layers was never inverted, one could say with confidence that the lower ones had been formed before the upper ones. He also pointed out that two strata in different parts of the country that contained the same types of fossils must be the same age. His intense interest in strata led to his nickname "Strata Smith," and to a tremendous advance in our understanding of the history of the earth. All this started with a fragile teacup.

By the middle of the nineteenth century, Charles Lyell had made a convincing case for the modern point of view that past changes on the earth's surface are adequately explained by proc-

Figure 3-47. An unconformity separating horizontal layers above from steeply tilted layers below. Gaspé Peninsula, Quebec. (*From Fundamentals of Physical Science, by K. Krauskopf, McGraw-Hill Book Co., 1948.*)

esses now in operation. This replaced the catastrophic theory, which held that a few world-wide catastrophes, such as floods and volcanic activity, were responsible for the present surface features of the earth. Darwin's theory of evolution (1859) did for biology very much what the theory of uniform change did for geology. In fact, the two theories strengthened each other, just as two quarter circles fit together to make a strong arch.

The most accurate method for dating our oldest rocks depends on a study of the radioactive decay of uranium and certain other elements. This method will be explained later (Unit on Atomic

Structure, p. 448). The age of the earth's crust, as estimated by the radioactive-decay technique, is nearly 3 billion years, and it is this time scale that we shall use in the following history of the changes that have taken place in the surface of the earth.

SUMMARY

1. A young landscape is characterized by jagged, rocky peaks; swift, straight streams with waterfalls, cascades, and lakes.

2. A middle-aged landscape is characterized by rounded mountain tops, mostly covered with soil and vegetation; vein-like pattern of streams; meanders and shoals in the rivers.

3. An old-aged landscape has developed a peneplain; sluggish, meandering streams; oxbows and deltas in the rivers.

4. Mountain-building forces have raised the bottoms of ancient seas up to be mountain tops.

5. An unconformity is the line separating two layers of rocks in certain special situations. These conditions are that one layer is igneous and the other sedimentary; or, if both are sedimentary, the layers are not parallel. The lower layer appears to have been extensively eroded before the upper one was laid down.

6. An era is a major division of geological time. Eras are so chosen in length that there are few of them, and they cover a fairly unified series of events.

7. A revolution is a time of extensive mountain building, which usually marks the break between geological eras.

8. In a sequence of strata, unless there is reason to suspect otherwise, it is assumed that lower strata were laid down before those above them.

9. We find a consistency among the fossils in any one stratum and an increase in diversity and complexity from older to younger strata.

10. Charles Lyell first stated, and it is now agreed, that past changes of the earth's surface are adequately explained by geological processes now in operation.

11. The age of the earth's crust, as estimated by radioactive-decay technique, is nearly 3 billion years.

QUESTIONS AND EXERCISES

1. What are the signs indicating that a stream has passed from youth to middle age?

2. In a situation like the Delaware Water Gap, in which a river cuts directly across a mountain range, what is the relative age of the river as compared to that of the mountain range?

3. Write a paragraph tracing the story of a grain of sand that was first part of a mountain range, was then carried away by erosion, and later returned to be deposited as part of the upper layer of an unconformity.

4. What is the relationship among the terms era, revolution, and unconformity?

5. What would be characteristic features of the landscape of the Cascade Mountains?

6. List some of the more obvious differences between sedimentary and igneous rocks.

7. Yosemite Valley now has a river running through it. What makes us think that this valley was once occupied by a glacier?

8. How many different unconformities can be seen in the Grand Canyon of the Colorado?

9. Can a river show signs of being both old and young at the same time? Explain.

10. Explain briefly but precisely the basic reasoning involved in interpreting geological records.

4

CHAPTER

Up from the Sea

1. GETTING A PERSPECTIVE

The geological history of the earth is divided into six major eras, some of which are subdivided into periods. As you can see by referring to Table 3-1, each is longer than the period that succeeds it. This is partly because we have more detailed information about the recent eras than about the ancient ones. Except for the Azoic era, the end of an era is marked by a revolution, a period of extensive mountain building.

A word should be put in here about an older scheme of classification in geology. Before time was divided into eras it had been divided into four parts, which were called Primary, Secondary, Tertiary, and Quaternary. The term Primary is now covered by the names of the first three eras—Azoic, Archeozoic, and Proterozoic. The Secondary period covered the time now included in the Paleozoic and Mesozoic eras; Tertiary refers to the first four periods of the Cenozoic era; and Quaternary, to the last one. The reason for including these older terms is that geologists have not yet eliminated the last two, and so you will still see rocks referred to as Tertiary or Quaternary, as well as by the name of the period.

As you can see from Table 3-1, the Azoic era occupied 33% of the entire time since the formation of the earth's crust, the Archeozoic 27%, and the Proterozoic 23%. It is not until we come to the Paleozoic era, with only 17% of the time remaining, that we find abundant fossil records. This era lasted 10% of the time, the Mesozoic 5%, and the Cenozoic only 2%.

TABLE 3-1

Notice that the space given to the eras is not related to the length of time they lasted.

Era	Period	Physical events in North America	Characteristic life
		3 billion years ago—formation of earth's crust	
Azoic			Nothing living
		2 billion years ago—appearance of first "living" thing	
Archeo-zoic			Graphite and limestone deposits
		1.2 billion years ago—Laurentian revolution	
Pro-tero-zoic		Erosion from Cascadia and Appalachia	Very scanty fossil records. Algae and primitive invertebrates
		500 million years ago—Killarney revolution	
Paleo-zoic	Cambrian	Continent gradually sinking after previous mountain building. Extensive erosion	First trilobites Earliest rocks with abundant fossils
	Ordovician	Large part of North America covered by sea	Dominance of trilobites and other invertebrates. Early vertebrates

TABLE 3-1 (*Continued*)

Era	Period	Physical events in North America	Characteristic life
Paleo-zoic	Silurian	Climate hot and dry Salt deposits formed	First land plants Rise of fish Dominance of trilobites
	Devonian	Most of North America above sea level	First land animals
	Mississip-pian	Center and eastern part of continent a shallow marsh that rose and fell several times	Rise of amphibians Complex invertebrates
	Pennsyl-vanian	Same as Mississippian	Coal deposits of east Many amphibians Dragonflies
	Permian	North American continent rose above sea level	Last of the trilobites Rise of the reptiles

200 million years ago—Appalachian revolution

Era	Period	Physical events in North America	Characteristic life
Meso-zoic	Triassic	Dry climate; much volcanic activity along west coast	Rise of dinosaurs Earliest mammals
	Jurassic	Coast Range and Sierra Nevada thrust up	Dominance of dinosaurs Flying reptiles and earliest birds Marsupials

TABLE 3-1 (*Continued*)

Era	Period	Physical events in North America	Characteristic life
Meso-zoic	Cretaceous	Rocky mountain area pushed up above sea level. Cooler, drier climate. Western coal and oil deposits formed	Early mammals and birds. Last of the dinosaurs. Many flowering plants and insects

60 million years ago—Rocky mountain revolution

Era	Period	Physical events in North America	Characteristic life
Ceno-zoic	Eocene	Mild climate and general erosion	Reptiles giving way to mammals
	Oligocene	Mild climate and general erosion	Modern plant life Mammals dominant
	Miocene	Cascades, Alps, and Himalayas formed. Yellowstone Park area formed	Many modern animals well developed
	Pliocene	Lava extrusions cover Columbia River basin	Manlike ape
	Pleistocene	Four great ice ages	Appearance of early man. Social behavior of man

2. AZOIC ERA

The Azoic (without life) era started with the formation of the earth's crust and lasted for about a billion years. The emergence of the first primitive form of life is the arbitrary mark of the end of this era. By definition, we have no fossils from this era, and very little is known about it. Our best guess is that it was a rather warm, rainy time, when there was extensive erosion. Somehow or other the necessary chemical reactions took place for the molecules to be organized into living things.

3. ARCHEOZOIC ERA

The Archeozoic (ancient life) era began about 2 billion years ago, lasted for about 800 million years, and ended with the Laurentian revolution. Extensive graphite and limestone deposits are evidence of life during this era, but the remains have been so altered that we cannot even guess at the details of their structure. It was probably to this era that Koko was referring when he said, in *The Mikado,* "I am in point of fact a particularly haughty and exclusive person of pre-Adamite ancestral descent. You will understand this when I tell you that I can trace my ancestry back to a protoplasmal, primordial, atomic globule." The best-preserved fossils are those of some blue-green algae. The Laurentian mountains are an igneous intrusion resting on sediment accumulated during the Archeozoic era. The Vishnu schist, which is the rock through which the Colorado River is now cutting in the Grand Canyon, is thought to have been formed at the same time as the Laurentian mountains.

4. PROTEROZOIC ERA

With the building up and erosion of the Laurentian mountains, we start the Proterozoic (early life) era. This was about 1.2 billion years ago, and it lasted for 700 million years. It ended with the Killarney revolution. Much of the mineral wealth of Canada—copper, nickel, silver, and gold—and the iron-ore deposits of northern Minnesota originated during this era. The

areas that are now the Rocky and Appalachian mountains were
great geosynclines being filled with sediment from the west and

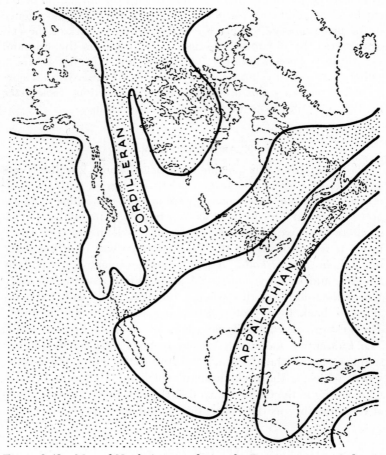

Figure 3-48. Map of North America during the Proterozoic era. Sediment
was being deposited in the Appalachian and Cordilleran geosynclines.

east respectively (Figure 3-48). There is no indication that
the Mississippi valley was ever very high above sea level, but the
east-coast and west-coast parts of this continent have changed
from high mountain ranges to below sea level more than once.

5. PALEOZOIC ERA

The Killarney revolution was a period of mountain building and erosion in central Canada along the Ontarian geosyncline. This was the time during which the curtain was down between the third and fourth acts of our drama. The curtain rolled up again to reveal the Paleozoic (old life) era. The rocks of this era are so rich in fossils and we can make out so many details that we have divided it into seven periods. So far we have covered five-sixths of geologic time; life is still confined to the sea and is very primitive. The Paleozoic era started about 500 million years ago and lasted for 300 million years. During this time, living things conquered the difficulties of existence on dry land and evolved many complicated forms, including seed plants, flying insects, and reptiles.

The first period in this era is the Cambrian. Since Cambrian rocks are the oldest containing extensive fossil remains, the early geologists lumped all the older rocks into one group and called them pre-Cambrian, or Primary. The most frequently encountered type of fossil in this period is the trilobite (Figure 3-49). In fact, the history of this era may be summarized as the rise, heyday, and disappearance of the trilobite.

During the second, or Ordovician, period, the Middle West was a vast shallow sea abounding in trilobites and many other marine invertebrates. Cephalopods, an early form of squid (Figure 3-50), reached a length of 15 feet, and the first vertebrate, a primitive fish, put in its appearance.

The third period in this era is called the Silurian. During this period, the various marine invertebrates evolved increasingly complicated forms. Many areas in North America that had been under water were lifted gently (without much faulting or folding). The drier climate resulted in the formation of extensive salt deposits in New York and Michigan. Plants which had been growing in shallow water either developed so that they could survive on dry land, or perished. This emergence of the plants from water to dry land is probably the most significant event in this period, because the animals had to stay in the sea until there were land plants for them to feed on.

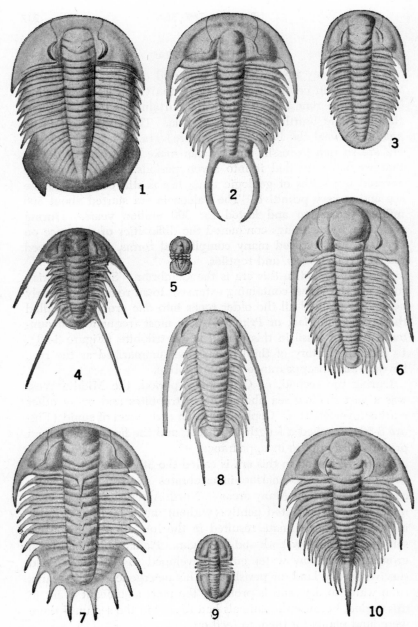

Figure 3-49. Cambrian trilobites. All natural size except 6, which is about
⅙ natural size. (*From Historical Geology, by C. O. Dunbar, John Wiley
& Sons, 1949. Drawn by L. S. Douglass.*)

In the next, or Devonian, period, the land plants developed rapidly. Ferns, club mosses, and even primitive trees (Figure 3-51) were abundant. Although an early type of air-breathing scorpion is found in late Silurian deposits, the first land animals are thought to have appeared in the Devonian. In the sea the

Figure 3-50. An Ordovician sea beach, on which specimens of the great cephalopod, Endoceras, are stranded. (*Chicago Natural History Museum, From a painting by Charles R. Knight.*)

trilobites and cephalopods, although more complex in structure, were becoming less important. A great variety of fish developed (Figure 3-52).

After the Devonian came two periods, the Mississippian and the Pennsylvanian, which have so much in common that it is convenient to consider them together. The climate was temperate and uniform for a long period of time. At the close of the Devonian nearly all North America was dry land, and it returned to this state by the opening of the Permian; but in the interval a shallow sea covered most of what is now the continental United States west of the Mississippi. The scene of the present Appalachian mountains had many ups and downs. For long periods, our present eastern coal beds must have been a huge swamp resembling the Dismal Swamp in Virginia. Luxuriant, primitive

Figure 3-51. Reproduction of a middle-Devonian seed-fern tree. These grew to a height of 25 to 40 feet. (*Courtesy of the New York State Museum.*)

vegetation flourished and fell into the water to be turned into coal. Giant dragonflies and cockroaches flew through the air; amphibians developed, flourished, and gave way to reptiles (Figure 3-53).

Figure 3-52. Model of a Devonian fish. Actual length about 2 feet. (*Yale, Peabody Museum.*)

Figure 3-53. Reconstruction of a Pennsylvanian landscape. (*Yale, Peabody Museum.*)

The last period of the Paleozoic is the Permian. The North American continent rose above sea level, never again to be extensively invaded. The climate became cooler and drier, and this change put the dry-land animals and plants to a severe test. From the amphibians, which have to breed in water, came the reptiles that could lay eggs on the ground (Figure 3-54). The plants had developed a sexual method of reproduction, which

Figure 3-54. Restoration of Permian reptiles. (*Chicago Natural History Museum.*)

made for more variety in each generation and, hence, for more rapid evolution. The characteristics which did not contribute to success were more rapidly eliminated and a greater variety of responses became possible as conditions changed. During the previous periods of uniformly favorable climate, the plants were characterized by giant size more than by daring experiment; during the Permian period of change, the smaller, more versatile types fared better.

Since the climate turned progressively colder during the late Permian, this period saw the most extensive ice age of any period before or since. Strangely enough, most of this glaciation took place in the neighborhood of the equator.

The close of the Paleozoic era is marked by the Appalachian revolution. Our present Appalachian mountains were being slowly pushed up, and there was a great amount of folding, faulting, and erosion as the process continued. With the Appalachian revolution the curtain falls on this era, which saw so many significant changes taking place. As erosion once more lays down sediment, we open the next act.

SUMMARY

1. The Azoic era lasted 1 billion years, from the formation of the earth's crust to the appearance of the first form of life. Very few details known about this area.

2. The Archeozoic era lasted 800 million years, from the first form of life to the Laurentian revolution. Fossil records include graphite and limestone deposits.

3. The Proterozoic era lasted 700 million years, from the Laurentian revolution to the Killarney revolution. Fossil records include algae and worm burrows. Erosion was filling up the Appalachian and Rocky mountain geosynclines. Important mineral deposits were laid down in Canada and the United States.

4. The Paleozoic era lasted 300 million years, from the Killarney revolution to the Appalachian revolution. Extensive fossil records occur thenceforth. Trilobites developed, flourished, and died out. First vertebrates, land plants, land animals, insects, amphibians, and reptiles. Eastern coal deposits formed.

QUESTIONS AND EXERCISES

1. On a scale in which all geological time is represented by 1 hour, how long would each of the eras be?

2. Arrange the following forms of life in the order in which they developed: fishes, land plants, reptiles, trilobites.

3. What is the nature of our oldest fossil deposits?

4. Would you expect to find fossils in the rocks of the Laurentian mountains? Explain.

5. Why do we suppose there was extensive erosion during the pre-Cambrian eras?

6. What kind of evidence indicates that the Appalachian geosyncline was being filled up by erosion from a mountainous area located east of it?

7. What would be a particularly useful type of fossil in dating Paleozoic sedimentary rocks?

8. Name several factors that make it more difficult for plants to live on dry land than in the sea.

9. What was the first living creature to fly, and when did it develop?

10. What is an important difference between amphibians and reptiles? Name a living example of each group.

5

CHAPTER

From Early Mammal to Early Man

1. MESOZOIC ERA

The Mesozoic (middle life) era began 200 million years ago and lasted for 140 million years. It is divided into the Triassic, Jurassic, and Cretaceous periods. The rugged climate of the Appalachian revolution eliminated many of the star players in the previous act of our drama and left all but part of the Far West above sea level (Figure 3-55). The trilobites have disappeared; the cephalopods and amphibians have been reduced to a minor role; the reptiles and seed plants have taken over. Just as the Paleozoic was outlined as the rise, heyday, and decline of the trilobites, so the Mesozoic was the scene for the reptiles.

The Triassic period saw the development of many forms of reptiles and of the earliest mammals. These primitive mammals had hair on their bodies, laid eggs, and suckled their young very much as the duck-billed platypus does now. In fact, this modern animal is probably a "living fossil" from this era (Figure 3-56). The ginkgo tree (maidenhair-fern tree) is another holdover from nearly 200 million years ago.

During the Jurassic period the reptiles developed into complex and fearsome beasts. To anyone but a scholar in Greek their names are equally impressive. The ichthyosaur (fish-lizard) (Figure 3-57) and the plesiosaur (near-, or semilizard) (Figure 3-58) swam the seas; the brontosaur (thunder-lizard) (Figure 3-59) and gigantosaur (giant-lizard) were so ponderous that they spent most of their time partially immersed in swampy water, munching the lush vegetation; the stegosaur (lizard-with-a-roof) was a plant eater and depended for protection on its heavy armor plate; the pterosaur (winged-lizard) (Figure 3-60) were flying dragons with a wingspread of as much as 25 feet. Along with the flying reptiles appeared the first true bird with feathers,

225

the *Archaeopteryx* (ancient-bird) (Figure 3-61). It could hardly be called an early bird, however, because worms had existed nearly a billion years. Intense volcanic activity, mainly by in-

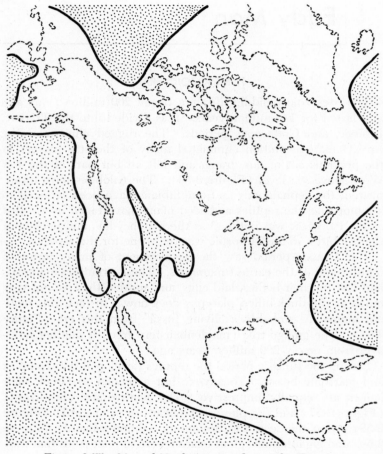

Figure 3-55. Map of North America during the Triassic.

trusion of granite, pushed up the Sierra Nevada and the Coast Range of California. With these were formed the gold ores that later drew the forty-niners to the West.

The Cretaceous period was one of a slow change in climate

from mild to cold. It saw the start of a mountain-building program (the Rocky mountain revolution) that was probably the most extensive the world has ever known. Along with this process came the rapid development of some types of life and the equally rapid disappearance of others.

Figure 3-56.   Duck-billed platypus.   (*New York Zoological Society.*)

Figure 3-57.   Skeleton of Jurassic ichthyosaur.   It is about 12 feet long. (*American Museum of Natural History.*)

Although the thrusting up of the Rocky mountains marks the end of the Cretaceous period (and of the Mesozoic era), it was a process that was going on gradually during most of this time. We have a repetition of the situation during the Permian period. There was a change toward a cooler and drier climate and an increased complexity in plants, and the giants among the animals gave way to the smaller and more clever creatures.

The most dramatic event in the plant kingdom was the appearance and phenomenal development of flowering plants. In this one period they rose from their first beginnings to dominance.

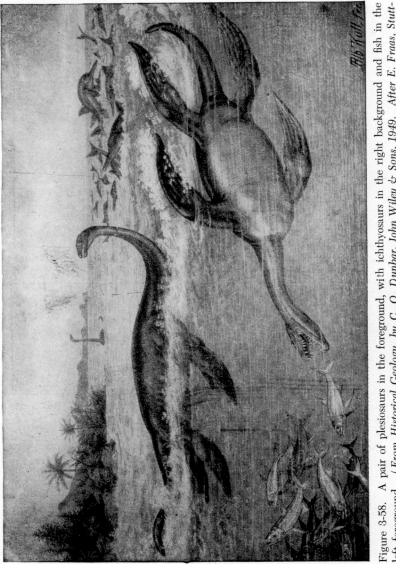

Figure 3-58. A pair of plesiosaurs in the foreground, with ichthyosaurs in the right background and fish in the left foreground. (From *Historical Geology*, by C. O. Dunbar, John Wiley & Sons, 1949. After E. Fraas, Stuttgart Museum.)

The ancestors of our present-day hardwoods, conifers, palms, and grasses were all present.

Among the reptiles, the terrifying flesh-eater *Tyrannosaurus rex* (tyrant-lizard) (Figure 3-62) represents their last fling in size and might. The dinosaurs decreased rapidly in importance and

Figure 3-59. Skeleton of a brontosaur. This specimen measures 67 feet from nose to tip of tail and stands about 18 feet high at the hips. (*Yale, Peabody Museum.*)

disappeared altogether by the end of the era. A number of factors contributed to the decline of the dinosaurs. One wonders whether some of these have a modern-day parallel. Since reptiles are cold-blooded (their body temperature changes with changing air temperature), the cooler climate made them more sluggish. Both the coolness and dryness cut down the luxuriant vegetable growth so necessary for feeding their huge bodies. They had such small brains that they must have been unbelievably stupid. They laid eggs on the ground, then went off and left them. At this point the life threads of the dinosaurs and the mammals cross.

Egg-laying mammals appeared during the Triassic, marsupials during the Jurassic, and those which give birth to well-developed young, the placentals, appeared during the Cretaceous, about 100 million years ago.   Mammals are warm-blooded, have a rela-

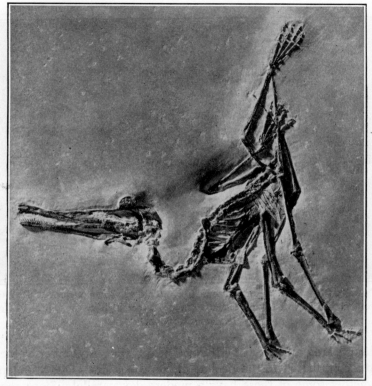

Figure 3-60.   Skeleton of a pterodactyl.   (*American Museum of Natural History.*)

tively large brain for their size, and nurse and train their young. Although the Cretaceous mammals were so small that *Tyrannosaurus rex* would have needed several for a mouthful, he could not catch them, and they found dinosaur eggs a convenient and delicious meal (Figure 3-63).   It is small wonder that the mammals began to displace the reptiles in importance.

The Rocky mountain revolution involved the formation of the

mountainous spine of two continents. From Canada through Central America the Rockies were formed, and in South America the Andes continued this range. The Appalachians had been eroded nearly to a peneplain, and they, too, were pushed up

Figure 3-61. The oldest known bird, *Archaeopteryx*. The bird was about the size of a crow. (*From Historical Geology, by C. O. Dunbar, John Wiley & Sons, 1949. After G. Heilmann.*)

again. In Virginia and Pennsylvania many old rivers cut directly through the more recently formed ridges. The Delaware Water Gap is an example of this activity. These events, which happened about 60 million years ago, mark the end of the Mesozoic era and the start of the Cenozoic.

2. CENOZOIC ERA

When the curtain goes up on our final act (which is still going on), we find the scenery and the players surprisingly familiar. The North American continent is about its present size and shape; the mountains are rather more rugged than we know them; important changes have yet to take place in the Northwest; but, by and large, we would recognize it readily.

The trees, flowering plants, and grasses look vaguely familiar.

Figure 3-62.   Restoration of *Tyrannosaurus rex*. (*Chicago Natural History Museum.*)

The animals would not be any more surprising than those we see on our first visit to the zoo (Figure 3-64). Instead of a widespread, uniform climate, there is our present distribution of hot, moderate, and cold.

This era started 60 million years ago and is divided into five periods: Eocene, Oligocene, Miocene, Pliocene, and Pleistocene. There are some who mark off the last 30,000 years as a separate period and call it the Recent. Since all these are so recent we have a wealth of detail in the fossils. Practically all this era will have to be passed over and just a few high spots indicated.

In the Eocene, the flowering plants and mammals were the dominant forms of life. In the sea, the seaweed, fish, oysters, crabs, etc., were practically the same as their present-day descendants. During the Oligocene, the climate was rather mild and general erosion was taking place. A sample of the type of

evolution that was occurring is shown by the horse. In the Eocene it was a terrier-like animal with paws (Figure 3-65). By the
Oligocene it had grown larger and was developing hooves (Figure 3-66). As it grew larger, it attained more speed, a larger
brain, and more specialized teeth.

The Miocene was a period of mountain building in certain
areas and of gentle uplift in others. The Cascade range of Ore-

Figure 3-63. A nest of fossilized dinosaur eggs. (*American Museum of
Natural History.*)

gon and Washington, the Alps in Europe, and the Himalayas of
Asia were formed at this time and remain the world's youngest
mountain ranges. The Rockies, Appalachians, and even the Mississippi basin were elevated a few hundred feet. Some of these
disturbances, particularly those along the West Coast, continued
intermittently and are still going on.

During the Pliocene, the Columbia River plateau was covered
by igneous extrusions. These lava fields are about 200,000
square miles in extent and reach a thickness of 3000 feet.

These four periods of the Cenozoic era make up the old Tertiary classification.

The Pleistocene, which covers the last million years, used to
be called the Quaternary. During even this relatively short pe-

Figure 3-64.   Some animals of the early Eocene.   (*Chicago Natural History Museum and Charles R. Knight.*)

riod of time there were some rather striking changes taking place. There were four great ice ages, which left their marks on the northern part of this country and which presented a challenge that speeded up the evolutionary process.

From two different centers in Canada, sheets of ice, thou-

Figure 3-65.   Restoration of Eohippus.   This horse was about a foot high at the shoulder.   Restoration by Charles R. Knight.   (*American Museum of Natural History.*)

sands of feet thick, ground and scraped their ways across New England and the North Central and the Northwestern states (Figure 3-67). They advanced and retreated four different times, leaving the lakes of Minnesota and Michigan and the rolling hills of Ohio and New York to mark their passage.   They bulldozed the topsoil of New England into a moraine we now know as Long Island.   Many small local glaciers left their marks in the Rockies and the Sierra Nevada. The Yosemite owes its broad central valley and its waterfalls to this period.   The last major glacier disappeared no more than 10,000 years ago.   With all this water

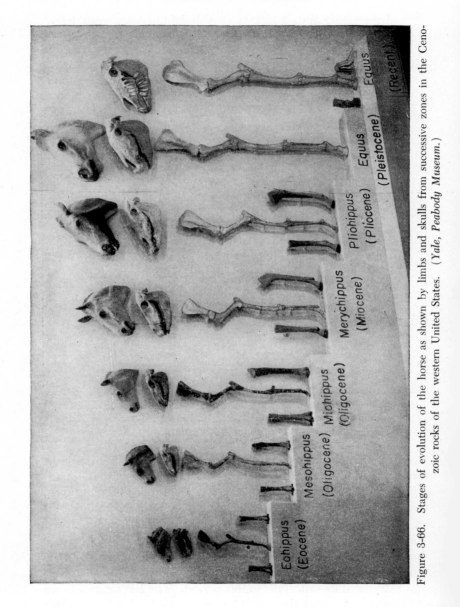

Figure 3-66. Stages of evolution of the horse as shown by limbs and skulls from successive zones in the Cenozoic rocks of the western United States. (*Yale, Peabody Museum.*)

tied up as continental ice, the oceans retreated and the rivers cut valleys far out into the continental shelf.

Figure 3-67.   The continental glaciers of the Pleistocene.

The generally cooler climate put a premium on the smaller and more adaptable forms of life.   At approximately the beginning of this period, the earliest form of man put in his appearance.   By modern standards, he was not particularly attractive, and, compared to the rest of the animals, he was poorly equipped physically. His fur was inadequate; neither his claws nor his teeth were sharp; nor could he run very fast. His brain and the shape of his hands were his two main assets. In a period of change he was better suited to meet the challenge than were some of his more specialized competitors. Figure 3-68 shows some early men. *Pithecanthropus erectus* lived about a million years ago, Neanderthal man at least 100,000 years ago, and the

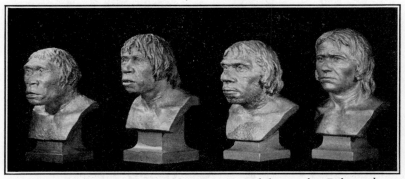

Figure 3-68. Restorations of early man. From left to right: Pithecanthropus, Piltdown, Neanderthal, and Cro-Magnon. (*American Museum of Natural History.*)

Cro-Magnon man about 40,000 years ago. There is no evidence that the Cro-Magnon man developed from these earlier types. Where he came from we do not know, but he seems to have moved into Europe and displaced his Neanderthal predecessor. There is recent evidence to suggest that a man as highly developed as Cro-Magnon man existed as much as half a million years ago, and so it is probable that several of these early types lived at the same time. As the study of these early human remains is only about a hundred years old, it is not surprising that there are many gaps yet to be filled in our picture of the past.

3. ANOTHER ICE AGE?

Considering the rather drastic effects of the last ice age, one may well wonder whether we are entering a new ice age or are still on our way out of the last. Many guesses have been made to explain the change in climate that led to these great sheets of ice. One recent theory based on data from the field of astronomy, seems to account very well for the repeated glaciation during the Pleistocene.

The accumulation of snow is due to unusually cool summers, not to abnormally cold winters. When the air temperature is below freezing, the moisture precipitates as snow, no matter how cold it is. But, if the summer is cool, not all the previous winter's snow melts. As it accumulates year after year, it pushes forward in the form of a glacier. You will remember that the reason for the seasons is the inclination of the earth's axis of rotation to the plane of its orbit around the sun. In January the sun's rays are falling more nearly perpendicularly on the southern hemisphere (Figure 2-2). In its elliptical path around the sun the earth is closest to it in January, so that the seasons of the northern hemisphere are less extreme than those in the southern hemisphere. The difference in distances is about 3%, but the chill of the northern winters and the heat of the northern summers are somewhat tempered. In Australia both the angle of the sun's rays and the distance to the sun combine to accentuate the seasons.

Has the situation always been as it is now? We know that the axis of the earth's rotation is swinging around just as a spinning top wobbles. The gravitational effect of the rest of the planets on the earth is not great, but it is enough to make small changes in the eccentricity of the earth's orbit and to change the angle between the orbit and the axis of rotation. At times in the past, all these factors have worked together to make summers as cool as possible. At other times both the eccentricity and the angle of the earth's axis were great; consequently, summers were particularly hot and winters cold. These changes can be calculated from the known orbits of the other planets. Figure 3-69 shows the calculated and predicted summer temperatures from astronomical data and the records of glaciation from geological data over a period from 600,000 years ago to 100,000 years in the future.

The coincidence of the calculated and observed glaciations is so close that it seems that the astronomical factors must be crucial. You can see that we are emerging from a glacial period and that the climate will continue to grow milder for about 20,-000 years before we head for another time of glaciation about 50,000 years from now and a really severe one 100,000 years hence. Of course, these predicted changes will come slowly, but

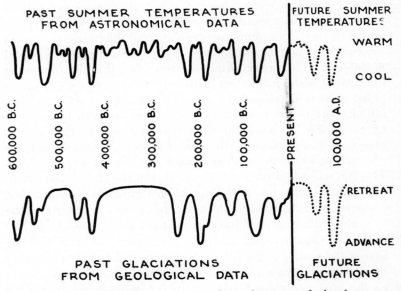

Figure 3-69. Graphs showing the correlation between calculated summer temperatures and glaciation in the past and a prophecy for the future. (*Redrawn from Scientific American.*)

it may not be too many thousands of years before palm trees will be growing in Montreal, and New York and the rest of our ports will be covered by the sea as the two polar ice caps melt.

The many theories attempting to explain the widespread glaciation occurring at about the times of the Appalachian and Killarney revolutions, and earlier, would take too much time to present here. None has been generally accepted, but the theories would make interesting reading and would be worth your critical examination.

4. EVOLUTION

The evolutionary process rests on two observed facts. The first is that offspring are never identical with their parents, and the second is that offspring are somewhat similar to their parents. In other words, we have variations from one generation to the next, and some of these variations tend to be inherited by future generations. If an individual is helped to survive by a particular variation, then it will have a better chance to live and to pass on that characteristic to its children. In this way, a useful variation will be encouraged, and what we call evolution will be the result. Many variations will be harmful, and the individuals bearing them will be weeded out gradually by the struggle for existence. The trilobites and dinosaurs are just two examples from the many dead ends in the evolutionary process. Some variations seem to have no noticeable effect on the struggle for survival. It is important to realize that evolution is a chance process; it is not purposeful.

The role of the environment in heredity is becoming clearer, although there is still much to learn. We have come to realize that the word "environment" of a plant denotes more than the soil and the climate in which it is growing. We must consider minute changes in the concentrations of the elements in the soil, the complete electromagnetic spectrum of radiation to which it is exposed, winds, drought, the presence of other plants, and many other factors. In fact, the division of the situation into plant on one hand and environment on the other is an artificial distinction that is useful for some purposes but confusing for others.

In a plant (or animal) there are certain extremely small (submicroscopic) structures called genes, which are principally involved in inheritance. Although these genes are extraordinarily stable they are subject to permanent change when attacked by certain chemicals, by radiation, etc. Any individual plant may be considered to be the result of the interaction of these genes and their environment (in the large sense). Some of the variations between one plant and the next may be inherited by future generations, and others may not. As the environment changes, the number of inherited variations increases. When the environment remains stable, changes in forms of life are slow. But when the environment changes rapidly, as when the tide pools dry up or the weather grows cooler, then the evolutionary process is speeded up.

In this unit we have followed the 3-billion-year-long story of the changes of the surface features of the earth and of the living things that populate it. We have seen how the landscape goes through a cycle of changes of mountain building, followed by erosion, and how the cycle may be repeated many times in any one region. We have seen how living things, on the other hand, have taken the path of progressive change. The few and simple gave rise to more variety and more complexity. The highly specialized prosper only so long as their environment remains stable. Abrupt change favors the versatile organism over the specialized one and accelerates evolution by increasing the frequency of variations and by intensifying the struggle for existence.

SUMMARY

1. The Mesozoic era lasted for 140 million years, from the Appalachian revolution to the Rocky mountain revolution. The Triassic period saw the rise of the dinosaurs and the earliest mammals. In the Jurassic period the dinosaurs were dominant and the Sierra Nevada were formed. During the Cretaceous period, the dinosaurs declined and disappeared, mammals and flowering plants flourished, and western coal and oil deposits were formed.

2. The Cenozoic era started 60 million years ago. Mammals and familiar plants were the dominant forms of life. The Cascade range was formed, and four great ice ages during the last million years left their mark on the northern part of the United States. Man developed and learned social behavior.

3. From astronomical data it appears that the climate of North America is due to grow progressively warmer for about 20,000 years, with another ice age in prospect after that.

4. Genes are extremely small units in a living organism, which are principally concerned with inheritance.

5. Some variations are inherited from one generation to the next, others are not. Some variations have survival value; others are injurious; and still others seem to make no difference.

6. A change in the environment tends to increase the number of variations.

7. Evolution is a chance process of progressive change that results from the interaction of the genes and their environment.

QUESTIONS AND EXERCISES

1. It is incorrect to say, "During the Silurian drought, plants changed in order to be able to live on dry land." How should this change be described?

2. What are some important differences between reptiles and mammals?

3. Trace the major steps in the evolution of plants during the Paleozoic and Mesozoic eras.

4. Trace the major steps in the evolution of animals during the Paleozoic and Mesozoic eras.

5. Take some region, such as the present Appalachian mountains, and trace it through its various ups and downs.

6. Which of the following mountain ranges consists principally of sedimentary deposits: Appalachian, Cascade, Laurentian, Rocky, Sierra Nevada?

7. Explain how it happens that several lakes which have a short geological life are found in the Adirondack mountains, which are very old.

8. What conditions are favorable for evolution in the direction of large size?

9. Explain how each of the following factors would affect the winter temperature of North America: (a) the earth's orbit nearly circular; (b) the earth's orbit fairly eccentric; (c) the earth's axis of rotation perpendicular to the plane of its orbit; (d) the earth's axis of rotation at a considerable angle to the plane of its orbit.

10. What are the various ways in which the environment affects evolution?

6

CHAPTER

A Pause to Take Our
Bearings

1. THE SCIENTIFIC METHOD

We have gone far enough now to have some examples to use in examining the way scientists work. It is important to do this because there are many decisions that you will need to make that can be approached by the same technique used on problems in science. As a home owner, you will have to evaluate conflicting claims before making purchases; as a voter, you will be faced with problems of school bonds, sanitation, traffic engineering, etc.; medical authorities will point out how impending antivivisection legislation would hamstring medical research; and the question of effective control of atomic energy will certainly be before us again. The methods used by scientists have been so amazingly effective in solving problems that it is high time they were used more widely.

The field of intellectual activity in which there has been the most substantial progress in the last 2000 years is the field of science. Progress implies more than trying something new and different. It implies a structural unity, with the old serving as a foundation for the new growth. Certainly there is no evidence of any significant change in man's brain during this period. His progress has been in his organization of his knowledge and in his techniques for acquiring new information.

In such a course as this you can learn something of the techniques that science has found so successful, you can learn something about the world around you, and you can develop your own critical thinking so that it will be more effective.

The so-called scientific method is a method of problem solving which has an entirely general application. The name is perhaps unfortunate, because it implies that it is to be used only by scientists. It is a genuine tragedy that this method has not been used more widely. Probably the greatest virtue of the scientific method is that it serves as a touchstone for identifying that which is false. There seems to be no lack of ingenuity in the human race for thinking up clever explanations. What is needed is a technique for examining this multitude of guesses and discarding the bad ones.

The Babylonians, the Egyptians, and the Greeks, Ptolemy, Copernicus, and Kepler, all had different ideas about the structure of the solar system. It is not so much a question of which idea is right, because none was entirely correct in all details. We want to know which theories are way off the track and what are the imperfections in those that are partly right. By this process of elimination we can build, piece by piece, a picture which comes ever closer to the thing it represents. Lucretius thought that we saw by means of a series of dart-like particles emitted from our eyes, which bounced off things we looked at and returned to our eyes—a sort of visual radar. Newton considered that light consisted of tiny particles, which he called corpuscles, and Huygens argued for the wave-like nature of light. We now see justification for both these latter points of view.

The scientific method is usually outlined as consisting of four steps, which follow the realization that a problem exists. These four steps may be labeled as (1) observation, (2) generalization, (3) deduction, and (4) examination. They will now be taken up and enlarged on in that order. The first step is the collection of information either by simple observation or by planned experiment. Sometimes this step is taken completely in the dark, but more often than not the experimenter already has a hunch by which he is guided in selecting his data and planning his experiments. The original hunch frequently is wrong; in fact, it usually is, but it forms a basis for action and can be revised as the experimenter goes along. Although Ptolemy's picture of the structure of the solar system was wrong in most details, it did serve to predict the rising and setting of the sun, moon, planets, and stars with passable accuracy for over a thousand years. A striking example of a completely wrong theory that led to an important discovery is to be found in the story of the discovery of radioactivity by Becquerel, which will be told later.

When we are faced with a number of related facts we always try to simplify the picture. We pick out the things that are similar and emphasize them. This thought process is generalization. Notice that when we do this we are ignoring the differences. We classify a group of individual animals as dogs; we say the Negroes are good singers; Newton saw the element common to the motions of a falling apple and the moon. The process is called generalization because we go from a number of particular events to a more general picture. Another name for it is inductive reasoning. Induction leads us to see things in a relationship which seems reasonable. We no longer are puzzled by a mass of separate facts. From a large number of observations "Strata Smith" was able to see that there were order and sequence in the fossils and in the types of deposits throughout England. He proposed the generalization or explanation that the lower ones were older than the ones on top. The kinetic-molecular theory of gases that is developed in the next unit gives us an over-all picture of the nature of gases and explains their behavior under changes of temperature and pressure.

The larger the number of experiments on which a generalization is based, the more likely it is to be accurate. One must be careful to avoid jumping to conclusions on insufficient data, and it pays to be critical and to ask to see the supporting data when someone propounds a theory that seems suspect. If you are the kind of person who insists on examining the data behind generally accepted theories, ones that "everybody knows are true," then you are already applying the skepticism characteristic of the scientific method.

The first two steps described above are common practice in all fields of learning. Collecting data (observation) is fun, and thinking up explanations for why things are as they are (generalization) is good exercise for the imagination. Some people are more gifted at it than others, but we all practice it more often than we realize. The third and fourth steps, however, give the scientific method its peculiar strength. They involve a conscious effort to undermine and demolish the brain child created in the second step.

The third step is usually called deduction. If the new generalization is correct, it follows that such and such must be the case.

Columbus held the theory that the earth was a sphere about 18,000 miles in circumference. He argued that, if this theory was true, it would be more convenient to sail westward from Spain to India than to sail eastward. Kepler constructed a model of the solar system with the sun at the center and the planets revolving in circular orbits at certain distances and speeds. He then calculated where they should be a certain length of time in the future. "Strata Smith" was able to predict from a surface deposit what type of deposit would be found beneath. This process of deduction involves prediction, and it is on the accuracy of its predictions that a theory is judged.

The fourth step, examination, follows inevitably. The predictions are checked. If they turn out to be correct, the investigator beams happily and feels that his brain child has a promising future. Since the predictions almost inevitably fall short of being completely correct, the theory is gone over carefully to see where it needs to be modified to make it accord with this new event. Kepler varied the distances of the planets from the sun, changed their speeds, recalculated the results of this change, and checked again. After a discouraging number of failures based on this general way of looking at things, Kepler tried elliptical orbits for his planets and soon was able to make predictions that came out right. His picture of the structure of the solar system was accepted, and those of Ptolemy and Copernicus were discarded, because his system was a more dependable guide to action. As we shall see later, Mendeleef's periodic classification of the elements was not taken seriously until some of his daring predictions about elements yet to be discovered were verified.

The terms generalization, hypothesis, theory, and law, as used above, mean much the same; they differ in degree. A generalization covers relatively few particulars; if it is more sweeping, but not yet carefully checked, it is called a hypothesis. After a large number of deductions from a hypothesis have been checked and found true the hypothesis advances to the status of a theory. The distinction between these two terms is not always observed, and the word "theory" is frequently used for either one. After a theory has become well established and generally accepted it may be called a law. The law of gravity and the law of uniform change are examples.

A theory is a brief statement, in general terms, that describes the way things behave. It outlines the results obtained from a large number of experiments and is revised whenever new evidence shows that it is somewhat inaccurate here or inconsistent there. To overthrow a theory completely requires the construction of an entirely new picture that is consistent with all the old evidence and that provides deductions differing from the results of the old theory. If the new deductions are checked and found to fit in with the facts, the old theory will gradually be discarded in favor of the new one. The death of an outmoded theory is seldom rapid, because there are always persons who would rather try to patch it up than to go over to a different point of view. The corpuscular theory of light advanced by Newton died a slow death even though all the facts known at the time were better explained by Huygens' wave theory. Subsequently discovered facts have shown, however, that both points of view must be taken into account. After a theory (such as the atomic theory) has been refined over the period of a century, it is extremely improbable that something completely new and different will replace it.

Notice the use of the expression "extremely improbable." Science is not the field of certainties that so many people seem to think. It is a field of probabilities, of suspended judgments, and it requires a willingness to let the evidence decide the case. A scientist realizes that any theory he may propose is not the final word; he tests it to find out how nearly right it is, not to prove that it is right.

2. TO GET SOME INFORMATION

The second objective mentioned as being important in the study of physical science was that you learn something of the world about you. Light, color, sound; the sun, moon, planets, and stars; and the story of the rocks and their fossils are experiences which touch you frequently. We will soon come to a consideration of rains, winds, and clouds; electricity and magnetism; and our ideas about the atoms and molecules that make up everything we see and touch. An attempt has been made to balance a basic understanding with a practical appreciation of how familiar things work. New things and ideas not yet dreamed of will come during your lifetime, and it is hoped that many of these will be extensions of material covered here, so that you will be able to follow the developments as they come along. Certainly life is poorer to the extent that you are blind to the physical world around you.

3. TO DEVELOP CRITICAL THINKING

A third objective in this course is to develop effective critical thinking. Many courses that you take will contribute to this important part of your education, but it will be worth while to examine some of the ways that a study of physical science helps.

All the logic in the world will not help you reach valid conclusions from faulty assumptions. In this book a consistent effort has been made to show the factual evidence on which the theories were based. Make it a habit to start from verifiable facts as a basis for your opinions. Aristotle was one of the most logical men the world has known in that he consistently followed the rules of logic in his thinking. In spite of this, he reached many absurd conclusions because he started arguing from what he thought things ought to be like because of what he considered to be their very nature. He failed to look at them and find out what they were really like before he applied his logical thinking.

Words have a chameleon-like quality of changing their meanings; but there is little chance of confusion when a definition, even though it is expressed in words, is based on a description of how one observes or measures the thing being defined. This way of defining terms is called operational definition (refer to the definition of polarized light, page 84), and, by consistently using it, scientists have reduced the amount of misunderstanding in their conversation and writing.

One of the greatest contributions you can make to your own clarity of thinking is to realize that you think in words. The words you use for expressing an idea are symbols, like a map, of the part of the world around you. The words are not the things they stand for, just as the paper map is not the actual countryside through which you are traveling. To the extent that your word map is accurate, your thinking can be accurate. Any details that are fuzzy or actually wrong in your word picture will lead you astray in your thinking, just as you will get lost on a trip if your map is inaccurate. No order or predictability was possible on the basis of the geological theory that each formation and fossil was a special act of creation. With a better understanding of the nature of geological change, it became possible to trace veins of ore, prospect more successfully for petroleum, and design buildings that were more resistant to earthquakes.

The great importance of this point makes it worth our while to consider a few more examples. Notice how the statement, "Now, let's look at both sides of the question," limits the discussion to two sides. There may be many different aspects that are important, but because of the way the statement was phrased, it is likely that only two will be brought out. Another example is the dismay felt by a scientist when he is asked if he believes in the theory of relativity, or of evolution, for instance. He is accused of hedging if he does not give a yes-or-no answer, yet either one is misleading. The word "believe" implies an unquestioning acceptance, and a scientist can give no more than a provisional acceptance to any theory. You may have noticed that the word "true" has been avoided in this text. There is a real difference between saying, "This is the true explanation," and, "This is the most nearly correct explanation that we have obtained so far." The first statement discourages further inquiry; the second suggests the need for it.

The subject of critical thinking is far too broad to be covered fully here, but it is hoped that this chapter will help you see some of the ways in which this course may contribute to your growth. Try consciously to start your thinking from operational definitions expressed in words that symbolize the things they stand for as accurately as possible. When you reach conclusions (hypotheses or theories), make deductions from them and test them to see whether they hold up. Do not hide or defend your mistakes; acknowledge them and learn from them.

Unit 4

▼

FORECASTING THE WEATHER

1

CHAPTER

Our Atmosphere as a Gas

1. WEATHER LORE

It would be hard to find a field of public activity that equals that of weather forecasting in the mixture of truth, half truth, and falsehood that has been handed down in our folk lore.

We have such sayings as

> An evening gray and a morning red
> Will send the shepherd wet to bed.
> Evening red and morning gray
> Two sure signs of one fine day.

and such signs as, "When rheumatic people complain of more than ordinary pains it will probably rain," "Smoke from the chimney descending to the ground means rain," "A ring around either the sun or the moon indicates rain within two days." These are consistent with what we know to be dependable signs of good and bad weather.

Then we have Izaak Walton's (1593–1683) advice to fishermen:

> When the wind is in the north,
> The skillful fisher goes not forth;
> When the wind is in the east,
> 'Tis good for neither man nor beast;
> When the wind is in the south,
> It blows the flies in the fish's mouth;
> When the wind is in the west,
> There it is the very best.

This could be true for some parts of the country, but it would be false for many others.

Finally, there are the sayings which do not contain a grain of truth:

> In this month is St. Swithin's day [July 15]
> On which, if that it rain, they say
> Full forty days after it will
> Or more or less some rain distill.

"If the new moon appear with the points of the crescent turned up the month will be dry. If the points are turned down it will be wet." The direct opposite of this is also quoted. The fact that the crescent of the new moon never does point down has apparently escaped the attention of the people who perpetrate this one. A last example of nonsense that is still believed in by many people is the rule:

> Go plant the bean when the moon is light,
> And you will find that this is right;
> Plant the potatoes when the moon is dark,
> And to this line you always hark.

The development of science has enabled us to predict the weather with much greater accuracy than we could on the basis of the rhymes and sayings given above. Today the United States Weather Bureau can collect data from stations all over the country. With this information it can advise farmers and stores about coming storms, freezes, hot spells, etc. Farmers have learned the value of using these forecasts in deciding whether or not to work late to get in a crop, to light their smudge pots, to insulate fruit in freight cars, etc. Stores plan sales campaigns; power companies, airlines, and road crews plan their work; small boats look for storm warnings; and you and I decide upon a picnic on the basis of the weather forecast we read in the paper or listen to over the radio.

2. AIR PRESSURE AND THE BAROMETER

(a) Observing Air Pressure

We are not ordinarily aware of the atmosphere around us. We breathe it in and out subconsciously. We walk around in it without hindrance. Nevertheless, however invisible they may be, stiff winds uproot trees. Steam from boiling water condenses and then disappears—it must go somewhere. On a cold winter day the windowpanes collect moisture on the inside—it must come from the atmosphere.

The air around you weighs about 1.3 ounces per cubic foot. This value can be determined rather easily by using a precision balance to weigh a glass container (a separatory funnel) before and after removing the air in it with a vacuum pump.   The air

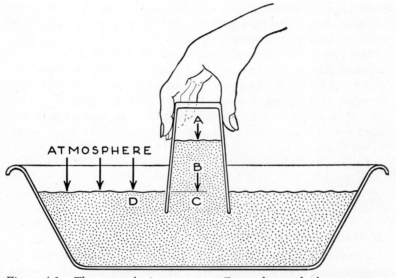

Figure 4-1.   The atmospheric pressure at *D* exactly equals the pressure at *C*, which is made up of the sum of the pressures of the trapped air, *A*, and the column of water, *B*.

in an ordinary two-story house would weigh close to a ton. Pressing down on us is a column of air that reaches high above the earth.   It thins out rapidly with altitude but is heavy enough to be noticeable even as high as 600 miles above us.   When you turn a partly filled glass of water upside down in the dishpan, the water level inside the glass stands higher than the level of the water in the pan (Figure 4-1).   What is holding up this column of water?   If the pressure at *D* and at *C* were not the same, water would be pushed from the place where the pressure is greater to the one where it is less.   Since the water is free to travel between *C* and *D*, and it is not doing so, we can assume that the pressure is the same at both places. The atmospheric column several hundred miles high is pressing down at D. At C, the pressure is the combination of that exerted by the column of water, B, and the air trapped above it at A. We can repeat the experiment with the glass completely full of water, and the whole column of water will still be held up. Is there any limit to the height of a column of water which would stay up in a glass tube under these circumstances? According to this analysis, the downward pressure of the column of water cannot be greater than the downward pressure of the atmosphere.

The Greeks and the medieval scientists did not approach the problem this way. They said that if a glass tube was filled with water and inverted into a bowl of water and the level in the tube dropped, then the space above the water would be empty. They argued that it was a logical absurdity to say that a space was filled with nothing, hence it could not happen. This was epitomized in the saying, "Nature abhors a vacuum." Many a farmer and miner had observed that a lift pump would not raise water more than 34 feet, and Galileo was probably the first scientist to remark, rather caustically, that nature's abhorrence of a vacuum seemed to be limited to 34 feet of water.

(b) Measuring Air Pressure

Torricelli (1608–1647), a pupil of Galileo, approached the problem much as we have. He used mercury instead of water, because its specific gravity is 13.6. In this way he could get the same downward pressure with a much shorter, more convenient column. A tube filled with mercury would have to be only a little over $\dfrac{34 \text{ feet} \times 12 \text{ inches/feet}}{13.6} = 30$ inches long. He found that no matter how much longer the tube was, the atmosphere would hold up a column of mercury only about 30 inches high (Figure 4-2). In this way he invented the first barometer in 1644.

Pascal (1623–1662) carried on the work in this subject and performed some spectacular experiments with long glass tubes, using water and wine for liquids. He had his brother-in-law take a mercury barometer to the top of Puy de Dôme (4805 feet high). He found that the mercury level dropped as they climbed. It stood at a little over 23 inches at the top. When he returned, a second barometer, left as a control with an observer at the base of the mountain, had not varied. Pascal published a description of this and other experiments, and concluded

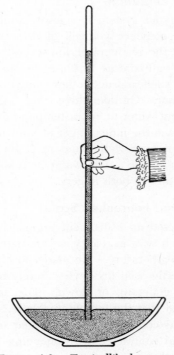

Figure 4-2.   Torricelli's barometer.

with the remark, "Nature has no repugnance for the Void; she makes no effort to avoid it. All the effects that have been attributed to this horror proceed from the weight and pressure of the air, and that is the sole and veritable cause; it is from ignorance of it that the imaginary horror of the void was invented, to make an explanation. This is not the only circumstance wherein, man's weakness having failed to find the true causes, he has expressed (the causes) by specious names which fill the ear and not the

mind." [1]   Pascal foresaw the usefulness of a barometer in measuring altitude and forecasting the weather.

3. TEMPERATURE AND THE THERMOMETER

(a) Physiological Sensation

The human nervous system is a most unreliable indicator of
temperature. To convince yourself of this, try leaving a small
block of wood in the refrigerator for several hours until it has
reached the same temperature as the metal shelves. Then touch
the wood and the shelf and notice how much colder one of them
feels than the other. Or take three cups: A containing warm
water, B containing water at room temperature, and C containing ice water. Place the index finger of your left hand in A and
the index finger of your right hand in C for 30 seconds, then
transfer both fingers to B. The water in B will not seem to be
the same temperature to both fingers.

(b) Centigrade and Fahrenheit Scales

Galileo constructed an instrument for measuring temperature
(Figure 4-3) which was, in reality, a barometer that was unusually sensitive to temperature. He made no effort to establish a
scale, and apparently used his device merely to tell whether the
temperature was going up or down. The early workers with
barometers noticed that the temperature affected the instrument
slightly, and it was common knowledge that substances, in general, expanded and contracted with changing temperature.

In the eighteenth century the thermometer took its present
form. It was realized that to construct a scale two fixed points
were necessary, and that there could be any convenient number
of degrees between them. Newton observed that a mixture of
snow and water always gave the same reading on his thermometer, and Amontons found that water always boiled at the same
temperature no matter how long he boiled it or how hot the fire
was. These two points of reference were the basis for the centi-

---

[1] Morris Bishop, *Pascal, the Life of Genius,* Reynal and Hitchcock, New
York, 1936.

grade scale invented by Celsius in 1742. He divided the interval into 100°. This is the scale used throughout most of the world and by scientists everywhere. Fahrenheit developed a scale which was sensible in that it tried to avoid negative numbers, but it was most illogical otherwise. He took for his zero the coldest temperature he could obtain by mixing ice and salt. For his upper reference point he chose body temperature, and called it 96. On this scale, the boiling point of water turned out to be 212. For some strange reason, the English-speaking countries have clung to this way of recording temperature.

There are numerous trick ways of changing back and forth from the centigrade to the Fahrenheit scales. Since $32°F = 0°C$, always subtract 32 from any Fahrenheit reading. Between the freezing and boiling points of water, the centigrade scale has 100° and the Fahrenheit has 180. Thus, there are $180/100 = \frac{9}{5}$ (nearly 2) Fahrenheit degrees for every centigrade degree: $68°F = (68 - 32)\ \frac{5}{9} = 20°C$; $104°F = (104 - 32)\ \frac{5}{9} = 40°C$; $15°C = 15 \times \frac{9}{5} + 32 = 59°F$. For very high temperatures the centigrade reading is slightly more than half the Fahrenheit

Figure 4-3. Galileo's thermometer.

reading. See if you can figure out at what temperature below zero the two scales have the same reading.

4. GAS LAWS

(a) Boyle's Law

Since the air around us is a gas that is constantly changing in pressure and temperature, we shall have to see what influences these factors have on the behavior of gases. We all know that increasing the pressure on a gas decreases its volume, and that, as we decrease the pressure, the gas tends to spring back to its original volume. Robert Boyle (1627–1691) investigated this situation quantitatively and showed that, for a given amount of gas at constant temperature, the volume is inversely proportional to the pressure. Stated in symbols, this is $V \propto 1/P$.

The type of experiment performed by Boyle is illustrated in

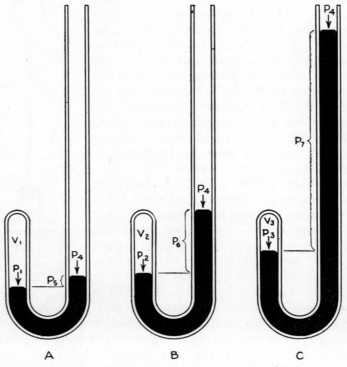

Figure 4-4. An experiment to demonstrate Boyle's law.

Figure 4-4. A volume V_1 of gas is confined in the short arm of a J-shaped tube. Its pressure is P_1 (Figure 4-4). The pressure of the gas is counterbalanced by the pressure of the atmosphere, P_4, and the pressure of the mercury, P_5, which stands higher in the long arm than in the short arm. $P_1 = P_4 + P_5$. In part B of this figure, more mercury has been added to the long arm, so that the pressure of the mercury is now P_6, and the atmospheric pressure, P_4, remains the same. $P_4 + P_6 = P_2$. The gas has been compressed to V_2. In part C, the gas has been further compressed to V_3, and it is exerting a pressure P_3. $P_3 = P_4 + P_7$. Expressing the volume in cubic centimeters and the pressure in millimeters of mercury, Table 4-1 shows the type of data that Boyle obtained in his experiments.

TABLE 4-1

	A	B	C
Atmospheric pressure	$P_4 = 760$	760	760
Pressure of mercury	$P_5 = 40$	$P_6 = 240$	$P_7 = 840$
Total pressure on gas	$P_1 = 800$	$P_2 = 1000$	$P_3 = 1600$
Volume of gas	$V_1 = 100$	$V_2 = 80$	$V_3 = 50$
$P \times V$	80,000	80,000	80,000

He found that in any one series of experiments the product obtained by multiplying each pressure by its corresponding volume was a constant. $P \times V = k$, or $V = k/P$, or $V \propto 1/P$.

(b) Charles' Law and Absolute Zero

The earliest thermometers made use of the expansion of air that was kept at constant pressure. This behavior was studied quantitatively by Charles (1746–1823) and Gay-Lussac (1778–1850) and they discovered that for a given amount of a gas kept at constant pressure the fractional increase in volume with increase in temperature was a constant. This is better illustrated with an example. Starting with 273 cc of any gas at 0°C, and increasing or decreasing the temperature by 1°C, the resulting volume would be 274 or 272 cc, respectively. At constant pressure, the change in volume was 1/273 for every degree change of temperature.

TABLE 4-2

Initial volume, cc	Change in temperature, °	Final volume, cc
273	+1	274
273	−1	272
273	−10	263
273	−100	173
273	−274	?

The figures in Table 4-2 raise the question of what would be the resulting volume if you lowered the temperature of 273 cc of gas from 0°C to −274°C, keeping the pressure constant all the time. According to the law of Charles and Gay-Lussac, there would be no volume left at −273°C. This was the first indication that there might be a bottom to the temperature scale. This lowest possible temperature, −273°C (?°F), is absolute zero. On the absolute scale, water freezes at +273° and boils at +373°. It is this absolute temperature that is represented by T, and centigrade temperature by t. The law of Charles and Gay-Lussac can now be stated as $V \propto T$, or $V = kT$. The two gas laws can be combined in an equation $V = kT/P$ or $PV = kT$, where k is a constant which depends on the units used for the other three terms.

SUMMARY

1. Weather lore is extremely unreliable as a basis for predicting the weather.

2. The normal pressure of the atmosphere at sea level will support a column of water 33.8 feet high, or a column of mercury 29.92 inches (76.0 cm) high.

3. Variations in atmospheric pressure are measured by the barometer, and since they indicate changing air conditions their detection aids in predicting the weather.

4. The fixed points on the centigrade temperature scale are the freezing point of water taken as 0° and the boiling point of water taken as 100°.

5. The Fahrenheit temperature scale uses the same two fixed points but assigns them the values of 32° and 212° respectively.

6. Interconversion between the centigrade and Fahrenheit scales may be made by using the formula (°F − 32) $\frac{5}{9}$ = °C.

7. Boyle's law states that for a given quantity of a gas at constant temperature the volume is inversely proportional to the pressure.

8. There is a lowest possible temperature called absolute zero. It is −273.18°C.

9. Charles' law states that for a given quantity of a gas at constant pressure the volume is directly proportional to the absolute temperature.

10. The two gas laws can be combined in the equation $P \times V = k \times T$.

QUESTIONS AND EXERCISES

1. Calculate the weight of the air in your classroom.

2. Calculate an approximate value for the weight of a cubic foot of air at the top of Puy de Dôme.

3. Calculate the approximate height in centimeters of Pascal's barometer column at the top of Puy de Dôme.

4. Of what countries were the following men native: Galileo, Pascal, Torricelli, Izaak Walton, Celsius, Fahrenheit, Boyle, Charles, Gay-Lussac, Amontons?

5. Make the following temperature conversions: $100°C = ?°F$, $0°F = ?°C$, $-40°C = ?°F$.

6. Is $20°C$ twice as hot as $10°C$? Is $473°C$ twice as hot as $100°C$? Explain.

7. If a balloon had a volume of 1 cubic foot at the base of Puy de Dôme, what volume would it have at the top of this mountain if there was no change in temperature?

8. Calculate the change in volume of a balloon having a volume of 5 cubic feet, if the temperature changes from $20°C$ to $30°C$.

9. Calculate the change in volume of the balloon in Problem 7 if the temperature at the base of the mountain was $20°C$ and at the top $10°C$.

10. What is the weight of air in an automobile tire whose volume is 4 cubic feet when the air is under a pressure of 3 times atmospheric?

2

CHAPTER

Kinetic Theory

1. HEAT AS MOTION

There was a great deal of confusion in the early nineteenth century about the use of the word "heat." What was the difference between two bars of iron, one of which was hotter than the other? Some said that there must be a substance, which they called caloric, that could flow from one thing to another. The amount of caloric in a body was thought to determine how hot it was. While supervising the boring of cannon in Munich, Count Rumford became impressed with the tremendous amount of heat evolved by the process. There seemed to be no limit to the quantity of heat that could be generated, and he suggested (1798) that the heat came from the friction and that it was an evidence of motion.

Soon after 1800 John Dalton had accumulated enough evidence to be able to show that matter is made up of small particles, which he called atoms. These could combine in characteristic groups called molecules. This theory and the evidence for it will be considered in a later unit. Because gases were so much more compressible than liquids or solids, it was assumed that the particles in gases were relatively far apart. The particles in liquids were thought to be touching each other but free to roll around like marbles in a box. In a solid, the particles were considered to be held in a fixed position with respect to each other. It was the motion of these particles that constituted heat. They were hotter when they moved faster.

2. SPECIFIC HEAT

The following experiments describe one aspect of the problem of heat that was very confusing to the early scientists and is of considerable importance for our study of the weather. If equal weights of water and dry sand are placed on an electric hot plate to warm up, the temperature of the sand will increase more rapidly than that of the water. If 100 grams of sand at 20°C is poured into 100 grams of boiling water (100°C) and the mixture is stirred, the temperature reaches about 80°C. If 100 grams of water at 20°C is mixed with 100 grams of water at 100°C, the temperature of the mixture comes to 60°C. It takes less heat to produce a given change in temperature in sand than in water. The term specific heat refers to the amount of heat necessary to change the temperature of 1 gram of a substance by 1°C. Water has the highest specific heat of almost any known substance, and our unit of heat, the calorie, is defined as the amount necessary to raise the temperature of 1 gram of water by 1°C (more precisely, from 15°C to 16°C). In cooling from 100°C to 80°C, the 100 grams of water gave up 20° $\times$ 100 g $\times$ 1 cal/g deg = 2000 cal. This amount heated 100 grams of sand through 60°, and so the specific heat of sand is $\dfrac{2000 \text{ cal}}{100 \text{ g} \times 60°}$ = 0.33 cal/g deg.

3. WORK AND ENERGY

We must now get a more precise idea of a few common terms before we use them in describing the behavior of gases.

Our muscles give us a fairly good idea of the term force. Force was discussed under Newton's laws of motion as something which overcomes inertia. It takes a force to start something moving, or to change the motion of something that is moving. Force may be expressed in units of pounds, grams, etc. You are exerting a pound of force when you lift a pound of oleo.

In Figure 4-5 you see a man dragging a package at a uniform rate across the floor. He is pulling the package by means of spring scales. The pointer on the scales reads 5 pounds and he drags the package 10 feet. He has done 10 feet $\times$ 5 pounds = 50 foot-pounds of work. The term work refers to a force acting through a distance. If you weigh 120 pounds and raise yourself 12 feet in running upstairs, you have done 12 feet $\times$ 120 pounds = 1440 foot-pounds of work.

Energy is an extremely important word which is in common use—atomic energy, solar energy, kinetic energy, electrical energy, etc. Energy is defined as the ability to do work. Innumerable experiments have established the fact that energy can be neither created nor destroyed. This statement is known as the law of conservation of energy. (The interconversion of mass and energy will be discussed later.) From this law of the conservation of energy we can get some help in calculating how much energy a system has. How much work is a 2-pound book

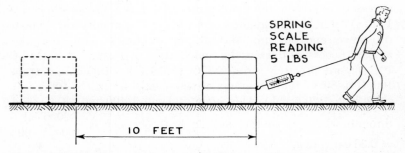

Figure 4-5. Work equals force times distance. This illustration shows 5 pounds × 10 feet = 50 foot-pounds of work being done.

able to do in dropping 3 feet to the floor? In other words, what is its energy because of its position (potential energy)? If we calculate the work that would have to be done on the book to raise it from the floor to its present position, the law of conservation of energy tells us that this will be the amount of work that it is able to do in returning to the floor. This amount of work would be 3 feet × 2 pounds = 6 foot-pounds. In the old-fashioned grandfather's clock in which the weights are wound up once a week, the potential energy of the weights is slowly transformed into the energy of the moving parts of the clock, of the sound waves of the ticking, and of the striking bell. Each week end, when the clock is wound up, we do as much work on the weights in a few seconds as they do in 7 days. The rate of doing work is very different. The term which applies to the rate of doing work is power. The familiar unit of power is horsepower. One horsepower is 550 foot-pounds per second.

A substance can do work because it is in motion. This type

of energy is called kinetic energy. Erosion by wind and running water is an example of the results of kinetic energy. If we know the mass, m, and the velocity, v, of a substance, we can calculate its kinetic energy from the equation: kinetic energy = $\frac{1}{2}mv^2$. Remember this the next time you are driving a car. When you double its speed, 4 times as much work is required to stop it. There are several other types of energy that we will encounter in this book, but it will be better to discuss them when we come to them. Right now let us see how the idea of kinetic energy fitted into the developing idea of the nature of gases.

4. KINETIC THEORY OF IDEAL GASES

You will remember that Count Rumford showed that heat is a form of motion, and that Dalton showed that matter is made up of discrete particles. In a gas these particles are relatively far apart and their motion gives them kinetic energy. Since a gas can be made to do work by expanding when it is heated, temperature is a measure of the kinetic energy of the particles.

The kinetic-molecular picture of an ideal gas can be outlined broadly as follows:

1. A gas is made up of molecules that are in rapid motion.
2. The molecules undergo frequent collisions.
3. The molecules move in straight lines between collisions.
4. The molecules are negligibly small in comparison with the space occupied by the gas.
5. The molecules have no attraction for each other.
6. There is no loss of kinetic energy as a result of these collisions (the collisions are perfectly elastic).

SUMMARY

1. Our present-day picture of the nature of matter includes the ideas that: (a) the elementary particles (atoms and molecules) of a solid are vibrating about points that have a fixed relation to each other; (b) the particles of a liquid are in motion relative to each other, but are touching their neighbors; and (c) the particles of a gas are in motion and are relatively far apart.

2. The motion of these elementary particles constitutes heat.

3. Calorie: the amount of heat needed to raise the temperature of 1 gram of water by 1°C.

4. Specific heat: the number of calories needed to raise the temperature of 1 gram of a suhstance 1°C.

5. Work: force × distance.

6. Power: rate of doing work.

7. Energy: the ability to do work.

8. Potential energy: energy possessed by a body because of its position.

9. Kinetic energy: energy possessed by a body because of its motion.

10. Kinetic-molecular picture of an ideal gas: (a) a gas is made up of molecules that are in rapid motion; (b) the molecules undergo frequent collisions; (c) the molecules move in straight lines between collisions; (d) the molecules are negligibly small in comparison with the space occupied by the gas; (e) the molecules have no attraction for each other; (f) there is no loss of kinetic energy as a result of these collisions.

QUESTIONS AND EXERCISES

1. Where was Count Rumford born?

2. Determine the specific heat of lead BB shot by the technique described in this section. What are a few serious sources of error in this experiment?

3. How far would you have to lift a 50-pound weight in 1 second in order to be exerting 1 horsepower?

4. One British thermal unit (Btu) is the amount of heat needed to raise 1 pound of water 1°F. How many calories are there in a Btu?

5. State in different terms the fact that there is no loss of kinetic energy when gaseous molecules collide.

6. Meteors do not "burn up," in the ordinary sense of that term. What makes them light up as they enter the earth's atmosphere?

7. How many foot-pounds of work do you do if you exert a force of 5 pounds over a distance of 10 meters?

8. When ice is in equilibrium with water at 0°C, is the average kinetic energy of the molecules in the ice the same as that of the water molecules?

9. Find out how many calories should be in the diet of the average 20-year-old student.

10. Calculate the kinetic energy of a 3000-pound car traveling at a speed of 50 miles per hour.

Real Gases

1. IDEAL VS. REAL GASES

With the picture of an ideal gas as a model, we can study real gases and see how they do or do not coincide with it. In either outcome we shall have learned something about real gases. The only points with which we find any disagreement are the fourth and fifth (page 267). The following evidence shows that the molecules have a small but appreciable volume and that their attraction for each other is important. When a liquid at its boiling point is turned into a gas at the same temperature and pressure, we find that the volume increases about a thousand times. Hence, the molecules in a gas occupy about 0.1% of the total space at room temperature and pressure.

The disagreement with the fifth point is more important. Most gases heat up when they are compressed and cool down when they expand. This means that there is an attraction between the molecules. How could you show that the heating of the barrel of a bicycle pump is due to compression of the air, not to the friction of the piston? By pressing the valve stem of an inflated tire you notice a stream of cold air emerging from the tire, yet the tire is not cold. This shows that the air molecules attract one another and slow down as they rush apart. The practical application of this will soon be apparent.

The pressure of these numerous small particles of air bombarding us from all sides is tremendous. It is this pressure on the surface of the well of mercury that holds up the column in the barometer. It is this pressure on the surface of the water in a well that pushes the water to as high as 34 feet in the pipe of the lift pump. An airplane wing is so shaped that, as it flies, the force of the molecules hitting the bottom side is greater than that of those which hit the top side. This, and this alone, keeps the airplane from falling. The pressure of the atmosphere at sea level is about 14.7 pounds per square inch.

2. CHANGE OF PHASE

We can extend this kinetic picture of gases to include liquids and solids. As a gas cools, the molecules slow down. At a temperature which is unique (depending on the pressure) for each gas, the speed is not great enough to overcome the force of attraction between the molecules, and they stick together. What we observe is that the gas condenses to a liquid. There is still plenty of motion; the molecules are darting around among each other, but they are always touching several neighbors.

As the liquid is cooled the motion becomes slower. Again, another temperature (which again depends on the pressure) is reached, which is peculiar for each substance, at which the speed is not sufficient to allow a molecule to pull away from the attraction of those around it. The whole mass of liquid begins to set, like a jelly, into a fixed pattern. We say that it has solidified, or frozen. There is still motion. The particles vibrate about a given point like a leaf caught in a spider web. This motion becomes less and less frantic with dropping temperature until it ceases altogether at absolute zero.

Let us reverse the process and follow the changes as a solid is heated. The motion of the molecules becomes more and more agitated. Occasionally a molecule on the surface of a crystal may be hit so hard by the one below it that it is knocked completely out of place and darts off into space. This passage from the solid directly to the gas phase is called sublimation. Dry Ice sublimes without melting and condenses from a gas to a solid without passing through the liquid phase. In dry, cold weather snow sublimes without melting. Usually, however, the solid remains intact. It expands, but remains solid until the melting point is reached. This is the same temperature as the freezing point. As energy is put into the molecules (as they are heated) their motion increases enough to overcome their mutual attraction, and they break out of the geometrical arrangement that was characteristic of the crystal.

As the liquid is heated the molecules move about more rapidly. Some of those near the surface may be hit from behind and knocked out of the liquid. Unless they have a high velocity they will drop back, but some will escape. We call this evaporation. Only the fastest-moving ones can evaporate. Fast moving and hot mean the same thing. The average speed of those that remain in the liquid is reduced by the loss of the fastest ones; or, to put it differently, evaporation produces a cooling effect. You have noticed this when your hands were wet, or when you dried your hair. The evaporation of a few drops of ether on your hand cools it even more than water, because ether evaporates much faster.

In the liquid, molecules dart around rapidly, although their motion is considerably restricted by the pull of their close neighbors. Above the liquid the molecules are relatively far apart. Like the oxygen and nitrogen molecules of the air, these vapor (evaporated liquid) molecules exert a pressure on everything they hit. It is impractical to build a pressure gauge to measure the pressure exerted by any one kind of molecule present in a gaseous mixture, but we can measure the pressure of water vapor by the technique shown in Figure 4-6. On the left (A) we have a regular barometer with the space above the mercury column containing only relatively few molecules of mercury vapor. On the right (B) we have introduced a drop of water into the mercury column. It has risen to the top and part of it has evaporated. Since these water-vapor molecules exert a downward pressure on the column of mercury, it does not stand quite so high as in A. The difference in height of the two columns represents the vapor pressure of water.

In Figure 4-6, the rate at which the molecules are evaporating from the drop depends on their average speed; that is, it depends on the temperature. The higher the temperature, the more rapidly they are evaporating. The rate at which the water-vapor molecules bump into the drop and condense back to a liquid will depend on their concentration in the vapor. As the drop is first introduced, the molecules are evaporating rapidly and few are condensing. As the concentration of vapor molecules builds up, the rate of condensation increases. Finally, the two rates become equal—as many are leaving as are entering the liquid in any one second. A dynamic equilibrium is established. This situation may be compared to a busy store where the number

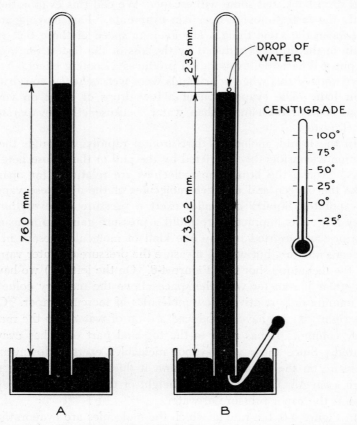

Figure 4-6. An experiment by which the vapor pressure of water may be determined.

of customers remains approximately the same although many are entering and leaving at any one time.

You can see from the above discussion that, for any given temperature, the equilibrium concentration of vapor molecules will have a certain value. The liquid will have a definite vapor pressure for that temperature. If the temperature is raised the rate of evaporation will increase and more molecules will be in the vapor state. With more vapor molecules, the rate at which they condense will increase and, finally, the rates of evaporation and condensation will again balance. A new equilibrium will be set up at this higher temperature. When the new equilibrium is established there will be a higher concentration of vapor molecules, which means a higher vapor pressure. If we carry out the experiment outlined in Figure 4-6 at two different temperatures we shall find a greater depression of the mercury column at the higher temperature. Table 4-3 gives the figures for the vapor pressure of water at several different temperatures.

TABLE 4-3. VAPOR PRESSURE OF WATER IN MILLIMETERS OF MERCURY FROM 0°C TO 100°C

t	vp	t	vp	t	vp
0	4.6	35	42.2	70	234
5	6.5	40	55.3	75	289
10	9.2	45	71.9	80	355
15	12.8	50	92.5	85	434
20	17.5	55	118	90	526
25	23.8	60	149	95	634
30	31.8	65	188	100	760

As the temperature of a liquid is increased its vapor pressure increases until, finally, the vapor pressure is equal to the atmospheric pressure above it. At this temperature the liquid boils. Instead of the condition where only a few molecules have a speed great enough to get away in spite of their mutual attraction, even the molecules moving with average speed are now going fast enough. Large bubbles of vapor form at the bottom of the container, where the heat is being applied, rise up through the liquid, and escape into the air. At a temperature just below the boiling point these bubbles of vapor no sooner form than they are collapsed by the cool liquid and the atmospheric pressure above them. You may have noticed the "singing" of water just below the boiling point.

A great deal of energy is required to overcome the mutual attraction of the liquid molecules and to separate them from a liquid into a vapor. This energy that is required to boil a liquid without increasing its temperature is referred to as the latent heat of vaporization. This amounts to 539.5 (540 approximate value) calories per gram for water. This is indeed a large amount compared to the 100 calories that are required to raise 1 gram of water from the freezing to the boiling point. When condensation (the reverse of evaporation) takes place the molecules are speeded up (by attraction) as they approach the liquid, and consequently the average speed of the liquid molecules is increased. The same amount of heat, 539.5 calories per gram, is added to water by condensation. This detailed, mechanical picture of the gaseous, liquid, and solid states has been given because it is the basis for understanding much of our ability to predict the weather.

3. HUMIDITY

When we have some form of precipitation such as rain, snow, hail, or fog, it means that water has been evaporated at some distant point, brought to where we are, and condensed. The principal sources of moisture for the atmosphere are the oceans and seas, which cover ¾ of the area of the globe. There is not enough evaporation from rivers and lakes to affect more than a small area in their vicinity. Great forests contribute a moderate amount of moisture to the air. It has been estimated that an average of about 5000 tons of water evaporates every day from each square mile of well-watered forest land. We need to be able to detect the presence of masses of humid air in our weather prediction. When the vapor pressure of the water in the air is at the equilibrium value for its temperature (Table 4-3) it is called its saturated vapor pressure. The actual vapor pressure of water in any sample of air is usually less than this, and the fraction

$$\frac{\text{actual vapor pressure}}{\text{saturated vapor pressure}} \times 100 = \text{per cent relative humidity}$$

The humidity is the term usually used for this. A value of less than 30% is considered very dry, and one of greater than 80% is very moist, or "humid."

SUMMARY

1. Real gases differ from an ideal gas mainly in that the volume occupied by the molecules may not be negligible and an appreciable force is acting between the molecules.

2. Atmospheric pressure is the result of the myriads of blows struck by the molecules of the air.

3. The boiling point is the temperature at which the vapor pressure of a liquid is equal to the atmospheric pressure.

4. The freezing or melting point refers to the temperature at which the liquid and the solid phases of a substance are at equilibrium with each other under normal atmospheric pressure.

5. Sublimation is the evaporation of a solid directly into the vapor phase.

6. The latent heat of fusion is the number of calories liberated when 1 gram of a substance solidifies at its freezing point. This is the same as the number of calories required to melt 1 gram of the solid at the freezing point. For water the latent heat of fusion is approximately 80 calories.

7. The latent heat of vaporization is the number of calories required to evaporate 1 gram of a liquid at its boiling point. This is the same as the amount of heat given off when 1 gram of a vapor condenses to a liquid at the boiling point. For water the latent heat of vaporization is approximately 540 calories.

8. Per cent relative humidity of water vapor in the air at any given temperature $= 100 \times \dfrac{\text{actual vapor pressure}}{\text{saturated vapor pressure}}$.

QUESTIONS AND EXERCISES

1. Why does a balloon expand as it rises above the earth?

2. Why must an airplane be moving very fast before it can rise from the ground?

3. Using graph paper, plot the data supplied in Table 4-3.

4. What would be the boiling point of water at the top of Puy de Dôme? (See Problem 3, page 263.)

5. What would have been the height of the mercury column in Figure 4-6, part B, if the temperature had been 95°F?

6. If 100 grams of ice were placed in 100 grams of water at 25°C

and left there until the water was cooled to 0°C, how much would the water weigh?

7. Look up a description of the modern process for preparing liquid air and notice how it makes use of the principles discussed in this and the previous chapter.

8. Devise an experiment to measure the volume occupied by the carbon dioxide gas which results from the sublimation of a measured volume of Dry Ice. (If you carry out the experiment be careful to avoid touching the Dry Ice with your bare hands.)

9. Describe the action of a vacuum-return coffee maker in terms of the ideas in this chapter.

10. Give several lines of evidence which show that there is an attraction between the molecules of water.

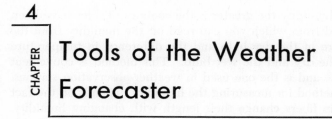

4

CHAPTER

Tools of the Weather Forecaster

1. HYGROMETERS

Instruments for measuring humidity are called hygrometers. We could make this measurement by drawing an air sample through some drying agent and then comparing the amount of moisture it contains with air that was saturated at the same tem-

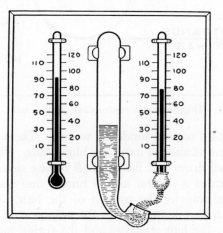

Figure 4-7. Wet-and-dry-bulb psychrometer.

perature. This would be direct but too expensive and time-consuming to be practical. There are indirect methods that are more suitable. One of these indirect methods makes use of the cooling effect of evaporation. In the wet-and-dry-bulb psychrometer, two thermometers are strapped together, one of which has a moistened wick around its bulb (Figure 4-7). Water is both condensing on and evaporating from the wick. Unless the humidity is 100% there is a net evaporation and cooling, and the lower the humidity the greater is the cooling. Tables have been constructed from which you can read off the humidity from the temperature of the dry bulb and the difference in temperature between the dry and the wet bulb. This method is convenient and precise and is the one used in weather-observation stations. Another method for measuring the humidity depends on the fact that certain fibers change their length with changing humidity. This is a familiar fact to sailors who work with ropes and to girls

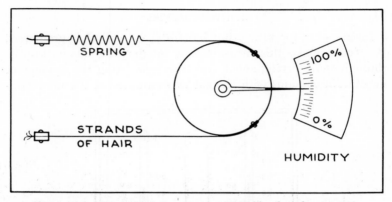

Figure 4-8.   Diagrammatic representation of a hair hygrometer.

whose hair has a natural tendency to curl. The weather-bureau instruments use strands of naturally blond hair. They are wound around a small drum and fastened off to one side (Figure 4-8). The drum carries a pointer and is turned one way by a spring and the other way by the tension of the hair. Low humidity makes the hair shrink and swings the pointer over the scale. At high humidity the hair stretches and the spring pulls the pointer in the opposite direction. This instrument is capable of only a moderate degree of precision, but it is sufficiently accurate and is so convenient that it is employed for most home weather guides and in the weather-bureau radiosondes that will be described later.

Another method for measuring humidity makes use of the dew point. The dew point is the temperature to which air must be cooled to start condensation. At the dew point the vapor pressure of the water in the air is the same as the saturated vapor pressure for that temperature, as given in Table 4-3. To make this measurement, ice and water are placed in a shiny metal tumbler. The water is stirred with a thermometer, and as soon as the first film of condensed moisture appears on the outside, the temperature of the water is recorded. If this temperature turns out to be 10°C we know that the actual vapor pressure of water in the air is 9.2 mm. If the actual air temperature is 20°C, then the saturated vapor pressure at this temperature is 17.5 mm and the per cent humidity is $\dfrac{9.2 \text{ mm}}{17.5 \text{ mm}} \times 100 = 52.6\%$. Of course, air containing water vapor must be cooled to its dew point before rain can fall. But more of that later.

2. THERMOMETERS

Since we are sufficiently well acquainted with the ordinary thermometer, a description of it can be passed over. In order to

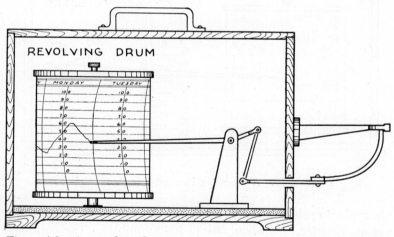

Figure 4-9. A recording thermometer, or thermograph. The curved tube at the right changes shape with changing temperature.

get a continuous recording of the temperature, we need a revolving drum carrying ruled paper and pen and ink on the end of a lever arm, and a thermometer to actuate them (Figure 4-9). The thermometer is a curved tube filled with alcohol and sealed.

With an increase in temperature the alcohol expands more than the metal and tends to straighten out the curve. This motion is transmitted to the lever arm so that the temperature is recorded on the graph paper. The drum moves so slowly that it makes only 1 revolution in 1 week.

3. BAROMETERS

The mercury barometer has been described. For precise readings a temperature correction must be made, because the column of mercury, the glass tube, and the brass scale expand differently with increasing temperature. The unit now in use for recording

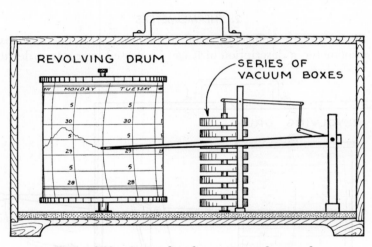

Figure 4-10. A recording barometer, or barograph.

atmospheric pressure is the millibar. At sea level the pressure normally varies from about 980 to 1040 millibars. The readings at stations above sea level are corrected for altitude so that they can all be compared. A portable type of barometer is called an aneroid barometer. A sealed metal box with a corrugated top expands and contracts as the pressure outside changes. The top of the box is connected to a pointer that indicates the pressure on a scale. Sometimes the scale is graduated to read in feet above sea level so that the instrument can be used as an altimeter in airplanes or by hikers on trips in the mountains. If the pointer is fitted with a pen that writes on a moving graph paper, the device is a recording barometer or barograph (Figure 4-10).

4. WIND- AND RAIN-MEASURING INSTRUMENTS

The best way to measure the direction from which the wind is blowing is still the old-fashioned weather vane. For recording

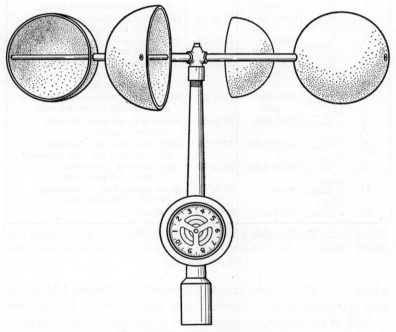

Figure 4-11. An anemometer.

the speed of the wind, the most common instrument is the anemometer (Figure 4-11). The rate of revolution of the cups is a measure of the speed of the wind. The speed of the wind in miles per hour is translated into a number on the Beaufort scale and recorded on the weather maps by arrows, as indicated in Figure 4-12.

The amount of rainfall is observed by catching the water in

Beaufort Number	Map Symbol	Descriptive Words	Velocity	Guide For Estimating Velocities
0	o	Calm	Less than 1	Smoke rises vertically.
1		Light air	1 to 3	Direction of wind shown by smoke but not by wind vanes.
2	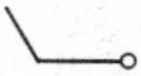	Light breeze	4 to 7	Winds felt on face; leaves rustle; ordinary vane moved by wind.
3		Gentle breeze	8 to 12	Leaves and small twigs in constant motion, wind extends light flag.
4		Moderate breeze	13 to 18	Raises dust and loose paper; small branches are moved.
5		Fresh breeze	19 to 24	Small trees in leaf begin sway; crested wavelets form on inland water.
6	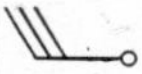	Strong breeze	25 to 31	Large branches in motion; whistling heard in telegraph wires; umbrellas used with difficulty.
7		Moderate gale	32 to 38	Whole trees in motion; inconvenience felt in walking against the wind.
8		Fresh gale	39 to 46	Breaks twigs off trees; generally impedes progress.
9		Strong gale	47 to 54	Slight structural damage occurs (chimney pots and slate removed.).
10		Whole gale	55 to 63	Trees uprooted; considerable structural damage occurs.
11		Storm	64 to 75	Rarely experienced; accompanied by wide spread damage.
12		Hurricane	Above 75	Devastation occurs.

Figure 4-12. The Beaufort scale. (*From The Physics of Blown Sands and Desert Dunes, by R. A. Bagnold, by permission of William Morrow and Co., New York.*)

a large can called a rain gauge (Figure 4-13). Figure 4-14 shows how this looks in cross section. The inner tube, A, has an area of 1/10 of the top of the funnel, and so the actual depth of rainfall is 1/10 the amount measured in A.

5. DATA FROM THE UPPER AIR

Only recently has it been realized that important information might be obtained by sampling the atmosphere up to as high as

50,000 feet. We now know that the first signs of a storm can be detected thousands of feet above us. Neither kites nor airplanes are practical for obtaining these data, so an extremely simple, lightweight radio set called a radiosonde was developed to be

Figure 4-13. Rain gauge. (*U. S. Weather Bureau.*)

carried aloft by a balloon (Figures 4-15 and 4-16). The pressure, temperature, and humidity are registered continuously, and the signals from the small radio sender relay this information to the weather station at regular intervals. The whole apparatus must be simple and cheap enough to be expendable.

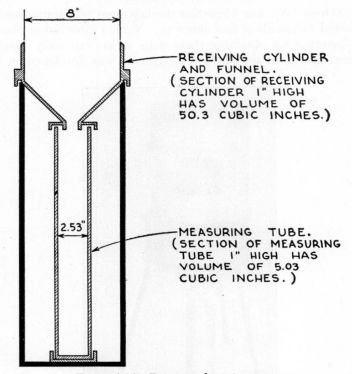

Figure 4-14.   Diagram of a rain gauge.

6. WEATHER MAPS

There are about 200 regular weather stations throughout the continental United States and its possessions. In addition, hundreds of amateur observers make regular reports of the weather in their localities, and ships at sea send in data by radio. The country is divided into seven major forecasting districts where the data are assembled and forecasts prepared. As the data from any one station come in, they are recorded in symbols on a map such as is illustrated in Figure 4-17. For our purposes it will be necessary to consider only a few of the symbols. With the data pared down to the bone, the notations for the above station would appear as shown in Figure 4-18. From left to right, these mean that the temperature is 31°F, the wind is blowing from the northwest with a force of 5 (19–24 miles per hour), and the barometric pressure is 995.3 millibars. In recording the pressure, the

Figure 4-15.   Figure 4-16.

Figure 4-15. Radiosonde. (*U. S. Weather Bureau.*)

Figure 4-16. Launching a radiosonde. One observer is prepared to launch the balloon, parachute, and radiosonde, the other will follow its flight by radar to determine upper-air wind directions and velocities. (*U. S. Weather Bureau, L. E. Johnson.*)

10 or the 9 at the beginning of the number is omitted, so that 235 would mean 1023.5 millibars. The black circle at the point of the arrow means that the sky is completely covered with clouds at this station.

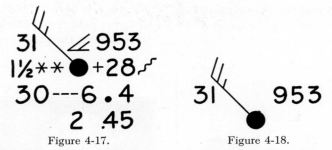

Figure 4-17.   Figure 4-18.

Figure 4-17.   An example of the way that data are recorded for a single weather station.

Figure 4-18.   A simplified version of Figure 4-17, showing only temperature, barometric pressure, wind direction and force, and cloud cover.

SUMMARY

1. Humidity is usually measured by a wet-and-dry-bulb psychrometer, a hair hygrometer, or a dew-point apparatus.

2. Dew point: the temperature to which air must be cooled to start condensation.

3. Temperature is usually measured by a mercury thermometer or a Bourdon gauge filled with alcohol.

4. Atmospheric pressure is usually measured by a mercury or an aneroid barometer.

5. The direction of the wind is observed by means of a weather vane.

6. The velocity of the wind is measured by means of an anemometer.

7. The amount of rainfall is measured by a rain gauge.

8. A radiosonde is a balloon carrying weather-recording instruments and a radio to send the information back to the weather-bureau station.

9. Weather maps for the United States are prepared each day. On them are recorded in symbols the weather data collected at each of the regular weather stations.   From these maps the weather forecasts are prepared.

QUESTIONS AND EXERCISES

1. Name and describe six instruments which are used to obtain weather data at a weather station.

2. If the dew point is within 2° of the air temperature, is the humidity very high or low?

3. What factor besides changing pressure would affect the reading of an aneroid barometer?

4. What two factors would you have to be careful about when using an aneroid barometer for an altimeter when mountain climbing?

5. What is the point of having the measuring tube of a rain gauge 1/10 the area of the catching funnel?

6. For as long as possible a radiosonde is tracked by radar. What additional information is thereby obtained?

7. Start cutting out and saving the weather maps from your local newspaper. As you study farther in this unit see if you can follow the tracks of storms across the country and try your hand at forecasting the next day's weather.

8. What number on the Beaufort scale represents a wind of 15 miles per hour? What would the arrow representing it look like?

9. If the air temperature is 77°F and the humidity is 38.7%, what is the dew point?

10. See how many simple but dependable weather instruments you can construct.

CHAPTER 5

Elements of Weather and Climate

1. SEASONS

You will recall that the changing angle at which the rays from the sun strike the earth is responsible for the changing seasons. As the sun is most nearly overhead at noon on June 21, we receive the greatest amount of heat from it then. However, we know that June 21 marks the beginning of summer, not its height. The seasons lag behind the sun by 2 or 3 months along the seacoast and by a few weeks in the interior of the continent. This geographical difference points to the explanation. Water has a much greater specific heat than soil. Since the oceans heat up more slowly than the continents, even after the sun's warmth has started to wane in July and August the water is still being warmed. Of course, the water also cools off more slowly than the continent, and so the coldest time of winter is delayed along the coast until early March. This relatively high specific heat of large masses of water gives coastal regions and islands a much more moderate climate at all seasons. The water cools the air in summer and warms it in winter. A continental climate is characterized by a short lag of the seasons behind the sun, rapid and extreme changes in temperature, and great seasonal differences in temperature. For instance, for St. Louis, Missouri, the average July temperature is 80.2, the average January temperature is 32.9; for San Francisco, California (which is at about the same latitude), the same two average temperatures are 58.9 and 49.8.

2. CLOUDS

A cloud is only one of the many treasures of nature that most of us take for granted. In spite of the fact that each cloud is a unique individual, clouds have been classified into a few simple

types. Once you come to know something about them you will
fall into the habit of observing them more carefully, and you will
find that a knowledge of them is very useful in predicting the

Figure 4-19.   Banner cloud.   (*U. S. Weather Bureau, C. D. Walcott.*)

weather. First of all, how does a cloud form? Figure 4-19 shows
a cloud over Mt. Assiniboin. If you were on top of the mountain
you would find the wind blowing hard, but the cloud remains
stationary. As moist air rises up the side of the mountain its

pressure drops, and it is cooled by expansion (page 304). When it is cooled below the dew point, the moisture condenses into droplets which form the cloud. The process of condensation releases heat (page 304) and the cloud is also warmed by the sun. The drops are carried a few miles through the cloud and eventually evaporate again. Thus, the cloud hangs over the peak, yet it is composed of a constantly changing population of drops that are forming at one edge and evaporating at the other. The conditions for the formation of a cloud are the cooling of moist air below its dew point. You can see from this that very moist air will form clouds at a lower altitude than fairly dry air. For any given set of conditions of temperature and humidity, there will be a definite height at which cloud formation starts, and you will observe the flat bottom to cumulus clouds and large cloud formations.

Clouds are classified according to their altitude. The prefix alto- is placed before the names of clouds between 10,000 and 20,000 feet, and cirro- before those above 20,000 feet. If the cloud formation is composed of individual clouds they are called cumulus clouds, and if they form a uniform layer across the sky they are called stratus clouds. Thus above the 20,000-foot level are (a) cirrocumulus clouds, which are commonly called mackerel sky; (b) cirrostratus clouds, which form a thin, milky sheet; and (c) cirrus clouds, which are the mare's tails, or thin, hooked wisps (Figures 4-20a, b and c). Since at this altitude the temperature is always below the freezing point, these clouds are composed of ice crystals. The refraction of light through the ice crystals gives rise to the large ring around the sun or the moon.

Between 10,000 and 20,000 feet are altostratus clouds, which usually form a thick, dark-gray blanket, and altocumulus clouds, which are large white or gray masses (Figures 4-21a and b). Below 10,000 feet the cumulus clouds are the fleecy cotton puffs with flat bottoms. The low, gray layers of clouds (high fog, in the West) are called stratus, and the low, heavy masses of distinct units that practically cover the sky are given the hybrid name of stratocumulus. The word nimbus refers to a cloud from which rain is falling, and cumulonimbus to a huge thunderhead that towers from near the ground up to 30,000 feet or higher

Figure 4-20a. Cirrocumulus clouds. (*U. S. Weather Bureau, U. S. Army.*)

Figure 4-20b. Cirrostratus clouds, with a few altocumulus clouds visible below the altostratus layer. (*U. S. Weather Bureau, L. A. Boyd.*)

Figure 4-20c. Cirrus clouds. (*U. S. Weather Bureau, F. Ellerman.*)

Figure 4-21a. Altostratus clouds near the horizon. (*U. S. Weather Bureau,
C. F. Brooks.*)

Figure 4-21b.   Altocumulus clouds.   (*U. S. Weather Bureau, A. C. Lapsley.*)

(Figure 4-22). Later, we shall see what sort of weather is associated with these types of clouds and how a sequence of them
indicates the presence and nearness of a cyclone.

Figure 4-22. Cumulonimbus cloud, with rain shower at its base. (*U. S.
Weather Bureau, U. S. Navy.*)

3. RAIN

The minute droplets in a cloud are usually too small to fall to
earth as rain. If the moist air that was cooled to form the cloud
is cooled further by being elevated, the drops grow in size and
eventually become heavy enough to fall. The conditions which
usually give rise to rain are the passage of warm moist air:
(*a*) up the windward side of a mountain range, (*b*) from the
warm ocean to cold land, (*c*) up over a wedge of cold air, and
(*d*) up into the air on ascending currents. Condition (*a*) is
responsible for the heavy rainfall on the western slopes of the
Cascade range in Washington and Oregon. Much of the rain
in California, the Middle West, and the East comes from conditions (*b*) and (*c*). The spring and summer rains in the North-

Figure 4-23. Microphotographs of snow crystals. (*U. S. Weather Bureau, W. A. Bentley.*)

Central States and much of the tropical rainfall comes from condition (*d*).

For many centuries superstitious groups have tried to bring rain by various mystic rites. Scientists have finally stepped into

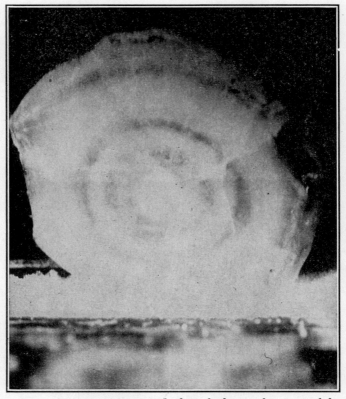

Figure 4-24. A cross-section view of a large hailstone, showing multilayered structure. (*U. S. Weather Bureau.*)

the picture with an understanding of the conditions necessary for making rain, and they are having a certain amount of success. It has been found that condensation takes place on small dust particles, which serve as nuclei for the formation of the drops. The long, white trails left by jet planes are the result of moisture condensing on the particles of dust in the exhaust fumes of the jets. Occasionally, the lack of nucleus particles in the air holds up condensation, and when these are supplied, rain results. More frequently, condensation has proceeded to the small-drop stage and something is needed to make the drops grow. By scattering crystals of Dry Ice or silver iodide into clouds that are at the correct temperature and altitude, further condensation is started. The heat of condensation (page 290) warms the surrounding air, producing an updraft that increases the condensation to such an extent that rain falls from a cloud that would otherwise have passed by.

4. SNOW AND HAIL

When moisture condenses from the vapor directly to the solid phase (below 32°F) it forms snow. Snow crystals are characterically hexagonal and beautiful in design when viewed under a low-power microscope (Figure 4-23). Hail is formed by the freezing of rain. When there is much turbulence in a cloud, raindrops may be swept up high enough to freeze. These balls of hail usually accumulate more moisture as they fall; if they make several round trips before finally hitting the ground, they have an onionlike structure and may be very large (Figure 4-24).

SUMMARY

1. The lag of the seasons behind the changing angle of the sun's rays is due to the specific heat of the earth.

2. Since water has a higher specific heat than soil, the lag of the seasons is greater along the coast than in the interior of the continents.

3. Coastal climates have a great seasonal lag and moderate temperature changes throughout the year.

4. Continental climates have a short seasonal lag and rapid and extreme changes of temperature.

5. Atmospheric moisture condenses into small drops to form clouds when air is cooled below its dew point and nuclei are present (usually dust particles) for the drops to form on.

6. Clouds are classified as cirrus, cirrostratus, and cirrocumulus above 20,000 feet altitude; altostratus and altocumulus be-

tween 10,000 and 20,000 feet; and stratus, cumulus, stratocumulus, nimbus, and cumulonimbus below 10,000 feet.

7. We have rain when the air is cooled sufficiently to produce drops large enough to fall to earth.

8. Techniques have recently been developed for obtaining rain from clouds that would not otherwise have produced it.

9. Snow is formed when water vapor condenses directly to a solid. Snow crystals have a characteristic hexagonal shape.

10. Hail is formed by the freezing of raindrops.

QUESTIONS AND EXERCISES

1. Why do cumulus clouds usually have flat bottoms?

2. If you are in doubt about the height of a cloud, how could its apparent speed help you decide?

3. Would you expect Nevada to receive less rainfall than Northern California? Why?

4. What type of cloud is indicated by a ring around the sun?

5. Keep a record for several days of the types of clouds that you see. If a storm comes during this period, compare the sequence of clouds with the description of a storm in Chapter 7.

6. Which of the conditions that produce rain is most important in your area?

7. Under what conditions would it be possible to have a humidity of 105%?

8. What are the three principal differences between a coastal- and a continental-type climate?

9. Discuss the legal complications that may very well develop from any widespread attempt at artificial rain-making.

10. Why is the hottest time of year in the interior of our continent later than June 21?

6

CHAPTER

Winds

1. GENERAL DISTRIBUTION OF WINDS AROUND THE EARTH

The blowing of the wind is such a common occurrence that you may well have taken it for granted. But when you stop to think about the blanket of air which covers the globe the questions arise: "Why does the air move around? Where does it come from, and where does it go?"

As the sunlight pours down on the earth it heats the air in the tropics more than that in the polar regions. The warmer air in the tropics expands and rises, and the colder air flows toward the Equator from the Poles. As the warm tropical air rises it continues to expand. As we learned earlier, a gas is cooled by expansion, and so the high-altitude tropical air flows poleward and sinks to replace the cold surface air which moved toward the Equator. This oversimplified scheme of circulation is shown in Figure 4-25. It resembles the circulation in a closed room heated by a single radiator. You can follow such air currents with a candle flame.

The rotation of the earth on its axis breaks up this simple pattern into three units in each hemisphere. If you were an observer on the moon looking at the earth, you would see that the surface features were moving from left to right across your field of vision. As the earth rotates, a spot on the Equator is moving around at a rate of 1050 miles per hour. The daily circular path through which St. Louis moves is only about 20,000 miles long, and so a spot here is moving 830 miles per hour, and at Nome, Alaska, the circular speed is slightly less than 420 miles per hour. The cold polar air moves southward with the rotational speed of the place from which it started, and it moves across land that has a constantly greater eastward speed. The north wind becomes a northeast and finally an east wind. A simple way to illustrate this for yourself is to place a piece of paper in front of you and hold a pencil at the top of it with your left hand. Draw the pencil straight down toward you as you move the paper to the right with your right hand. You will draw a curve that

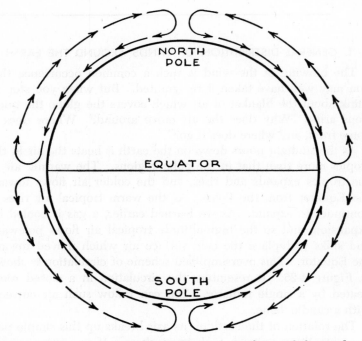

Figure 4-25. An oversimplified scheme of circulation of the winds.

shows the way the wind changes in direction. By the time the winds from the region of the North Pole reach the Canadian-American border, they are blowing so nearly directly from east to west that they get no further south. They warm up, rise, and return to the Pole at high altitudes.

Air from north of the Equator flows in to take the place of the heated air which has risen there. This southward-moving air curves in from the northeast just as the polar air did. The heated air rises and moves poleward to cool and descend again. By the time it has traveled approximately to the Tropic of Cancer (or Capricorn) it has cooled sufficiently to sink. It comes down and returns to the Equator along the ground.

In between these two circulating units in each hemisphere there is a third which is carried along by the other two. In the middle latitudes the air is moving northward along the ground. As it does so, it reaches latitudes that are rotating more slowly. It curves to the right and becomes a wind from the southwest. There are three circulating units in the southern hemisphere, and Figure 4-26 shows the prevailing winds in broad outline. The details of this broad picture are modified by the unequal heating of the oceans and the continents, by mountain barriers, and by the shifting of the sun with the changing seasons.

The line of contact between the polar easterlies and the stormy westerlies is called the polar front. This region of frequent storms shifts north into Canada during the summer, and south into the central United States during the winter. The horse latitudes are a region of gently settling air which is rather dry. The name comes from the days of the sailing vessels, which would frequently find themselves becalmed near the Tropic of Cancer. Any horses in the cargo would be thrown overboard to conserve the supply of drinking water. On the continents, the horse latitudes are the typically dry regions: northern Mexico, North Africa, Arabia, and Central Australia.

Between the Tropic of Cancer and the Equator is the region of the northeast trade winds. This name also comes from the days of the sailing vessels. Here the skipper could count on a steady wind which would carry him nearly to the Equator. Once the ship was near the Equator, the sails would flap in the gently rising air. It was hot, humid, and showery, and no progress could be made for days on end. This region was named the doldrums, and from that name we get the common expression "in the doldrums." During the summer, all these regions in the northern hemisphere are compressed and shifted northward, and during the winter they shift southward and spread out. The wind roses in Figure 4-27 show the remarkable consistency of the northwest and southeast trade winds and the high percentage of calm periods in the doldrums.

The birthplace of much of the weather for the continental

United States is the polar front. Here the warm air from the south meets the cold air from the north. The two masses are

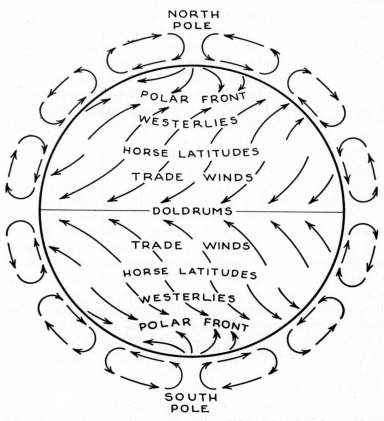

Figure 4-26. The prevailing winds of the world, in broad outline. These are modified considerably by surface features.

moving in nearly opposite directions, and a counterclockwise whirlpool of ascending air results. This is a low-pressure area and is given the name cyclone. Do not confuse this use of the word with its common meaning of a rapidly whirling, destructive wind. Tornado and hurricane are names applied to special kinds of cyclones. A descending mass of air with the surface winds blowing out from the center is characterized by high pressure, usually fair weather, and a generally clockwise distribution of

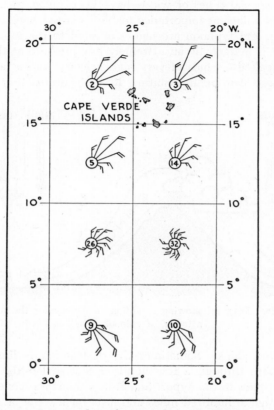

Figure 4-27.   Northeast and southeast trades and doldrums over the Atlantic Ocean, June, 1922.   The wind rose is given for each 5-degree square. Arrows fly with the wind.   The length of the arrow is proportional to the frequency of the winds from that direction.   The figure in the center gives the percentage of calms, light airs, and variable winds.   (*From U. S. Hydrographic Office Pilot Chart.*)

wind direction, and is called an anticyclone.   We will examine the weather conditions associated with typical cyclones and anticyclones in the next chapter.

2. SPECIAL TYPES OF WINDS

A few special types of winds have been given special names and are of sufficient importance to be discussed here. Tornado, hurricane, and typhoon are names applied to the same kind of wind. It is marked by an extremely low pressure at the center, counterclockwise winds of very high velocity, and a heavy rainfall. These can be devastating in their destruction of trees,

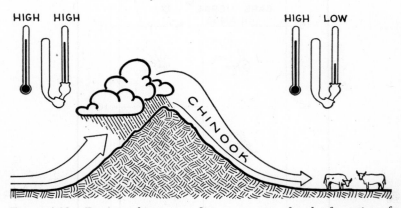

Figure 4-28. Diagram showing conditions necessary for the formation of a foehn, or chinook, wind.

houses, and ships. Sometimes the destruction is limited to a narrow path through a few hundred feet in length. Tornado usually applies to this type. Sometimes the storm covers a front of more than a hundred miles and lasts for a week or more as it moves over the earth. The autumn hurricanes of the east coast are of this type. In mountainous regions there is a peculiar type of wind called a foehn or chinook. As air rushes up one side of a mountain range it is cooled by expansion. When the cooling carries the temperature below the dew point there is condensation and rain. The condensation removes most of the moisture from the air and also warms it. When the partially warmed, dry air descends the range on the lee side, it is further warmed by compression, so that a hot, dry foehn wind results (Figure 4-28). In the West these are called chinook (or Santa Ana) winds, and they are of considerable economic importance. They usually blow in the wintertime, and they can melt many feet of snow in a single day, thus uncovering feed and water for range cattle.

Along the coast and for a few miles inland there is generally a period of calm followed by a reversal of the wind direction at sunrise and sunset. The land heats up faster than the sea when the sun first strikes them in the morning, and it cools down faster in the evening. The warmed air rises above the land, and a sea breeze (from the sea toward the shore) sets in soon after sunrise. In the evening there is a calm at sunset and then a land breeze springs up. Of course, this is a small-scale phenomenon and it is easily overcome by a storm with strong prevailing winds.

SUMMARY

1. The northern hemisphere has three general systems of winds, which result from the unequal distribution of heat from the sun and from the rotation of the earth.

2. In one of these systems the wind moves southward from the Pole in an ever-increasing westerly direction to about the northern border of the United States.

3. In the second of these systems the settling air moves northward from about the Tropic of Cancer in an ever-increasing easterly direction.

4. In the third of these systems the settling air moves southward from the Tropic of Cancer in an ever-increasing westerly direction toward the Equator.

5. The polar front is the line of meeting of the northeast winds of the polar system with the southwest winds of the central system.

6. A cyclone is a low-pressure area with a counterclockwise system of winds blowing toward it.

7. An anticyclone is a high-pressure area with a clockwise system of winds blowing out from it.

8. A trade wind is a seasonal prevailing wind which blows consistently from a certain direction.

9. A wind system characterized by a very low-pressure area, high wind velocity, and heavy rainfall is variously called tornado, hurricane, or typhoon.

10. A foehn, or chinook, is a warm, dry wind flowing rapidly from a high to a low altitude.

QUESTIONS AND EXERCISES

1. Would you expect the humidity at the Tropic of Cancer and at the Equator to be about the same or very different?

2. Would you expect the equivalent of the trade winds to exist in the upper atmosphere? Would this be of any importance for intercontinental air travel?

3. Why are the conditions typical of a coastal climate less pronounced along the Atlantic Coast than along the Pacific Coast of the United States?

4. At what seasons of the year would the area called the doldrums be right at the Equator?

5. When you pull the plug out of the bathtub, which way does the water whirl as it goes down the drain? Why?

6. From what direction does a chinook wind usually blow?

7. The difference in specific heat between water and soil has been used to explain a number of different things. See how many of them you can list.

8. What determines where the Tropic of Cancer is drawn on the globe?

9. Would a cyclone or an anticyclone be found regularly in the neighborhood of the North Pole?

10. Why does a chinook wind have a high temperature and a low humidity?

Cyclones and Anticyclones

It was mentioned earlier that when a mass of warm, moist air blowing from the southwest meets a mass of polar air blowing from the northeast a cyclone is developed. Figure 4-29 shows the sequence of events. The cooling of the warm, moist air as it rides up over the polar air results in an increasing amount of precipitation as the cyclone develops. As the cyclones that affect the weather of the United States seem to originate somewhere in Siberia, they usually reach us in a fairly well-developed stage.

Figure 4-30 shows a horizontal section through a well-developed cyclone. The symbol ⌢⌢⌢ represents a warm front, which is the line between a mass of cold air and an advancing mass of warm air. The symbol ⌃⌃⌃ represents the cold front where the cold air mass is advancing toward the warm air. Since the cold front advances faster than the warm front, it eventually catches up with it. This situation is called an occluded front, and is indicated by the symbol ⌃⌢⌃ . The solid black lines are lines of equal barometric pressure, isobars, drawn at intervals of 3 millibars, and they represent a typical distribution of pressures around a cyclone or a low-pressure area.

If a vertical section is taken between X and Y we have Figure 4-31. Let us consider the series of changes that would be observed at Y as the storm moves eastward from its present position. This is indicated by the successive positions of Y as $Y1$, $Y2$, $Y3$, $Y4$, $Y5$, and $Y6$. These changes are outlined in Table 4-4.

A storm of this type may cover an area of a thousand miles on a side, and the changes described may take place over a period of 1 to 4 days. If you are located north of the center of the low-pressure area, the storm is less severe and lasts for a shorter time, and there is no intermediate clearing. At the extreme south end of the storm there is very little precipitation.

An anticyclone, or high-pressure area, consists of a mass of

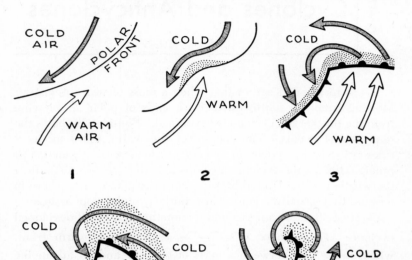

Figure 4-29. Five stages in the life of a cyclone. From a kink in the polar front, warm front and cold front develop. The dots represent areas of precipitation. At 4 the storm is at its height, at 5 the cold front is rapidly overtaking the warm front and the storm is dissipating. (*After Trewartha.*)

descending air that spreads out along the surface with a distribution of winds rotating in a clockwise direction. Since this mass of air is descending from an altitude of 30,000 or 40,000 feet, it is rather dry to begin with and the increase in pressure warms it. Therefore, fair weather usually accompanies a high. The clockwise swing of the winds draws in cold air from the north on the east side of the anticyclone and warm air from the south

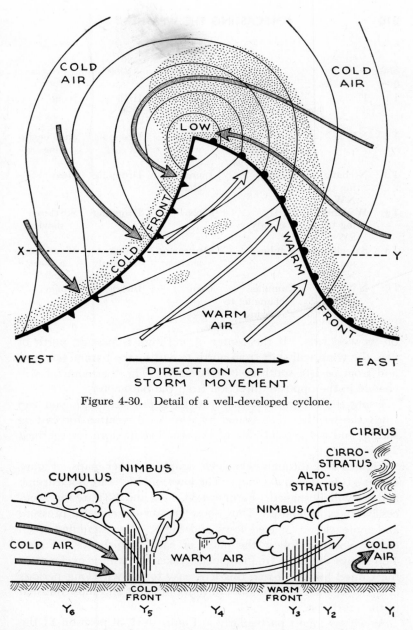

COLD AIR

COLD AIR

LOW

COLD FRONT

WARM FRONT

WARM AIR

X — — — — — — Y

WEST

EAST

DIRECTION OF STORM MOVEMENT

Figure 4-30. Detail of a well-developed cyclone.

CIRRUS

CIRRO-STRATUS

ALTO-STRATUS

NIMBUS

CUMULUS   NIMBUS

COLD AIR

WARM AIR

COLD AIR

COLD FRONT

WARM FRONT

Y_6 Y_5 Y_4 Y_3 Y_2 Y_1

Figure 4-31. A vertical cross section along the line $X-Y$ of the cyclone shown in Figure 4-29. (*After Trewartha.*)

TABLE 4-4

Sta-tion	Wind direction	Type of clouds	Tempera-ture	Pres-sure	Precipi-tation
Y1	E	Cirrus changing to cirrostratus	Cool	High	None
Y2	NE	Altostratus changing to nimbus	Slightly warmer	Dropping	Just beginning
Y3	N changing to NW	Nimbus	Increasing sharply	Dropping	Heavy
Y4	W changing to SW	Partly cloudy	Warm	Dropping	Scattered showers
Y5	SW changing to NW	Nimbus	Decreasing sharply	Rising sharply	Heavy for a short time
Y6	NW	Cumulus changing to clearing	Cool	Increasing	None

on its west side. If the center of the high is passing north of you, the wind will shift from north to east as the barometer rises, and from east to south as it falls again. The thermometer will change in the opposite direction from the barometer.

Using the information that you have just acquired, you can study the weather map issued by your local weather-forecasting station and get a good idea of the weather in store for the next 24 hours.

Figures 4-32 through 4-35 show sample weather maps. Figure 4-32 is a typical summer map. The lows and highs are not extreme and are widely spaced. Figures 4-33, 4-34, and 4-35 are for 3 successive days in winter. They show greater extremes in pressure and more closely spaced lows and highs. By examining them closely you can follow the paths of each disturbance. Figure 4-36 shows the most frequent paths taken by winter cyclones in the United States. From this it is easy to see why long periods of good weather are common in the southwest and most unusual in the northeast.

As we saw, most particularly in Figure 4-31, at position Y1 the air high above the ground was warm and moist while that close

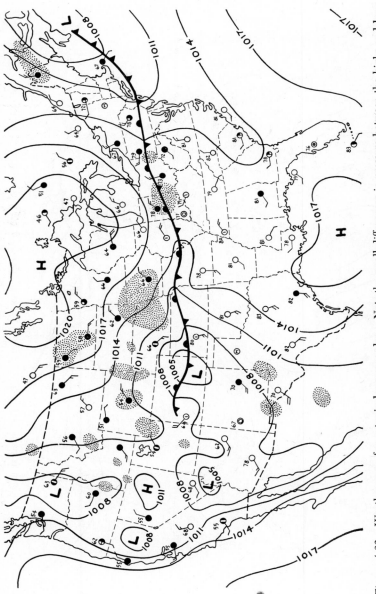
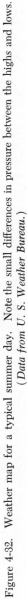

Figure 4-32. Weather map for a typical summer day. Note the small differences in pressure between the highs and lows. (*Data from U. S. Weather Bureau.*)

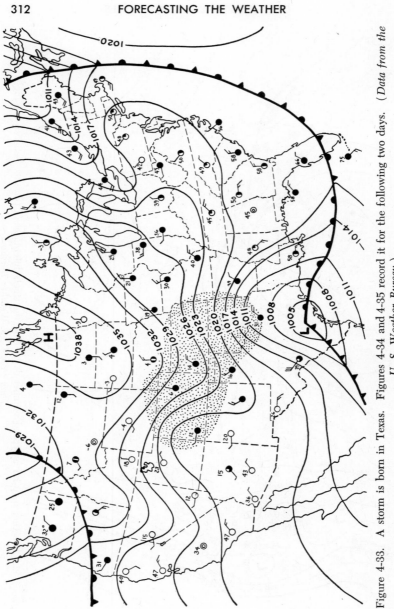

Figure 4-33. A storm is born in Texas. Figures 4-34 and 4-35 record it for the following two days. (*Data from the U. S. Weather Bureau.*)

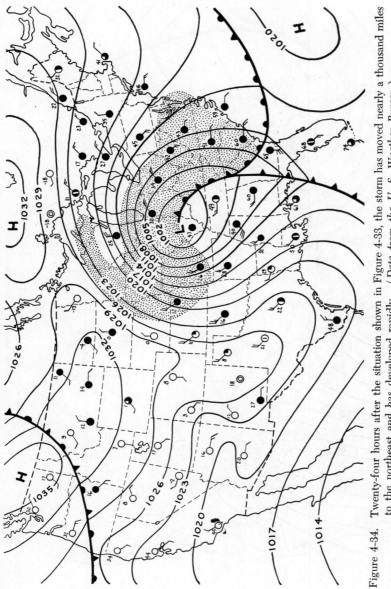

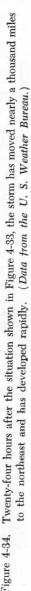

Figure 4-34. Twenty-four hours after the situation shown in Figure 4-33, the storm has moved nearly a thousand miles to the northeast and has developed rapidly. (*Data from the U. S. Weather Bureau.*)

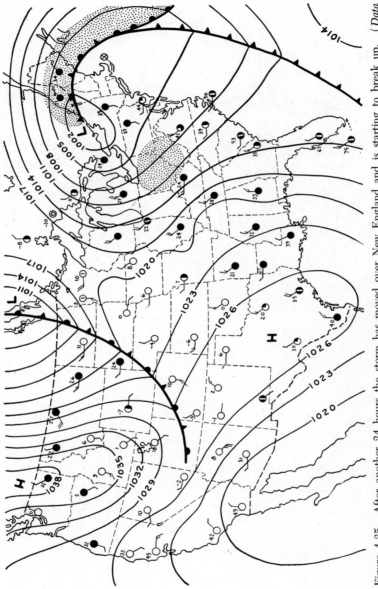

Figure 4-35.   After another 24 hours the storm has moved over New England and is starting to break up.   (Data from the U. S. Weather Bureau.)

to the surface was cold and dry. The importance of radiosondes is that they locate these high masses of air that give warning of weather which is still a day or so away.

As weather data have accumulated, we have learned that a few large masses of air are relatively stationary and consistent in composition (Figure 4-37). Our storms come from the inter-

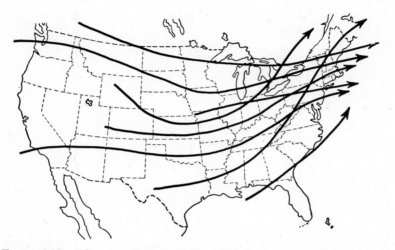

Figure 4-36. The most frequent paths taken by winter cyclones in the United States. (*After Trewartha.*)

action of these masses. When a region has unusual weather for a number of weeks at a time, we find that one of these masses of air has moved beyond its usual boundaries. A knowledge of how and why these move will be valuable for long-range weather prediction, but our understanding of these factors is not yet sufficiently advanced to be of much help to the layman.

SUMMARY

1. A warm front is the line between a mass of cold air and an advancing mass of warm air.

2. A cold front is the line between a mass of warm air and an advancing mass of cold air.

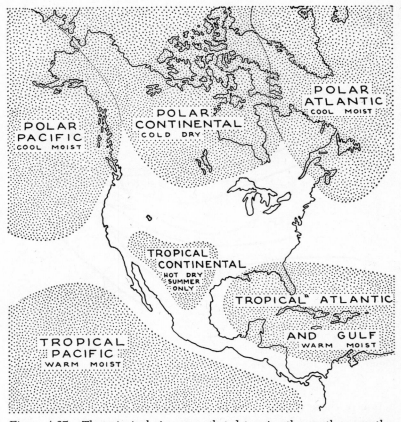

Figure 4-37. The principal air masses that determine the weather over the continental United States. (*After Trewartha.*)

3. An occluded front is the line between two masses of cold air which have met and pinched off the contact between a mass of warm air and the ground.

4. A typical well-developed cyclone is characterized by a low-pressure area of ascending air, with a counterclockwise whirlpool of winds blowing in toward it, a warm front extending southeast and a cold front extending southwest from its center, precipitation east of the warm front and west of the cold front, and a sequence of clouds that starts with cirrus at the eastern edge and drops to lower altitudes near the warm front, with

cumulus clouds following the clear-up shower at the cold front.

5. A typical anticyclone is characterized by a high-pressure area of descending air that moves out from the center in a system of winds rotating in a clockwise direction.

6. Summer highs and lows are usually spaced far apart, with only moderate differences in pressure between them.

7. In the winter, the lows and highs show greater extremes in pressure and they are spaced closer together.

8. A few large masses of air surrounding our continent are relatively stationary and consistent in composition over long periods of time. The position of these masses with respect to each other is a major factor in determining our weather.

QUESTIONS AND EXERCISES

1. Copy the chart shown in Figure 4-30.

2. Draw a north-south line through the center of the low-pressure area in the chart made in Problem 1, and make a sketch of a vertical section along this line.

3. Choose five representative points along the north-south line drawn in Problem 2, and describe the weather conditions at each point.

4. Assume that the center of an anticyclone passes about 200 miles north of you. Describe the sequence of weather conditions that you would observe.

5. What is the sequence of clouds that accompanies a cyclone?

6. Does the rain accompanying a cyclone come from the air that is already in it or from the air that is drawn in as it proceeds?

7. What stage in the life of a cyclone is indicated by an occluded front?

8. What are the principal differences between a typical summer and winter weather map?

9. If a radiosonde were sent up from position Y2 in Figure 4-31, what sort of a record of temperature and humidity would it send back as it ascends?

10. Explain a long period of unusual weather that you have had this year in terms of an extraordinary location of some of the principal air masses shown in Figure 4-37.

Miscellaneous Weather Conditions

1. TYPES OF ANNUAL DISTRIBUTION OF RAINFALL

Figure 4-38 shows the annual distribution of rainfall over the United States. For many agricultural purposes the distribution throughout the months of the year is extremely important. Figure 4-39 shows how different the pattern is for various parts of the country. No absolute significance can be attached to the figures on the vertical axes; the significant part of these curves is their shape. The Pacific Coast gets most of its rain in the winter months. During the summer little or none falls in California, a few inches are expected in Oregon, and about 10 inches is normal for Seattle, Washington. The polar front retreats northward in the summer, so that any storms enter the country at its northwest corner. The Rocky mountain region has a low total rainfall with a slight minimum during the summer. The plains region has its maximum rainfall in the spring and summer. Most of this results from local ascending air currents heated by the ground. The Gulf States have a coastal climate; the hottest time of year lags behind the season, and their maximum rainfall occurs in late summer and early fall. As New England is the funnel through which most of our storms leave the country, its rainfall is evenly distributed over the year.

2. CLOUDS AS BLANKETS

We have mentioned several times that the earth receives energy from the sun by radiation. However, the process is not one-way, with the earth receiving energy and giving none out. One of the fundamental laws of radiation states that every object in the universe is radiating energy to every other object at a rate which depends upon its temperature. The earth also radi-

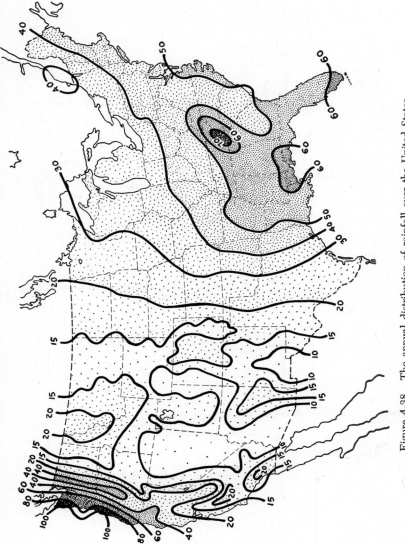

Figure 4-38. The annual distribution of rainfall over the United States.

ates to the sun, but since the earth is cooler, it receives more than it gives. You have certainly noticed that clear nights are colder

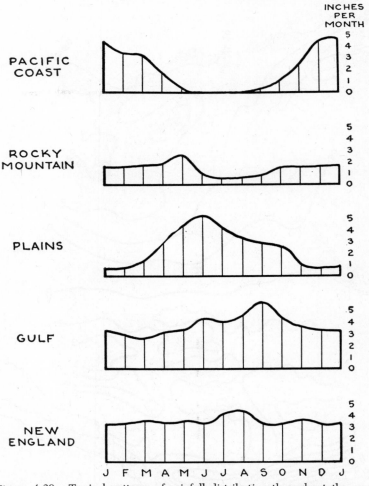

Figure 4-39. Typical patterns of rainfall distribution throughout the year.

than cloudy ones. At night the earth is giving off more energy than it is receiving. Clouds act like a blanket and hold in this energy, so that the earth does not cool off as fast as it does when the sky is clear.

3. FOG AND FROST

When a cloud is resting on the ground it is called fog. Along our West Coast the term "high fog" is applied to a cloud that is within a thousand feet or so of ground level. Fog occurs most frequently near large masses of water such as the Pacific Ocean, the Gulf of Mexico, the Atlantic Ocean, and the Great Lakes. Warm, moist air will condense into fog if it is blown from the land over cold water, or from the warm ocean over the colder land mass. Where hills hem in a saucer-like area, air that has been cooled by radiation will flow downhill and collect at the lowest point. If the cooling reduces the temperature below the dew point, a radiation fog results. This is usually thick, and it sticks close to the ground until the morning sun evaporates it. If the air is dry and the cooling carries it below the freezing point, a frost results. Frost is always heavier in the bottom of valleys than on their sloping sides. In southern California and Florida frosts are rare, but they do occur. It is of the greatest importance that the weather bureau warn the citrus farmers when a frost is to be expected, so that they can protect their crops with orchard heaters.

4. THUNDERSTORMS

Thunderstorms are most frequent in the southeastern part of this country, and they occur with less frequency farther north and west (Figure 4-40). Since they are so dangerous to aviation, they are being studied intensively. An updraft in warm, moist air is needed for the formation of a thunderstorm. Its development may be outlined in three stages. In stage 1 (Figure 4-41) a strong updraft of air turns a cumulus cloud into a towering cumulonimbus one. Air is drawn in from the sides as well as through the base. The air rises rapidly, attaining a speed greater than 35 miles per hour. As the cloud reaches a height of 20,000 to 25,000 feet, the precipitation of rain and snow is heavy. This precipitation falls near the leading edge of the storm and carries a stream of cold air with it. With the formation of the down-draft, the second stage in the thunderstorm has been reached.

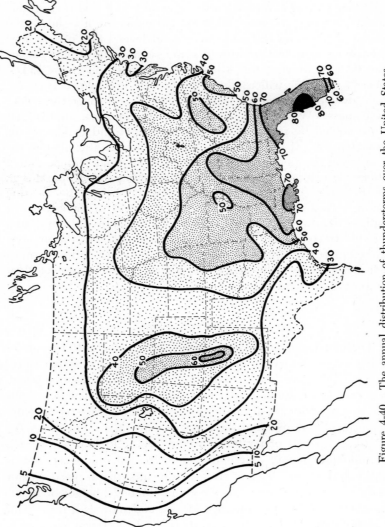

Figure 4-40.   The annual distribution of thunderstorms over the United States.

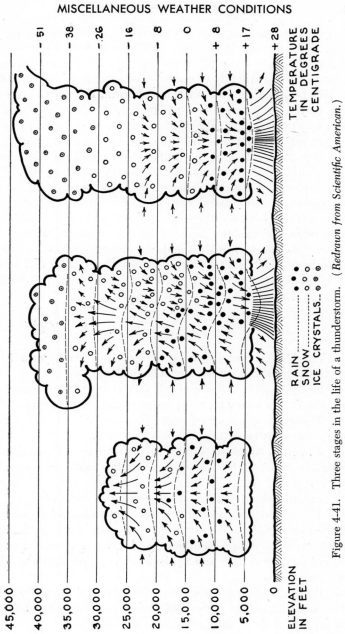

Figure 4-41. Three stages in the life of a thunderstorm. (*Redrawn from Scientific American.*)

Much rain reaches the earth, but some is swept back up by the ascending currents. It becomes mixed with snow, freezes into hail, and descends again. After a few round trips the hailstones are large enough to fall to earth. As several such circulating cells will be found in any one thunderstorm, the pattern of rainfall is spotty. What falls is usually of short duration, and adjacent towns may get very different amounts.

Lightning results from the difference in electric charge between the drops of water that fall and the fine mist that breaks off them and stays in the cloud. It consists of a huge spark between regions of opposite charge. The heating effect of this spark makes the air expand with explosive violence. By checking the interval between the time you see the lightning and hear the thunder, you can tell how far off the lightning struck. Remember that sound travels a mile in about 5 seconds. As the thunderhead reaches 40,000 or even 50,000 feet, the fall of rain is so great that the updraft is blocked and the third, or dissipating, stage is reached.

SUMMARY

1. The United States may be divided into five regions which have characteristic distributions of annual rainfall.

2. Every object in the universe is radiating energy to every other object at a rate which depends upon its temperature.

3. The earth cools off at night because it is radiating more energy than it is receiving.

4. A cloudy night is warmer than a clear one because the clouds are warmed by radiation from the earth and reradiate energy to it.

5. Fog is a cloud resting on the ground or close to it.

6. A thunderstorm contains several separate cells of violently turbulent air. Warm, moist air is swept up until its moisture condenses; these drops circulate up and down several times till they fall as rain or hail; and finally the heavy precipitation dissipates the storm.

7. Lightning results from the difference in electric charge between the drops of water that fall rapidly and the fine mist that breaks off them and falls slowly or not at all.

8. Thunder is the noise produced when the stroke of lightning heats the air very rapidly.

QUESTIONS AND EXERCISES

1. Why is the Rocky mountain region low in total rainfall?

2. How would you expect the total annual rainfall to change as you go north from Louisiana to Iowa?

3. Obtain the average annual rainfall data for your locality and plot it on a graph like the ones in Figure 4-39.

4. Plot the rainfall data for last year as you did in Problem 3. The chances are good that there will be important differences between the two graphs.

5. Why is there less danger of frost when the humidity is high than when it is low?

6. Can you have thunder without lightning?

7. How does the formation of rain aid the updraft in a thunderstorm?

8. What is responsible for the "roll" of distant thunder?

9. What would be some of the dangers of flying an airplane through a thunderstorm?

10. What are the different kinds of conditions that produce a fog?

CHAPTER

Climate and Comfort

1. MAINTAINING BODY TEMPERATURE

So far, we have been talking mostly about the day-to-day changes in the weather. When we take into consideration the weather conditions averaged over several years, we are referring to the climate of a region. There are days when the temperature at Chicago is higher than it is at New Orleans, and there are days when it rains in Los Angeles and not in Seattle. Yet we know that the climate of New Orleans is, in general, warmer than that of Chicago, and that the average annual rainfall of Seattle is greater than that of Los Angeles. In this section we shall be considering the effects of various elements of the climate on our bodily comfort, our ability to work, and our intellectual efficiency. Later, we shall see how important a factor the climate of a region is in limiting the type of civilization which can develop there.

Numerous investigations have shown that the effect of climate on bodily comfort is almost exclusively connected with the ease of maintaining a constant body temperature. The normal body temperature varies with the location at which it is measured. Under the tongue (orally) it is 98.6°F, rectally it is 99.6°F. The skin temperature is about 88°F (except for the hands and feet), and in the body cavity it may be as high as 107°F. In healthy individuals there may be a variation of about 1° either way from the averages given above. Any greater variation is probably a sign that something is wrong.

The principal way in which the body gains heat is by burning food. After we have attained full growth, practically all the food we eat is burned up in our bodies. Just as much heat is produced by burning food in our bodies as there would be by burning it in a furnace. One of the important ways in which the body loses heat is by the evaporation of water from the skin and the lungs. There are other ways in which the body gains or loses heat, depending on the conditions. It is convenient to divide these into radiation, convection, and conduction.

Earlier we learned the law of radiation, which states that every object radiates energy at a rate depending on its temperature. Applying this law to the way in which our bodies gain and lose heat, we see that our skin is losing energy to all objects which are cooler than 88°F and it is gaining energy from all objects that are warmer than that. The term convection refers to the air which blows past our bodies. We either gain heat from or lose it to the air molecules that strike our skin, depending on whether they are warmer or colder than our skin. The same situation holds with respect to solid objects that remain for a while in direct contact with our skin. This last method of gain or loss is called conduction. The distinction between these last two is a minor but convenient one. You can put your hand into a hot oven with safety for a few seconds, but you are burned by even a brief contact with the oven rack. This illustrates the fact that gases are much less efficient in transferring heat than solids or liquids.

2. CONTROLLING THE CLIMATE INDOORS

At present, our homes are made comfortable mainly by convection, and they are made uncomfortable mainly by radiation. In the wintertime, air is heated either in a furnace or by steam condensing in radiators, and it circulates around us to keep us warm. One difficulty with this system is that since the circulating system is never very efficient the air near the ceiling of a room is usually 10° or more warmer than the air near the floor. Another drawback is that heating air reduces its relative humidity. The range of winter humidities in most of our homes is far too low. While we are gaining heat by convection we are also losing it by radiation. The floor, all outside walls, and any windows are nearly always colder than our skin, so we must keep the air warm enough to make up for this loss by radiation. In the summertime the walls heat up during the day and then keep us hot by radiation after the air has cooled in the evening.

In what way can we modify our present techniques of construction to improve this situation? The most obvious answer is to make radiation work for our comfort instead of against it.

The space between our inside and outside walls can be insulated with products like rock wool or glass fibers. These materials hold air in their porous structure and prevent it from circulating. One inch of rock wool is as effective a heat insulator as 12 inches of solid stone or concrete. Insulation will keep the walls warmer in winter and cooler in summer. Windows made with double panes of glass separated by a dead-air space lose much less heat by radiation than do regular single-pane windows. Actually heating or cooling the walls would be an excellent idea, but it is not yet economically practical. With new construction, it is now possible to put heating pipes under the floor, above the ceiling, or in both places (Figures 4-42a and b). Radiation from such a large area as the floor is so effective that the floor does not need to be very warm, and the air temperature can be about $10°$ cooler than we usually need it. Another advantage of radiant heating in the floor is that we do not have to overheat the top half of a room in order to make the lower half comfortable.

For climates which are too hot in the summer, the best solution seems to be the forced circulation of cooled air. In private homes this is about all that can be done. In office buildings, stores, etc., the air is filtered and cooled by refrigerating coils. This lowers the humidity by condensing moisture. Sometimes it is necessary to put some moisture back, and a spray of water or steam will do this.

3. THE COMFORT ZONE

With the increasing ability to control the temperature and humidity of our environment, studies have been made to determine the best conditions to maintain. For any given temperature, evaporation of perspiration will have more of a cooling effect the lower the humidity. Actually, we are comfortable over quite a range of humidities at any one temperature, and over several degrees of temperature at any one humidity, so that it is proper to speak of the comfort zone. Measuring such a subjective thing as comfort is difficult at best, but by controlling conditions carefully and getting reactions from a large number of people, satisfactorily objective data can be obtained. Figure 4-43 gives a general idea of the results of many such experiments.

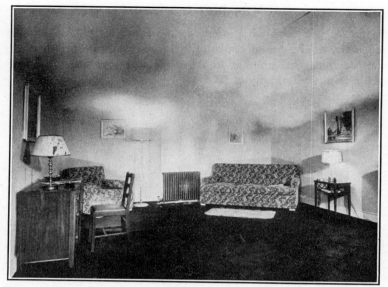

Figure 4-42*a*.   Room heated with conventional steam radiator.   Smoke shows that warm air has collected near the ceiling.   (*Courtesy Life © Time.*)

Figure 4-42*b*.   Room heated by radiant heat from pipes under the floor and above the ceiling.   Smoke shows even distribution of warm air.   (*Courtesy Life © Time.*)

Evidence will soon be presented to show that we work most efficiently at the cool end of this comfort zone, so it would seem that 65 is a good number to strive for—a temperature of 65°F and a relative humidity of 65%.

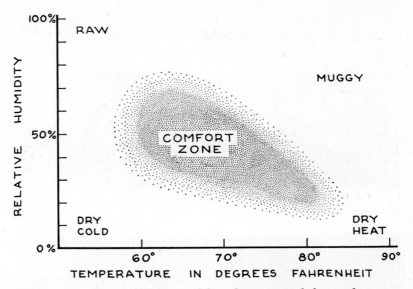

Figure 4-43. The temperature and humidity ranges of the comfort zone.

4. CLIMATE AND ENERGY

As a result of his studies of factory workers doing piecework and of the grades of college students, Huntington has drawn the graph shown in Figure 4-44. The temperature recorded was the 24-hour average outdoor temperature. The graph indicates that the most stimulating climate for both mental and physical work would have a daily average temperature variation from about 40°F to 55°F. Other factors that he found to contribute to mental and physical energy were a humidity varying between 30% and 80%, storms about once a week on the average, and frequent changes of weather which were neither abrupt nor violent.

An analysis of weather data from all over the world results in

Figures 4-45 and 4-46. These illustrations show the areas of the whole world and of the United States rated according to the above definition of a stimulating climate. It is interesting to pursue this topic further and to try to see how this distribution of climate correlates with the distribution of the characteristics

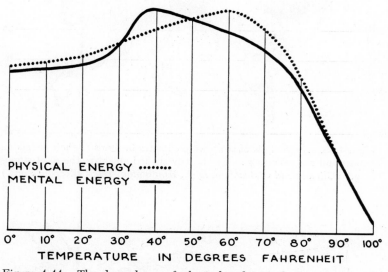

PHYSICAL ENERGY ⋯⋯⋯

MENTAL ENERGY ⎯⎯⎯

0°   10°   20°   30°   40°   50°   60°   70°   80°   90°   100°

TEMPERATURE   IN   DEGREES   FAHRENHEIT

Figure 4-44. The dependence of physical and mental energies upon the outside temperature. (*Civilization and Climate, by E. Huntington, Yale University Press.*)

of Western-type civilization. Such factors as amount of transportation, manufacturing, income, health, scientific and artistic creativity, and education were the ones taken into account. Figures 4-47 and 4-48 show the results of this study. There is a convincingly close correlation between those areas which are high in climate energy and high in the characteristic features of civilization and between those which are low in both. The conclusion to be drawn from these data seems inescapable. It is that a certain peculiar type of climate is one of the factors essential for the development of a Western-type industrial civilization. You should be careful to notice that there is nothing in this state-

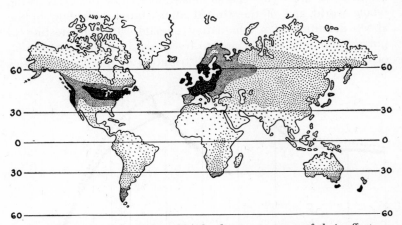

Figure 4-45. An analysis of worldwide climates in terms of their effects on physical and mental energy. The heavily shaded areas are the most stimulating. (*Climate and Civilization*, by E. Huntington, Yale University Press.)

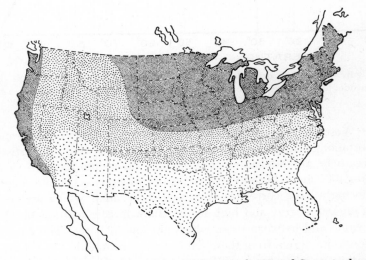

Figure 4-46. The same as Figure 4-45, showing the United States in detail. (*Climate and Civilization*, by E. Huntington, Yale University Press.)

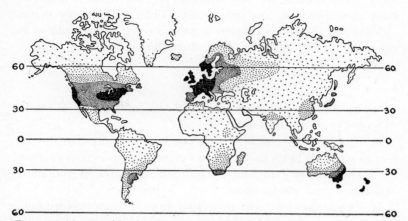

Figure 4-47. Worldwide distribution of factors characteristic of western civilization. The heavily shaded areas indicate the greatest concentration of these factors. Compare with Figure 4-45. (*Civilization and Climate, by E. Huntington, Yale University Press.*)

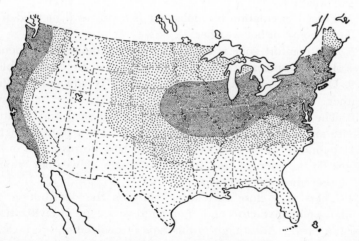

Figure 4-48. The same as Figure 4-47, showing the United States in detail. Compare with Figure 4-46. (*Civilization and Climate, by E. Huntington, Yale University Press.*)

ment which implies that any one kind of civilization is better or more desirable than any other kind. But it does imply that a vigorous, industrial civilization cannot develop in such places as the tropical parts of Africa, Asia, Australia, and Brazil.

SUMMARY

1. By climate is meant the weather conditions of a region averaged over several years.

2. The weather contributes to our bodily comfort to the extent to which it helps us maintain our normal body temperature.

3. Our bodies gain heat by burning food and by radiation, convection, and conduction.

4. Our bodies lose heat by evaporation of water and by radiation, convection, and conduction.

5. Insulation of our homes helps control heat radiation in both hot and cold weather.

6. Radiant heating is an excellent method for heating a house in cold weather.

7. Forced circulation of cooled air is a practical method for cooling a house in hot weather.

8. The comfort zone is the rather narrow range of temperatures and corresponding humidities at which we are comfortable.

9. Our physical and intellectual energy is affected by the weather.

10. The most stimulating conditions for physical and mental activity are a daily average temperature variation from 40°F to 55°F, humidity varying between 30% and 80%, storms about once a week on the average, and frequent changes of weather which are neither abrupt nor violent.

11. There is a close correlation between the distribution of the above climate factors and of an aggressive type of civilization over the earth. Areas high in this type of civilization are invariably high in climate energy, and areas low in climate energy are invariably low in this type of civilization.

QUESTIONS AND EXERCISES

1. Why do we seem to perspire more freely when the humidity is high?

2. Think up some examples illustrating the body gaining or losing heat by radiation, convection, and conduction.

3. On a day that is below 50°F outside, measure the temperature of a room heated by convection. Compare the temperature taken a few inches from the ceiling with that taken a few inches from the floor. If possible, make the same measurements in a room with radiant heating in the floor.

4. Why is tightly woven cloth uncomfortable in hot weather?

5. What is the principal type of heat energy received from a fireplace?

6. If the air in a building is at 65°F and 65% humidity and it becomes necessary to increase the temperature to 80°F, what change in the humidity would be necessary to keep the conditions within the comfort zone?

7. What is the point of pumping out the air between the walls of a Thermos bottle?

8. Why can you stand being exposed to air at 65°F much longer than to water at that temperature?

9. What use could a manufacturer make of the map of climate energy?

10. What seems to be the principal factor, other than latitude, that determines climate?

10

Climate and Civilization in the Past

A scientific hypothesis not only gathers together a large number of assorted facts into one simple generalization, but it also suggests new correlations which had not been thought of previously. If an aggressive civilization can develop only where the climate is suitable now, the same situation also should have prevailed in the past. In ancient history we studied vigorous civilizations centered in Persia, Egypt, and Greece. The climate of these regions now rates low in its ability to stimulate mental and physical activity. This lack of correlation suggests either a weakness in the theory or that climates may change over the centuries.

A large fund of information on climates of the past has been assembled. There can be no question about the fact that rather extensive changes in the amount of rainfall in Asia and Europe have occurred during the last 5000 years. Changing shore lines of lakes and seas, villages abandoned to either the water or the desert, dried-up forests, etc., are convincing evidence that many sections of the earth have experienced long periods of alternating rain and drought. Dating these periods accurately is another matter. The dating of the climatic swings in Europe and Asia is still so controversial that it will be better to confine our study to a much more certain example on our own continent.

The Mayan civilization on the Yucatan peninsula in Mexico once flourished in a region which is now a dense, malarial jungle with a subtropical climate. It would be hard to imagine a more unpromising location for a civilization which built magnificent temples, made accurate astronomical observations, and developed a high degree of artistic expression. The Mayan culture had its ups and downs. From a high point about A.D. 600 it declined to a low point about 700. It rose again from about 900 to 1100, but thenceforth the record is difficult to trace.

In the Sierra Nevada of California are growing giant redwood trees, many of which are 2000 years old, and some patriarchs can look back on 3000 years. The width of the annual growth rings on these trees is an excellent measure of the rainfall for the year in which the growth was made. Several hundred of these trees have been studied carefully, and an accurate graph of the rainfall in that area for the last 2000 years has been made. Figure 4-49 shows this graph. You can see that from A.D. 200 to 400 the

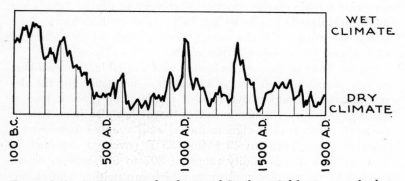

Figure 4-49. Variations in the climate of Southern California over the last 2000 years, as judged from the annual growth rings of redwood trees. (*Civilization and Climate*, by E. Huntington, Yale University Press.)

rainfall dropped from a large amount to a moderate amount. After 400 it varied irregularly, with a peak at 600. From 600 to 640 it dropped to a very low level, where it remained until around 770. By 800 there was again a moderate rainfall, and it increased to a large amount by 1000. A real low was not again reached until 1150; a high peak was attained in 1330; and an extreme low in 1480 has been followed by an irregular pattern at a rather low level. The low period in Mayan culture from 700 to 900, its recovery about 1000, and its final decline about 1500 fit in with the swings of the graph of rainfall in southern California.

At present, the horse-latitude belt of dry climate lies across northern Mexico. It is bounded on the south by the moist region of the trade winds and on the north by the moist region of the stormy westerlies. If this whole pattern of climate shifts north and south for some reason or other, we would have Yucatan dry at the time southern California is moist, and vice versa. From the evidence of the tree rings we know that just such a shift in climate did take place. At the peak periods of Mayan culture, southern California was unusually moist, indicating that the horse-latitude belt of dry climate had shifted south into Yucatan. The predictions of our theory are borne out by the way the vigor of the civilization kept pace with the climate of the region.

There is yet no satisfactory explanation of the north-south shift of the climate zones. One naturally turns to the explanation that was used for the glacial epochs. The curve in Figure 3-69 is not sufficiently detailed to be of any help. The explanation may lie in this direction or in the direction of a study of the effect of sunspots on the weather of the earth.

On the basis of the best evidence now available, it seems that certain peculiar conditions of climate are necessary for the development of an aggressive type of civilization. This is true at present, and our evidence indicates that it has also been true in the past. This special climate includes an average annual temperature range between $40°F$ and $55°F$ (average extremes of $30°F$ to $70°F$), a humidity range of 30% to 80%, storms on an average of once a week, changes which are neither abrupt nor violent, and no long periods with very little change. If this is true, it must be taken into account in decisions to relocate displaced persons, to invest funds for industrial expansion, and in general plans for the development of backward areas of the earth.

SUMMARY

1. The width of the annual growth rings of trees is a measure of the corresponding annual rainfall of the locality.

2. The rainfall of southern California was formerly much heavier than it is now. Times of maximum rainfall occurred in A.D. 200, 600, 1000, and 1330.

3. This fact indicates a north-south shift of the horse-latitude belt of dry climate.

4. At the times when the dry belt was south (maximum rainfall in California) the Mayan culture in Yucatan was at a high level, and when the dry belt was north (maximum rainfall in Yucatan) the Mayan culture declined.

5. Evidence from the past and the present indicates that certain peculiar conditions of climate are necessary for the development of an aggressive type of civilization.

QUESTIONS AND EXERCISES

1. Draw a graph showing how it is assumed that the rainfall varied in Yucatan from A.D. 200 to 1150.

2. Make a graph of the ups and downs of Mayan culture from A.D. 600 to 1100, and notice the inverse relationship between this and the one drawn in Problem 1.

3. What would this theory predict about the level of Mayan culture in A.D. 200?

4. Why do we not study growth rings of trees in Yucatan to obtain information about the rainfall of the period under discussion?

5. Describe the type of climate which seems most suitable for the development of an aggressive, Western-type civilization.

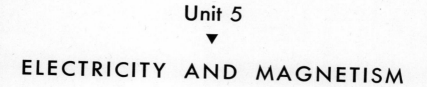

Unit 5
▼
ELECTRICITY AND MAGNETISM

CHAPTER

Static Electricity

1. THE INTERACTION OF CHARGES

Electric motors start our cars and run our tools and washing machines; all long-distance communication depends on electricity; the majesty of lightning and the crackle of cat's fur are two extremes of the same thing—a spark of electricity. Two of the three basic particles of atomic structure bear electric charges. We shall study some of the laws of this subject that reaches into so many aspects of our lives.

There are many examples of static electricity that you may have noticed on dry days. On a clear, cold day the air indoors is almost sure to be dry. Your hair follows the comb; the cat's fur crackles when it is stroked; you get a shock from a metal object or another person after scuffing your feet on the carpet; rayon or nylon slips or shirts cling to your body as you take them off.

Phenomena similar to the above ones have intrigued mankind for well over 2000 years, yet it was not until 200 years ago that someone worked out a reasonable explanation. With a few well-planned experiments, this explanation will become apparent to you in a few minutes.

We shall use two rods, one of hard rubber and one of glass; two pieces of material, one of cat's fur and one of silk; and two pith balls suspended on silk threads. First touch one of the pith balls with your finger, then rub the hard-rubber rod with cat's fur and bring the rod close to the pith ball. The ball will jump toward the rod, cling to it for a second or so, and then spring away from it (Figure 5-1). As you follow the ball with the rod, it keeps swinging away. Now repeat the above experiment with the glass rod, the silk cloth, and the other pith ball. The results will be exactly the same. We say that we have charged the pith balls with electricity.

Now let us perform three more experiments which will give us further insight into the behavior of electricity. After our ex-

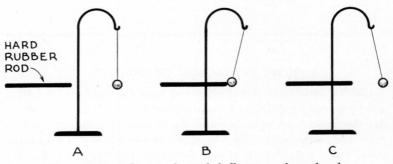

HARD
RUBBER
ROD

A   B   C

Figure 5-1.   Behavior of a pith ball near a charged rod.

perience with light we know better than to ask the question, "What is electricity?" Electricity is no more than a word which applies to the action of matter under certain conditions. Charge each of the two pith balls with the hard-rubber rod rubbed with cat's fur, then bring them close to-

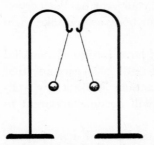

Figure 5-2.   Behavior of two pith balls when charged alike.

gether. Figure 5-2 shows how they will repel each other. Repeat the experiment, charging the two balls with the glass rod rubbed with silk. Again the balls repel each other. Finally, charge one pith ball with the hard-rubber rod rubbed with cat's fur and the other ball with the glass rod rubbed with silk. When the two balls are brought close together they swing toward each other (Figure 5-3) and touch.

Whatever we may decide later about electric charges, it is reasonable to assume that the two pith balls charged by the hard-rubber and cat's-fur technique received the same kind of charge. That experiment indicates that like charges repel each other.

The experiment in which the pith balls were charged with the glass-rod and silk technique supports this conclusion. When the two balls charged by the two different techniques are brought close and show attraction, we are forced to the conclusion that there are at least two different kinds of electricity. Like charges repel in each case, but unlike charges attract each other. The names negative and positive have been given to these two kinds of electricity, and they are the only kinds discovered so far. The name negative is applied by definition to the kind of electricity left on the surface of a hard-rubber rod after it has been rubbed with cat's fur. This is the basic definition in the field of electricity.

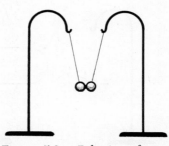

Figure 5-3. Behavior of two pith balls when they carry opposite charges.

As we shall see in the unit on atomic structure, we now think that all matter is composed of three fundamental types of particles, which are called electrons, protons, and neutrons. The electrons bear a single negative charge; the protons, a single positive charge; and the neutrons have no electric charge. The protons and neutrons constitute the mass and the structural unity of any substance, and the electrons are relatively free to wander through matter and to be transferred from one substance to another.

2. INDUCTION

After one more experiment we can start talking about these effects in terms of the motion of electrons. Use a blunt, cigar-shaped, metal cylinder, as in Figures 5-4A and B, with negatively charged pith balls hung near the ends as indicators. The + − charges at either end of the cylinder indicate that it is electrically neutral and that the charges are evenly distributed. In Figure 5-4B a negatively charged rod, R, has been brought up near the left end of the cylinder. The left pith ball swings toward the cylinder, and the right one swings away from it, indicating that the left end of the cylinder is charged positively and the right end is charged negatively. The excess electrons on the rod have repelled the free-moving electrons on the cylinder, so that they are crowded toward the far end. When the charged rod is removed

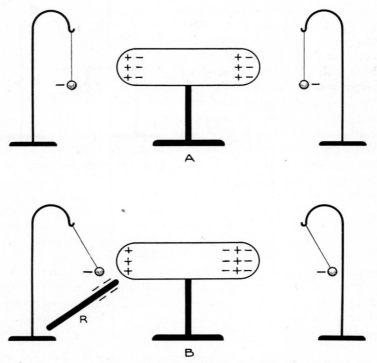

Figure 5-4. Part *A* shows a neutral metal cylinder with charges evenly distributed. Part *B* shows these charges separated by induction. Pith balls on stands show up this separation of charges.

from the vicinity of the cylinder the two pith balls will again hang vertically, showing that the charge on the cylinder is again distributed uniformly. This temporary separation of charges is called induction.

In the process of charging the pith balls as described on page 343 the cat's fur and the hard-rubber rod each had approximately the same number of electrons as protons. The rubbing transferred some electrons from the fur to the rod, and we represent these extra electrons by (−) around the rod, as in Figure 5-4B. The pith ball was touched to neutralize any excess charge which it may have had from a previous experiment. When the rod was brought near the pith ball, induction forced electrons to the far side and the excess protons were attracted to the electrons on the rod. This made the ball swing toward the rod and cling to it. Some electrons then flowed from the rod to the ball, and the ball soon had more electrons than protons. It was now charged negatively as a whole and was repelled by the rod, which was still left with a negative charge.

If experiments of this type are carried out with metal rods, or if the pith ball is suspended by a metal thread, no charge can be detected. Electrons flow along some substances much more easily than along others. Substances along which electrons flow easily are called conductors. Metals are good conductors, and copper is one of the very best. Substances along which electrons do not flow readily are called insulators. Glass, rubber, dry thread, and paper are examples of insulators. Your body is a moderately poor conductor, but it is good enough to conduct a charge from the earth to any charged body that you touch. You are sufficiently well insulated to acquire a fair charge by scuffing your feet on the carpet on a dry day. You might plan and carry out an experiment to test whether this charge is positive or negative.

3. THE GOLD-LEAF ELECTROSCOPE

Another sensitive instrument that can be used to detect an electric charge is a gold-leaf electroscope. This device consists of two strips of gold leaf attached to a metal rod and enclosed in a box with glass sides to protect the fragile gold leaf from air currents. The metal rod projects through an insulator in the top of the box, and the strips of gold leaf hang vertically beside each other (Figure 5-5). When a positively charged rod is brought close to the knob, some of the electrons are drawn up from the gold leaf. Both leaves are left charged positively, and so they repel each other and diverge (Figure 5-5). When a negatively charged rod is brought near the knob, the electrons on the knob are driven down to the gold leaves, acquire a negative charge, and again diverge. Thus, an uncharged electroscope detects the presence of a charge but not its sign.

If the positively charged rod is touched to the knob of the electroscope and then withdrawn, some electrons will jump from the knob over to the rod and the electroscope will be left with

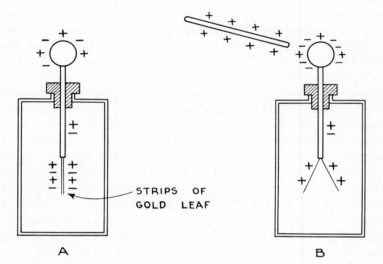

STRIPS OF GOLD LEAF

A   B

Figure 5-5. Gold-leaf electroscope used to detect charge on rod.

more protons than electrons. It will be charged, and the leaves will remain diverged. If a negatively charged rod is brought near the knob of this positively charged electroscope, the leaves will approach each other. Why? The approach of a positively charged rod will make the leaves diverge farther. A charged electroscope can be used to indicate the sign of the charge on a body.

An electroscope can be charged by induction, as indicated in Figure 5-6. Notice that the rod does not touch the knob and that the charge acquired by the electroscope is the opposite of the one on the rod.

If there are charges in the air surrounding a charged electroscope, they will be attracted to the leaves and neutralize them.

This kind of device has been most useful in studying X-rays and radioactivity, and it will be discussed again in the unit on atomic structure.

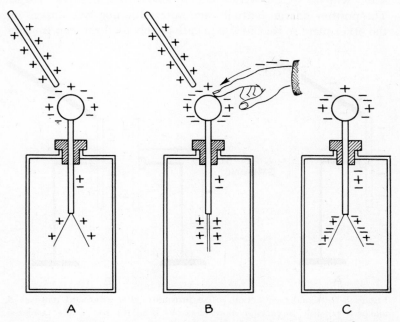

A   B   C

Figure 5-6. Charging an electroscope by induction. In part *B*, electrons move from the hand to the knob so that the leaves receive a charge opposite to that on the rod.

4. CONDENSERS

An insulated metal plate can be charged by contact with a charged rod (Figure 5-7). After a certain number of electrons have been transferred from the rod, the ones on the tip of the rod are repelled as much by those already on the plate as by those behind them on the rod. You can say that the plate has been filled to its capacity with electrons. A similar situation would hold if the rod were positive and electrons were being removed from the plate. Now let another plate (the left one in Figure 5-7), which is connected by a wire to the ground (notice the symbol), be brought up close to the first one. There is a force of repulsion between the electrons on the two plates, and those on the left-hand plate can move through the wire to the ground. They will do so, and that plate is left with a positive charge. The positive charge partially neutralizes the negative charge on the other plate so that now a negatively charged rod can transfer

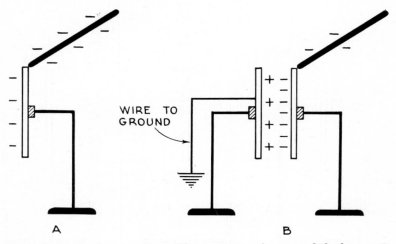

WIRE TO GROUND

A   B

Figure 5-7. Condenser action. The proximity of a grounded plate at *B* makes it possible to transfer more electrons from the rod to the insulated plate.

more electrons to it. Its capacity has been increased by the proximity of the grounded plate. Such a combination of parallel plates is called a condenser. The symbol for a condenser is ⊣├── or ─⊏═⊐── . One of the plates of a condenser does not have to be connected to the ground, but both should be made of material that is a good conductor, so that the electrons can distribute themselves over the surface readily.

One form of condenser which is convenient for lecture demonstration and laboratory work is the Leyden jar (Figure 5-8). A large glass jar has a metal lining inside and outside. With the outside lining grounded a very high charge can be put on the inside lining, and a juicy spark can be drawn from it. You should be extremely careful in handling a charged Leyden jar.

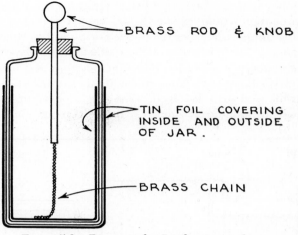

BRASS ROD & KNOB

TIN FOIL COVERING INSIDE AND OUTSIDE OF JAR.

BRASS CHAIN

Figure 5-8. Diagram of a Leyden jar condenser.

5. USING METALS TO OBTAIN AN ELECTRIC CHARGE

We have learned that different nonconductors have different tendencies to hold on to electrons. Cat's fur will give up electrons to hard rubber and to glass. Glass will give electrons up to silk, and silk will give them up to hard rubber. Arranging them in increasing order of their tendency to hold on to electrons, we would have cat's fur, glass, silk, and hard rubber.

Metals also have different tendencies to hold on to electrons. This is best illustrated by the following type of experiment. Drop a strip of zinc into a solution of copper sulfate and a strip of copper into a solution of zinc sulfate. The strip of metallic copper will remain unchanged for days. The zinc will be covered with a dark deposit, and after a few hours the blue color of the copper sulfate solution will fade. By the end of 24 hours the zinc strip will have disintegrated, leaving a dark, reddish-brown deposit, and the solution will be clear.

In the solution of the metal salts, the metals are in the form of atoms that have lost two electrons. (Atomic structure is described in Unit 6.) These charged particles are called ions. The zinc and copper ions can be represented as zinc^{++} and copper^{++}. In the metal strips the atoms of zinc and copper are neutral—they have the same number of electrons and protons and they can be represented as zinc$^{\mp\mp}$ and copper$^{\mp\mp}$.

Both the disappearance of the blue color typical of copper ions in solution and the formation of the reddish-brown deposit indicate that copper^{++} ions have taken on electrons and have been deposited as copper$^{\mp\mp}$. This explanation is strengthened by the fact that the zinc strip dissolved. The zinc$^{\mp\mp}$ gave up electrons and went into solution as zinc^{++}. In the competition for elec-

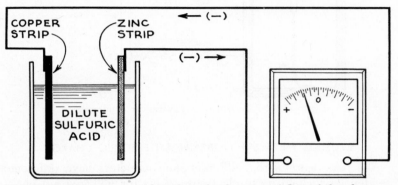

Figure 5-9. A meter is used to show the direction of flow of the electrons in the circuit.

trons the copper was able to take them away from the zinc. In the experiment in which the copper strip was placed in the zinc sulfate solution there was no change. The zinc ions were not able to take electrons away from the copper atoms. From this observation we can conclude that, in the competition for electrons, copper will win out over zinc.

Copper and zinc strips can be placed in the same solution of very dilute sulfuric acid and connected through a meter that indicates which way the electrons are flowing through the wire (Figure 5-9). In this case the zinc is going into solution and giving up electrons to the wire. They pass through the meter and go over to the strip of copper.

This experiment will show you which way the needle swings for a known direction of the flow of the electrons. Now you can compare different pairs of metals and arrange them in a series with the one having the greatest tendency to give up electrons at the top and the one having the strongest tendency to hold on to electrons at the bottom. An example of a list of metals arranged in such a series is: potassium, calcium, sodium, magnesium, aluminum, zinc, iron, tin, hydrogen, copper, silver, gold.

In the setup illustrated in Figure 5-9, the electrons will continue to flow through the wire so long as there is any zinc left to dissolve. We will have a current of electricity instead of just a temporary charge put on a rubber rod or Leyden jar. The discovery of current electricity was made in 1800, and it introduced a whole new era in the study of electricity.

SUMMARY

1. Electrons are fundamental units of atomic structure that bear a single negative electric charge.

2. The electrons are mobile, but the other two fundamental units, protons and neutrons, are relatively fixed.

3. Any two different substances have different tendencies to hold on to electrons.

4. Negative electricity is the kind of electric charge left on the surface of a hard-rubber rod that has been rubbed with cat's fur.

5. Like electric charges repel each other.

6. Unlike electric charges attract each other.

7. Induction is the displacement of electrons by the force of a nearby electric charge.

8. A conductor is a substance along which electrons flow easily.

9. An insulator is a substance along which electrons flow with considerable difficulty.

10. A gold-leaf electroscope is charged with the same kind of electricity as the charging rod by contact and with the opposite kind by induction.

11. A condenser is an arrangement of metal plates such that the number of electrons that can be stored on (or withdrawn from) one is increased by the presence of the other.

12. The elements have been arranged in an electromotive series that lists them in the increasing order of their tendency to hold on to electrons. Those listed first (at the top) have the

least tendency to hold on to electrons. They have a tendency to give up electrons to those listed below them and to go into solution as positively charged ions.

QUESTIONS AND EXERCISES

1. Describe, in terms of the motion of the electrons, the process of charging a pith ball positively.

2. In the experiment with induction illustrated in Figure 5-4, what would have been the position of the pith balls if the rod had been touched to the cylinder and then removed?

3. In the experiment with induction illustrated in Figure 5-4, what would have been the position of the pith balls if, when the rod was near the cylinder, the operator had briefly touched the right-hand end of the cylinder with his finger and had then withdrawn the rod?

4. Describe in detail an experiment that you could perform at home to test the sign of the charge you acquire by scuffing your feet on the carpet.

5. Pith balls and gold leaf are used in studying static electricity because they are so light. Why is this quality important?

6. Describe the behavior of an uncharged pith ball when a Lucite plastic rod which has been rubbed with wool is brought near it.

7. In the experiment illustrated in Figure 5-9, the pointer on the meter is shown swinging to the left. Which way would it swing if, for the zinc strip, there was substituted one of aluminum? iron? silver?

8. As in Problem 7, which way would the pointer swing if, instead of the copper strip, there was substituted one of aluminum? tin? silver?

9. What is the sign of the charge left on a gold-leaf electroscope that has been charged by induction by means of a glass rod rubbed with silk?

10. If you bring a negatively charged rod near an electroscope that has divergent leaves, and if the leaves are spread apart even farther, what is the sign of the charge on the electroscope?

The Development of Our Ideas about Electricity

Thales (640–560 B.C.) was the first to record an observation of static electricity; he noticed that after amber had been rubbed with cloth it would pick up small pieces of straw and lint. Not until 1600 were there any significant new discoveries in the field

Figure 5-10.   Von Guericke's electrostatic machine.

of electricity.   William Gilbert, the physician to Queen Elizabeth, prepared a list of substances that he could charge by friction and another list of those that he could not charge.   From the Greek word for amber, "elektron," he coined the word electricity.

In 1650 Otto von Guericke described his experiments using a large ball of sulfur which was rotated on an axle (Figure 5-10).

He could give the ball a charge by holding his hands against it as it turned. Many other experimenters used this same technique to study static electricity.

In 1735 Du Fay came to the conclusion that there must be two types of charge, resinous and vitreous, and that like charges repel each other and unlike charges attract each other. The Leyden jar was discovered in 1745. This was the first condenser, and it

Figure 5-11. Franklin proving that lightning is a form of electricity. (*Courtesy of the Museum of Science and Industry, Chicago.*)

furnished a means for storing large amounts of charge. With this more potent source of electricity many new discoveries were made.

In 1747 Benjamin Franklin suggested that we did not need to assume that there were two different kinds of electricity. He argued that a neutral body had just its normal amount of electricity, and when the body was charged we had either given it more or taken some away. This led to his suggestion that we use the terms plus and minus to describe how a body was charged. As you can see, we have combined his terms with the theory of Du Fay.

In 1752 Franklin carried out his famous experiment with the kite (Figure 5-11). The report of this experiment caused much excitement in Europe, and many scientists repeated it. Lightning, which had been looked on with superstitious awe, was now understood to be no more than a large-scale spark. With his practical turn of mind, Franklin invented the lightning rod, and this represents the first practical application of the knowledge of electricity to everyday life.

The large charges available from a Leyden jar had made many an experimenter jump. A systematic study of the muscular effects of electricity was made during the last half of the eighteenth century. When the exposed nerve of a frog's leg was touched with even a small charge the leg twitched. If the leg muscle was removed and stretched on a board, a shock would make it contract. This similarity between the behavior of the muscle in a live frog and a dead one added fuel to the philosophical controversy over the nature of life and death.

In 1780 Galvani, an Italian physician, was carrying out some experiments with frogs' legs. A static machine was in the same room. One of his assistants noticed that there was a muscular contraction if a frog's leg was touched with a metal scalpel at the same time that a spark was drawn from the static machine. There was no metallic connection between the machine and the frog's leg. It was not realized at the time, but this was actually a radio-broadcasting and receiving experiment of sorts.

Although the observation was accidental, Galvani was quick to see that it was important, and he followed it up with detailed experiments. He reached the erroneous conclusion that the source of the electricity was in the frog's nerve and that the metal scalpels were significant only as conductors. He came tantalizingly close to the truth when he observed that the muscle twitched when two points of the nerve were touched by the ends of two different metal rods that were crossed.

It remained for Volta, in 1800, to realize that the source of the electricity was in the two different metals and that the frog was only a detector. Working on this hypothesis he built up a "pile" of discs of silver, zinc, and moist cardboard. When he combined several layers in that order he was able to draw a large spark from the two ends. This was the first battery (Figure 5-12). He discovered that the more discs he had in his pile the more vigorous was the effect, and that it would give a continuous current. The previous static machines had to be recharged after each spark.

The battery opened up even more exciting possibilities than had the Leyden jar. Sir Humphry Davy (1778–1829) discovered that a spark could be obtained between two pieces of charcoal. This furnished a steady, brilliant light and was used to make the first projection lantern. Later it was used in street lamps. The introduction of street lights had a considerable effect in cutting down petty crimes in big cities.

By the use of the steady current available from a battery it

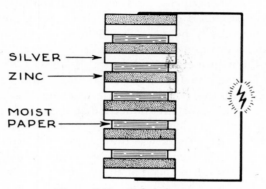

Figure 5-12. Volta's battery.

was soon discovered that molten salts could be decomposed, and that certain materials dissolved in water would deposit at the electrodes as the current passed through the solution. The forcing of a current through a salt or a solution is called electrolysis; it is the reverse of the action in a battery. At least one of the two different kinds of plates in a battery is used up as it generates electricity. In electrolysis something is deposited at at least one of the two electrodes.

When an electric current is passed through a solution of sodium hydroxide (caustic soda), oxygen is released at one electrode and hydrogen at the other. This is one important commercial method for making pure hydrogen. Plated silver is made by depositing a thin coat of silver from solution onto a steel electrode shaped like a spoon, fork, etc. Chromium, copper, many other metals, and rubber can be electroplated this way. The aluminum industry uses tremendous quantities of electricity in obtaining the metal from its ore by electrolysis.

SUMMARY

1. Some facts in the field of static electricity were observed by the early Greeks.

2. Gilbert coined the word electricity, and he found that some substances would hold a charge (insulators) and others would not (conductors).

3. Von Guericke made the first machine for generating static electricity.

4. Du Fay suggested that there must be two different types of electricity.

5. The first condenser, in the form of the Leyden jar, made it possible to accumulate much larger charges than had been available before.

6. Franklin contributed the terms positive and negative electricity, although he thought there was only one kind.

7. Franklin demonstrated that lightning is only a large-scale example of the common electric spark.

8. Galvani discovered that different metals have different tendencies to hold on to electrons. He misinterpreted his results and did not realize the significance of his discovery.

9. Volta correctly interpreted Galvani's experiments and constructed the first electric battery. This made possible a continuous current of electricity for the first time.

10. Current electricity soon led to practical applications like street lights, electrolysis of solutions, and electroplating.

QUESTIONS AND EXERCISES

1. Gilbert experimented with metals, among other substances. How would he have classified them?

2. Name five different nations whose scientists contributed to our understanding of electricity.

3. In Volta's battery, as illustrated in Figure 5-12, which way are the electrons traveling in the wire outside the battery?

4. Give an example of a scientist who was working with an incorrect theory but who obtained valuable information. There are many such instances in the history of science.

5. Why is an insulator, like glass, used to separate the two metal plates of a Leyden jar?

3

Paying Your Bill for Electricity

1. VOLTS, AMPS, AND WATTS

There are various adjustments possible on a static machine (Figure 5-13) that can change the type of spark. With the con-

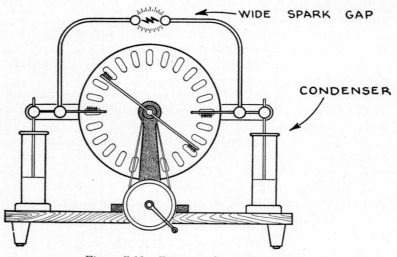

Figure 5-13. Diagram of a static machine.

densers in use and the sparking knobs an inch or more apart the sparks come every second or so; they are bright and make a loud crack. With the condensers disconnected and the knobs less than half an inch apart the sparks are very frequent, but they are hard to see and make little noise. Clearly two different quantities are involved; one is the amount of electricity flowing in each spark, and the other is the distance it will jump, or the drive behind it.

An analogy may be helpful in this situation. If a turbine or water wheel is being turned by water falling on it, the rate at which work can be done depends on both the height through which the water falls (the head, or pressure) and the rate of flow of the water in gallons per second. In electricity the quantity that measures drive or pressure is the volt, and the quantity that measures the rate of flow is the ampere, abbreviated amp. There is no need to go into a precise definition of either of these quantities here, but we shall be concerned with relationships between them.

As mentioned above, the measure of electric power (rate of accomplishing work) involves both volts and amperes. The product of these two quantities gives the power available and is called watts. Volts times amperes = watts. Household appliances are rated according to the power they consume in watts. Light bulbs usually run from 25 to 300 watts. An electric mixer may use 70 watts and an iron 575 watts. One thousand watts is called 1 kilowatt, abbreviated kw. An electric stove may use 2.5 kw. We pay for electricity by the kilowatt-hour, and the rates vary tremendously, depending on how much you use and what part of the country you live in. Using an average value of 3 cents per kw-hr, you can figure the cost of operating several of the above appliances for 1 hr. Ten 100-watt bulbs burning for 1 hr will use 1 kw-hr of electricity.

2. RESISTANCE AND OHM'S LAW

The analogy of a current of electricity flowing through a wire and of water flowing through a pipe holds very well for most of the examples that we will take up. For a given piece of pipe, the greater the pressure, the greater the rate at which water will flow through it. For a given piece of wire, the greater the voltage, the greater the current in amperes. For a constant pressure, different pieces of pipe will carry water at different rates. Some pipes offer more, and others less, resistance to the flow of water. In electricity, for a given voltage, different wires will carry different numbers of amperes. Wires offer varying resistances to the flow of electricity, depending on their size and composition. The unit of electrical resistance is the ohm. Volts, amperes, and ohms are so defined that a wire on which there is an electrical force of 1 volt and which has a resistance of 1 ohm will be carrying a current of 1 ampere. Electromotive force (EMF) or potential are terms that are frequently used to refer to electrical pressure. As explained above, this force is measured in volts.

In order to illustrate experiments and appliances in this field we shall need a few symbols. A few common ones are illustrated and defined in Table 5-1.

TABLE 5-1

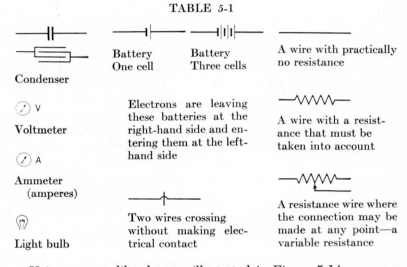

Condenser

Voltmeter

Ammeter (amperes)

Light bulb

Battery
One cell

Battery
Three cells

A wire with practically no resistance

Electrons are leaving these batteries at the right-hand side and entering them at the left-hand side

A wire with a resistance that must be taken into account

Two wires crossing without making electrical contact

A resistance wire where the connection may be made at any point—a variable resistance

Using a setup like the one illustrated in Figure 5-14, you can study the current (amperes) that a constant voltage will drive through a resistance that can be varied. On the reasonable assumption that the resistance of the wire is directly proportional to the length of it used in the circuit, you will find that the current (I) is inversely proportional to the resistance (R). $I \propto 1/R$. Using a fixed resistance and different numbers of cells or batteries, you will find that the current is directly proportional to the voltage (E). $I \propto E$. Ohm's law I (amperes) $= E$ (volts)$/R$ (ohms) combines these two statements into one equation.

Two different types of Christmas tree lights are now on the market. One of them, the old-fashioned kind, has eight small bulbs with a single wire running from one socket to the next and with both ends meeting at the same plug. When one of these bulbs burns out or becomes loose in its socket the whole string

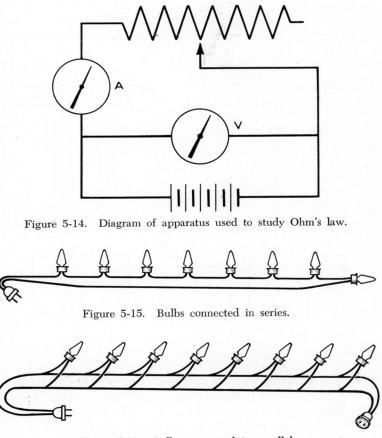

Figure 5-14. Diagram of apparatus used to study Ohm's law.

Figure 5-15. Bulbs connected in series.

Figure 5-16. Bulbs connected in parallel.

goes out. The wiring of this type is illustrated in Figure 5-15. The other kind of light has a male plug at one end, a female plug at the other, two wires going to each socket, and larger bulbs. When one of these bulbs burns out the rest stay lighted. This is illustrated in Figure 5-16. In the first type the current passes through each light in turn, and if the circuit is broken at any point no current can flow. This is called wiring in series. In the second, part of the current is diverted to pass through each bulb, so that the rest stay on when any one or several of them are not connected. This is called parallel wiring.

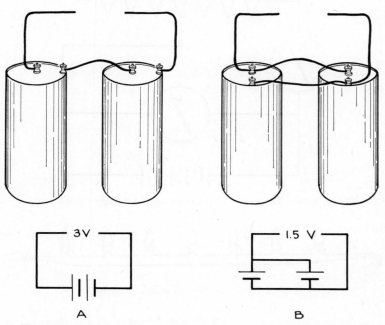

Figure 5-17.   Batteries connected in series, A, and in parallel, B.

Figure 5-17 shows two dry cells connected in series (A) and in parallel (B). These batteries give a potential of about 1.5 volts each. When they are connected in series they furnish a voltage which is the sum of the two, or 3.0 volts. When they are connected in parallel the voltage is no greater than that from one cell. The series connection is like two irrigation pumps, of which one takes water from a river and pumps it up 50 feet into a reservoir and the other pumps it from the reservoir into a ditch 50 feet higher. The flow of water is the same as from one pump, but the level reached is twice as high. The parallel connection is like the same two pumps taking water from the river and pumping it into the reservoir. The volume of flow would be twice as great but the height is no greater than one pump can supply.

There are two common ways in which electricity is supplied. The most frequently used system is 60-cycle alternating current (AC), wherein the electrons in the wires move first in one direction and then in the other, 60 times each second. They swing back and forth like a pendulum without ever getting anywhere. In direct current (DC) they flow along the wires like a current of water. Throughout almost the whole of the United States current is furnished at either 120 or 240 volts AC. Most home-generated current is 25 or 60 volts DC, and some cities use this voltage.

Now we can tackle some practical problems of electricity in your homes. Since the lights and base plugs in your homes are wired in parallel, you can use any one or all of them at once. Although the insulated copper wires that carry current to the lights and plugs have a very low resistance, they do have some. This frictional resistance to the flow of electricity results in the wires' warming up when they are being used. The electricians who wired your house used a wire heavy enough to carry all the current that would normally be used. But if a short circuit develops or you connect too many appliances at one time, then there is danger of the wire's overheating and setting fire to the house. To guard against this a fuse is placed in the line. A fuse contains a short piece of metal which will melt and break the circuit if more than a predetermined amount of current flows through it. Fuses are rated according to the maximum number of amperes that they will carry. Most household fuses will carry from 15 to 30 amp.

How many 600-watt waffle irons can you safely connect on the same line when it has a 20-amp fuse? Practically everything electrical in your house uses 120 volts except the stove, which uses 240 volts; so, using the relationship watts = amperes × volts, you can figure the amperes flowing through one waffle iron. Amperes = watts/volts = 600 watts/120 volts = 5 amp. Therefore, four such waffle irons would be the maximum that you could use on one circuit, and that would be crowding it.

Sometimes the label on household appliances lists amperes instead of watts. How much would it cost to run a washing machine for 1 hr if it draws 6 amp? Watts = 6 amp × 120 volts = 720 watts = 0.72 kw. At 3 cents per kw-hr this would come to 0.72 kw × 1 hr × 3 cents/kw-hr = 2.16 cents.

What is the resistance of the wires in an electric toaster that is rated at 500 watts? Here it is best to work the problem through in units first; in fact, it is always wise to do so to see whether the problem can be simplified. Since $I = E/R$, then $R = E/I$. E is 120 volts, but we do not know I. $I = $ watts$/E$. Substituting this in the previous equation, we get $R = E^2/$watts. We do not need to figure I separately. $R = \overline{120}^2$ volts$^2/500$ watts $= 28.8$ ohms.

3. SOME MORE SOURCES OF POTENTIAL

If a semicircular piece of iron and one of copper are put to-gether to form a ring (Figure 5-18), there is a tendency for the

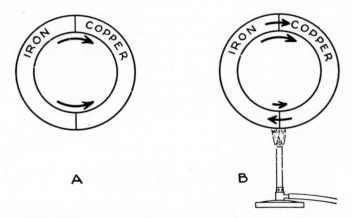

A   B

Figure 5-18. Both copper-iron junctions are at the same temperature in A, and no current flows. In B, one junction is warmer than the other, and current can flow around the ring.

iron to give up electrons to the copper at both junctions. Some electrons do flow across the junctions, but the copper is given such a high negative charge that the current soon stops. Since the voltage is the same at both junctions, the two opposing pressures balance each other and no continuous current can flow around the circle. If anything can be done to alter the voltage at one of the junctions, then the balance will be thrown off and a current can flow around the circle. In Figure 5-18 the voltage at the lower junction has been weakened by heating it (symbolized by the shorter arrow over the junction). At the cold junction electrons move from the iron to the copper, and at the hot junction they are pushed from the copper to the iron. A current flows around the circle, and the amount of current flowing is a measure of the difference in temperature between the two junctions. A sensitive meter can be put into the circuit and calibrated to read directly in degrees. This kind of thermometer, called a thermocouple, is useful for measuring the extremely high temperatures encountered in furnaces and the extremely small amounts of energy received from distant stars.

Another peculiar electrical effect is observed in certain crystals, such as quartz and Rochelle salt. If one of these crystals is compressed a difference in potential will develop between the two faces. Conversely, if a difference of potential is applied to two faces, the crystal will expand or contract. Thus, it can be set vibrating by a rapidly alternating current. Each crystal has a characteristic frequency of vibration which is determined by its thickness. Crystals that behave this way are said to be piezo-electric.

Light has three important effects on the electrical behavior of certain substances. In the effect called photoconductivity, the electrical resistance of selenium and several metallic sulfides is lowered when light strikes them. The change in resistance is approximately proportional to the intensity of the light. This effect could obviously be used to construct a lightmeter. It has been used in this way, but the effect mentioned in the next paragraph is the basis for a more convenient one.

In the photovoltaic effect a continuous current will flow around a circuit between two substances in contact when one junction is illuminated. This action is analogous to that of the thermocouple. The modern exposure meter used in photography is constructed on this principle (Figure 1-30). The current generated is small, but a sensitive galvanometer will record it or it can be used to operate a relay (Figure 5-37). When a steady light is focused on one of these light-sensitive cells anything coming between the two interrupts the current. Many uses for such a "photoelectric eye" have been devised. They open doors as you approach, ring burglar alarms, count or inspect objects on a conveyer belt, etc.

When light strikes certain metals (such as cesium) in a vac-

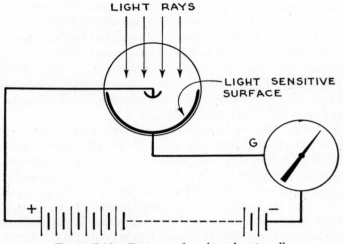

Figure 5-19.   Diagram of a photoelectric cell.

uum it knocks electrons out of the surface layer. By connecting the negative pole of a battery to the metal film and placing a positively charged collector near the film a continuous current will flow through the circuit as long as it is illuminated. This photoelectric cell (Figure 5-19) can do the sort of job handled by the photoelectric eye mentioned above, and it has found recent use in sound movies and television, as will be described later on.

Behavior similar to that of cesium in a photoelectric cell is shown by crystals of cadmium sulfide. Light of X-ray wavelengths will liberate swarms of electrons from these crystals. They are the most sensitive detectors of X-rays and are finding use where X-rays are employed to inspect opaque objects.

SUMMARY

1. A volt (E) is the unit for measuring the driving force or pressure of an electric current.

2. An ampere (I) is the unit for measuring the rate of flow of an electric current.

3. A watt is a measure of electric power.

4. Watts = volts × amperes.

5. An ohm (R) is a unit of electrical resistance.

6. Ohm's law is $I = E/R$.

7. A series connection in an electrical circuit is an arrangement of parts in which all the current passing through one also passes through the others.

8. A parallel connection in an electrical circuit is an arrangement of parts in which the current divides, some going through one part and some through another.

9. For resistances in series, $R = R_1 + R_2 +$ etc.

10. For sources of potential in series, $E = E_1 + E_2 +$ etc.

11. For sources of potential in parallel, when $E_1 = E_2$, $E = E_1 = E_2$.

12. Most household current is 120-volt AC.

13. A fuse is a sort of safety valve which breaks a circuit when it is overloaded.

14. Certain crystals will develop a difference of potential between two faces when they are compressed. With these crystals a difference of potential imposed on the two faces will distort the crystal. Such crystals are said to be piezoelectric.

15. The tendency of electrons to flow from one substance to another in contact with it is influenced, among other things, by (a) the temperature of the junction and (b) the amount of light striking the junction.

16. Electrons can be knocked out of (vaporized from) certain substances by the action of light.

QUESTIONS AND EXERCISES

Note to students: Unless stated otherwise, all numerical problems in electricity assume 120-volt AC.

1. Rearrange the equation $I = E/R$ to read: $E = ?$ and $R = ?$

2. Using the proper symbols, draw a circuit showing a two-cell battery that is driving electrons, first through a fixed resistance and then through a light bulb connected in series with it.

3. Is the fuse placed in parallel or in series with its circuit in the house?

4. How many amperes will flow through a toaster rated at 500 watts (see note above)?

5. What is the resistance of the wires in an electric iron that draws 1 ampere of current?

6. With electric power costing 3 cents per kw-hr, how much would it cost to use the iron in Prob!em 5 for 2 hours?

7. List several ways for obtaining a current of electricity.

8. How could you use two photoelectric cells to measure the speed of an automobile?

9. How does increasing the temperature affect the tendency of electrons to flow from iron to copper?

10. What voltage would be obtained from five dry cells connected in series? in parallel?

4

Magnetism

1. EXPERIMENTS WITH MAGNETISM

For our experiments with magnetism we shall need only a few simple pieces of apparatus. Using a bar magnet and some steel tacks, we find that we can pick up a string of tacks with either end, but not very easily along the middle of the bar. You can show that the magnetic attraction operates through a piece of paper or glass. Another very illuminating experiment is to place a magnet under a sheet of glass, sprinkle iron filings on the glass, and tap it gently. The iron filings are lined up in a typical pattern around the magnet. Each small sliver is lined up the way a small compass needle would point in this same position. Two or more magnets can be arranged under the glass and the resulting pattern of iron filings studied. These patterns make more real to us the entirely imaginary concept of a magnetic field of force that we say exists around a magnet.

If one bar magnet is suspended in the middle by a string and another bar magnet is brought near either end, we find that the ends either attract or repel each other. Bar magnets are usually stamped N on one end and S on the other. The ends with the same letter repel each other, but the N end of one attracts the S end of another. Magnetic attraction and repulsion are thus similar to attraction and repulsion in static electricity.

In passing, it would be well to observe that there are also striking differences between the phenomena of electricity and magnetism. In magnetism we do not need to be careful to insulate our magnets. The bar can as well be suspended by a flexible wire as by a string. We observe strong magnetism in only a very few substances, such as iron, steel, special alloys, and a mineral called magnetite. When two magnetic poles are touched together, the magnetism does not jump across from one to the other so that they both end up non-magnetic. Positive and negative charges of electricity exist separately from each other, but magnetic poles always occur in pairs.

When a bar magnet is floated on a cork in a dish of water you will see that it orients itself so that one end points north and the other end south. A compass needle is a lightweight magnet mounted on a pivot so that it can turn readily. If a compass is held on its side in a north-south direction, the needle does not lie horizontally; the north-pointing end dips down at a steep angle (Figure 5-20).

Figure 5-20. A magnetic dip needle.

2. EARLY KNOWLEDGE OF MAGNETISM

A knowledge of magnetism seems to have been arrived at independently in several parts of the world. We have records from China, India, and Greece, all of which date back more than 2000 years. Thales, who experimented with static electricity, also knew about magnetism. In the *Arabian Nights* is a story of a magnetic island that pulled the nails out of the planks of ships, whereupon the ships fell to pieces and the dismayed sailors were dumped into the sea. The mariner's compass was in use in Europe before A.D. 1200. It soon became apparent that the compass did not point to the north geographic pole. Or, more precisely, the compass did not point north as determined from the North Star. In Europe it pointed several degrees west of north.

On his first trip across the Atlantic Columbus discovered that this variation, which is called magnetic declination, decreased as he proceeded. It soon reached zero, and from then on the compass pointed east of north. This unexpected behavior of the compass nearly demoralized his superstitious crew, and it must have bothered Columbus himself. Later explorers recorded and mapped the magnetic declination all over the globe. Figure 5-21 shows a magnetic map of the United States. As you can see, the effect is considerable. Compasses in the states of Washington and Maine stand at half a right angle to each other. The north magnetic pole is northwest of Hudson Bay in Canada and considerably south of the north geographic pole. It shifts its position slowly through the centuries, for reasons which are not understood.

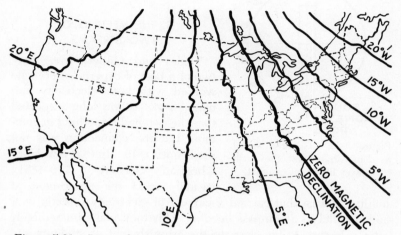

Figure 5-21. Lines of equal magnetic declination in the United States.

William Gilbert, another scientist whom we met in connection with electricity, carried out extensive investigations with magnetism. One of his most important contributions to science was his use of a small-scale model to illustrate the behavior of nature. This is a commonplace technique today, but Gilbert seems to have been the first person to employ it consciously. He constructed a globe with a bar magnet inside to represent the behavior of the earth as a magnet. By putting his magnet in just the right position he could show magnetic declination and inclination by means of small compass needles moved over the surface of the globe (Figure 5-22). Kepler tried to utilize Gilbert's ideas in explaining the motion of the planets around the sun.

Although the earth behaves as though it had a huge bar magnet buried deep in its interior, we know that this is not the explanation of the earth's magnetism. The iron-nickel core must be far too hot to be strongly magnetic (see Section 4 of this unit). It is too early to evaluate Blackett's theory (1951) that a rotating gravitational field generates a magnetic field. All previous efforts to explain the earth's magnetism have failed.

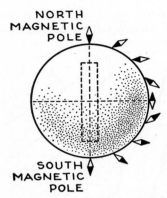

NORTH
MAGNETIC
POLE

SOUTH
MAGNETIC
POLE

Figure 5-22. Gilbert's model to demonstrate that the earth behaves like a big magnet.

3. THE MEETING OF TWO STREAMS

Thales and Gilbert were only two of a host of experimenters who worked with both electricity and magnetism. It was long suspected that the two had something in common, but the connection was not made until 1819. In that year Hans Christian Oersted (1770–1851) casually tried the experiment of holding a wire that carried a current of electricity directly over and parallel to a compass needle. This took place immediately after a lecture to his class; to the astonishment of students and teacher, the needle swung around at right angles to the wire. He reversed the electric current and the needle swung in the opposite direction. This was something new under the sun—a force (the electric current) was showing an effect at right angles to its line of motion. The communication of this discovery touched off a regular chain reaction of experiments which soon established most of our basic laws of electromagnetism. Oersted had discovered that a wire carrying a current of electricity is surrounded by a magnetic field.

It occurred to Michael Faraday (1791–1867) that the inverse effect should be observable. He tried thrusting a bar magnet into a coil of wire, hoping to observe a current induced into the coil. His instruments for detecting the current were not sensitive enough, and it was not until 1831 that he succeeded in observing the phenomenon of magnetism generating electricity. If the magnet is held stationary in or near the coil no current is generated, but when the magnet is in motion there is a current.

One of the earliest applications of Oersted's discovery was the electromagnet. A coil of insulated wire was wrapped around an

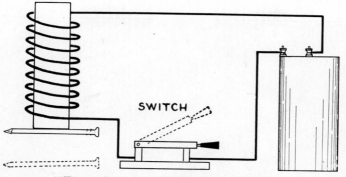

SWITCH

Figure 5-23. Model of an electromagnet.

iron bar and a direct current was sent through the wire (Figure 5-23). This produces a magnetic field that can be turned on or off at will; consequently, pieces of iron that are large or awkward to handle can be moved about with ease (Figure 5-24).

4. THEORY OF MAGNETISM

Before exploring some of the practical applications of the new discoveries about electricity and magnetism, let us sort out some of the facts that will help us understand what happens when a bar of iron is magnetized.

The black oxide of iron, magnetite, was the earliest known magnetic substance. It was discovered that rods of iron could be made magnetic by stroking them with magnetite and by hammering them while they were held with one end pointing north. You will find that few objects made of iron or steel around the laboratory do not affect a compass needle. It was observed that, when a chunk of magnetite was broken in two, both pieces were magnets. If a magnetized bar of iron is sawed into a number of small pieces, each one will be a small magnet (Figure 5-25).

A bar of iron can be more or less strongly magnetized. To observe this, find out how close a magnet must be brought to a certain compass needle to deflect it through 10° (Figure 5-26).

Make the same measurement using the same compass and a different bar magnet. You will find that the various magnets available differ considerably in their strength. There is a maximum

Figure 5-24. A large industrial electromagnet. (*General Electric Co.*)

amount to which any given bar can be magnetized. When a highly magnetized bar is heated and then cooled, or dropped on the floor several times (do not try this without permission), it loses much of its magnetic strength.

The facts mentioned in the previous two paragraphs give us enough to go on to construct a simple theory of magnetism. Let us suppose that a bar of iron is made up of a great number of small particles, each of which is a small magnet. Before the bar is magnetized, these tiny individual magnets are arranged in a random fashion; consequently, there is no appreciable resultant magnetic field (Figure 5-27A). The kinetic theory tells us that

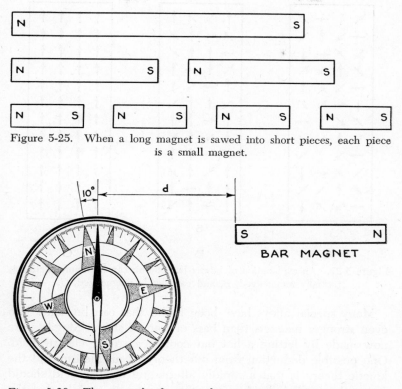

Figure 5-25. When a long magnet is sawed into short pieces, each piece is a small magnet.

Figure 5-26. The strength of various bar magnets may be compared by this type of experiment.

these particles are being jostled around constantly. If the bar is stroked with a piece of magnetite or hammered while it is held in line with the earth's magnetic field, several of these individual magnets will be lined up so that they work together. The bar will be magnetized weakly (Figure 5-27B). When substantially all of them are so lined up, the bar will be as strong a magnet as it can be (Figure 5-27C). Heating the magnet or dropping it will tend to break up this regular pattern and weaken the magnetism. Thus, with a rather simple theory, we can organize these many facts about magnetism.

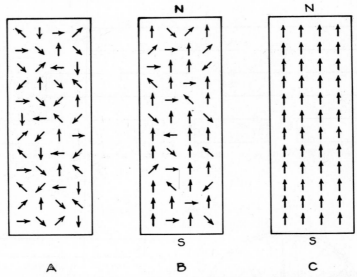

Figure 5-27. An explanation of how a bar of iron can be nonmagnetic, A, partially magnetized, B, and completely magnetized, C.

Many special alloys have been found that can be made into even stronger magnets than bars of iron or steel. Magnets are now made by letting a hot bar cool in a strong electric field. One possible deduction from our theory of magnetism and the kinetic theory is that a rapidly alternating electric field should swing the small individual magnets around so rapidly that the temperature of the bar would be increased. This technique has been developed to the point where a large bar of steel can be heated red hot.

SUMMARY

1. There are two kinds of magnetic poles, which are called north and south.

2. Like magnetic poles repel and unlike poles attract each other.

3. Although many substances possess magnetism, only magnetite, iron, and a few alloys show this property strongly.

4. The earth acts like a huge magnet. The north and south poles of the earth's magnetic field do not quite coincide with the geographic poles.

5. The early knowledge of the magnetic properties of magnetite was widely spread over Europe and Asia. The mariner's compass was in use before A.D. 1200.

6. Gilbert investigated magnetism as well as electricity.

7. Magnetic declination is the angle at any place on the earth between true north and magnetic north.

8. Magnetic inclination is the angle at any place on the earth between the horizontal and the position of a dip-needle compass.

9. Oersted discovered the fact that an electric current is surrounded by a magnetic field at right angles to the direction of flow of the current.

10. Faraday discovered that a changing magnetic field could generate an electric current.

11. When a magnet is broken in two, each piece is a complete magnet. Magnetic poles always occur in pairs.

12. Magnetism seems to depend upon the orientation of the particles of a substance. Any mechanical disturbance which tends to make this arrangement more random weakens the magnetism.

QUESTIONS AND EXERCISES

1. If you had an unlabeled magnet, how could you find out which pole was north and which south?

2. From Figure 5-21, determine the magnetic declination in your locality. Check this with the value given on a geological survey map of your district.

3. Why is it unlikely that the Norsemen used a compass in their explorations of Iceland, Greenland, and Labrador?

4. Will a steady electric current produce a magnetic field? Will a steady magnetic field produce a current of electricity?

5. Take a soft iron bar and increase its magnetic strength by one of the techniques suggested.

6. Use a diagram to explain the fact that a magnetized bar can be cut into several small pieces, each one of which is a magnet. (Combine the features of Figures 5-25 and 5-27.)

7. Mention several ways in which the facts observed in the field of magnetism support the kinetic-molecular theory of matter.

8. Give one good reason why the connection between electricity and magnetism was not discovered until after 1800.

9. Explain why a magnet will attract only something that can be magnetized.

10. At approximately what part of the globe would a magnetic dip needle remain horizontal?

CHAPTER

Electricity and Magnetism
at Work

1. THE INDUCTION EFFECT

Although Faraday failed to detect the current generated by pushing a magnet into a coil of wire, he finally did succeed when he used an electromagnet. His apparatus was similar to that sketched in Figure 5-28. A current is induced in the right-hand

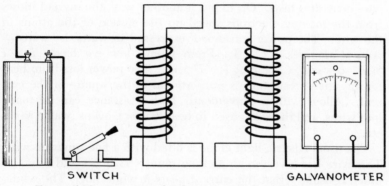

SWITCH   GALVANOMETER

Figure 5-28. Apparatus for demonstrating an induced current.

coil at the moment that the key either makes or breaks the circuit on the left, but no current is flowing through the right-hand coil when that in the left-hand coil is running steadily. When the key is first pressed down, the magnetic field in the left-hand coil builds up from zero to its normal value. It holds this steady value while the current flows, and when the key is released it drops again to zero. Thus, it is a changing magnetic field that induces a current in another coil.

Experiments were carried out with various numbers of turns of wire in the two coils. The coil through which the current is driven is called the primary, and the coil in which the current is induced is called the secondary. It was found that the ratio of the primary to the secondary voltage was the same as the ratio of the number of turns of wire in the two coils. This gives us a device for transforming voltage from any given level to a more convenient one, and it is appropriately named a transformer. If a transformer steps up the voltage there must be a corresponding decrease in amperage to keep the power output the same as the input. Actually, a transformer is not 100% efficient, and there is a slight power loss.

2. ELECTRIC HEATERS

As electrons move through a wire under the pressure of the applied voltage, the frictional resistance of the particles of the wire generates heat. Or, to put it another way, the myriad blows from the moving electrons speed up the motion of the atoms in the wire. The power consumed, expressed in watts, is: watts = volts $\times$ amperes = $E \times I$. From Ohm's law we have: $E = I \times R$, so watts = $I \times R \times I = I^2 \times R$. The power loss from heat for any given resistance is proportional to the square of the current. Alloys with a conveniently high resistance can be made into wires, and these are used to heat toasters, ovens, waffle irons, etc.

The usual electric-light globe is fitted with a fine tungsten wire. This wire has a very high melting point ($3370°C$) and offers so much resistance that the current heats it white hot. The white-hot wire gives off a good light, but a large fraction of the energy used is wasted as heat.

The lines carrying electric current from the generating stations to our homes have a certain resistance. Because many of these lines are hundreds of miles long it is important to keep the heat loss of transmission as low as possible. Since the power transmitted is proportional to $E \times I$ and the power loss from heat is I^2R, it is desirable to keep the current (I) as low as possible. This means that we must transmit current at a very high voltage. As an extremely high voltage in our homes would be dangerous, it is cut down from the many thousands of volts used in the distributing system to 120 volts as it enters our homes. Since a transformer requires a changing magnetic field, the current we use is not a steady, direct current but it alternates at the rate of 60 cycles per second.

3. MOTORS AND GENERATORS

By the proper timing of the approach of a bar magnet, we can keep a compass needle spinning. How can we use this to make a motor? When the north pole of the magnet is brought near the north pole of the compass, the compass starts swinging. When the south pole comes around, it is attracted by the north pole of the magnet, and the swing stops. Instead of a compass needle we can use a coil of wire around an iron bar for our rotating magnet and run an alternating current through it. If the rotating bar, which is called an armature, keeps time with the alternations of the current, there will always be a north pole at the top end of the armature and a south pole at the bottom end. Thus, there will always be a force of repulsion between the armature and the fixed magnet, which is called the field. Once a motor of this type is started running it cannot possibly get out of step with the alternations of the driving current, and it is this kind that is used for driving electric clocks (Figure 5-29).

It is desirable to be able to control the speed of a motor and also to have a more powerful motor than can be obtained by means of permanent magnets. Using alternating current, the connection to the armature is made through a commutator (Figure 5-30). The commutator consists of two semicircles which are connected to the two ends of the armature coil and which turn with the armature. They have sliding connections (brushes) with the source of current. As the armature turns, first one and then the other arc of the commutator touches the sliding contact at A. If the current is entering at A and leaving through B, it goes through the coil first in one direction and then in the opposite one as the armature turns. With this arrangement, the end of the armature that is up is always magnetized in the same direction (always a north pole, for instance), no matter how fast the armature is turning. The greater the voltage used, the greater is the force of repulsion and the faster the motor turns.

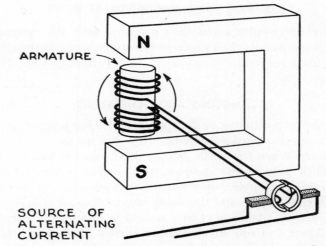

ARMATURE

SOURCE OF
ALTERNATING
CURRENT

Figure 5-29. A synchronous motor. Alternating current enters the armature through a commutator and the field is a permanent magnet.

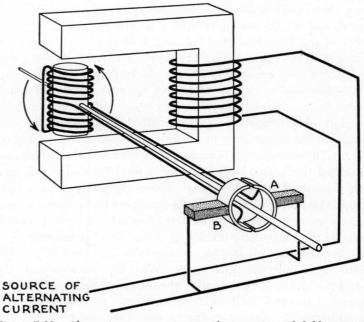

SOURCE OF
ALTERNATING
CURRENT

Figure 5-30. Alternating-current motor with armature and field connected
in parallel.

More power can be obtained from such a motor when the field and the armature are wired in parallel.

We have seen how a current driven through a coil in a magnetic field will force the coil to move at right angles to this field. If the coil is forced by mechanical means to move across a magnetic field, will the electrons in the wire of the coil receive a

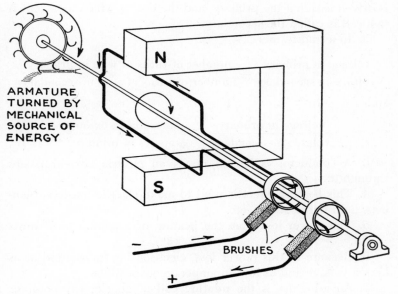

Figure 5-31.   An electric generator.

thrust?   Faraday had discovered that the answer was "yes."   An electric generator is just like a motor except that the armature is turned by waterpower, a steam engine, a gasoline motor, etc., and an electric current is pushed out through the line (Figure 5-31).   When the current is drawn off through the usual commutator, it is direct current; if a slip ring is used, alternating current is obtained.

It would be hard to imagine what our life would be like without the many electric motors we depend on each day.   A single modern airplane has over 200 electric motors to control various operations.   The people of the United States annually use more than 250 billion kilowatt hours of electricity, much of which goes for running electric motors.

SUMMARY

1. A transformer is a device consisting of two coils of wire insulated from each other. The one through which the current is driven is called the primary, and the one in which a current is induced is called the secondary.

2. In a transformer

$$\frac{\text{voltage in primary}}{\text{voltage in secondary}} = \frac{\text{number of turns of wire in primary}}{\text{number of turns of wire in secondary}}$$

and

$$\frac{\text{voltage in primary}}{\text{voltage in secondary}} = \frac{\text{amperes in secondary}}{\text{amperes in primary}}$$

3. A conductor is heated up as an electric current passes through it.

4. This heating effect is used to make electric toasters, blankets, light bulbs, stoves, etc.

5. The power loss from the heating of a conductor is watts $= I^2R$.

6. Because of this power loss, electricity is transmitted at as high a voltage and as low an amperage as possible.

7. An armature is the rotating coil of an electric motor or generator.

8. A field is the stationary coil of an electric motor or generator.

9. A synchronous motor uses a fixed magnet for a field and 60-cycle AC on the armature. With this arrangement its speed is strictly controlled by the rate of alternation of the current.

10. A commutator is a connection to an armature in the shape of two semicircles insulated from each other.

11. A generator is similar in construction to a motor. Mechanical power turns the armature, and an electric current is generated in the coil.

QUESTIONS AND EXERCISES

1. How much power is used from a 120-volt line by a resistance of 12 ohms? from a 240-volt line by a resistance of 48 ohms?

2. Why is it the general practice to use alternating rather than direct current?

3. What would be an undesirable result if our AC operated at 20 instead of 60 cycles per second?

4. If a coil carrying 60-cycle AC were held near the north pole of a compass needle would the needle be deflected?

5. How many turns would there be in the secondary coil of a transformer that has 120-volt AC running through 100 turns in the primary and which delivers 24 volts from the secondary?

6. If 3 amp are flowing through the secondary circuit of the transformer in Problem 5, what is the current flowing in the primary?

7. In the experiment illustrated in Figure 5-28, if the needle swings to the left when the key is first pressed down, which way will it swing when the key is let up?

8. What is the resistance of the tungsten wire in a 300-watt light bulb?

9. Why does an electric motor heat up when it is running?

10. List the parts of an electric motor.

Communication I

1. TELEGRAPH AND TELEPHONE

In using electricity to carry messages we must have some way of modifying or modulating the current at the sending end of the

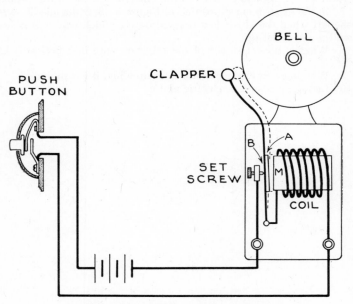

Figure 5-32. Diagram of a doorbell circuit.

circuit, and the modulated current must have some way of making a signal at the receiving end.

One of the simplest signal circuits is the one used to ring a doorbell (Figure 5-32). When you put your finger on the bell push, the circuit is completed so that the battery can send a current and magnetize *M*. The iron bar, *A*, is drawn over to *M*, and the clapper hits the bell. While this happens, the circuit is broken at *B*, so that the clapper bar springs back, makes a new contact, and again sounds the bell. These circuits are now operated through a step-down transformer from the regular house current.

The telegraph, invented by Samuel Morse in 1837, has a circuit similar to the house bell except that it does not have a current

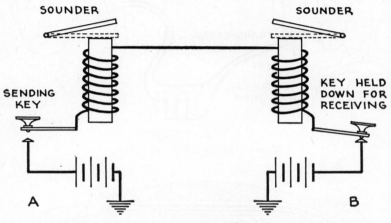

Figure 5-33.   Diagram of a telegraph circuit.

interrupter. The sender can hold down the sounding bar at the receiving end for any length of time he wishes and can spell out his message in short and long pulses called dots and dashes. There is no return wire to complete the circuit; only one wire is used, and the current returns through the earth.

Figure 5-33 shows a simple telegraph circuit. In the example shown, *A* is sending to *B*. The key at *B* must be held down mechanically so that the circuit can be completed at will by the key at *A*. In the circuit used here, both sounders would click in rhythm with the key.

A telephone operates much like a telegraph. Here the problem is to find a way to modulate the current so that it follows the frequencies of the human voice. Alexander Graham Bell (1847–1922) invented the first successful telephone, and Thomas Edison (1847–1931) improved it with his carbon-granule transmitter. Figure 5-34 shows a diagram of a telephone circuit, and Figure 5-35 is a diagram of a modern instrument. The transmitter is like a pillbox full of small pieces of coke put in series in the circuit. Any pressure on the lid of the box squeezes the carbon

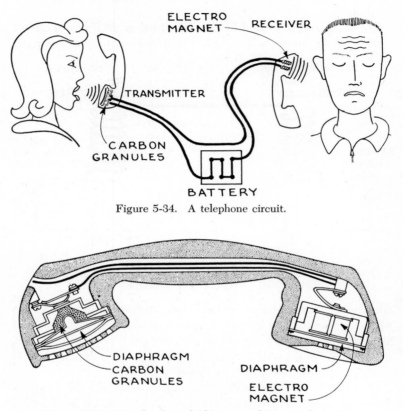

Figure 5-34. A telephone circuit.

Figure 5-35. Details of a telephone mouthpiece and receiver.

granules closer together and increases the current that is flowing (Figure 5-36). This changing pressure is provided by the sound waves of your voice. The current, which has been modulated by your voice, operates an electromagnet in the receiver. The electromagnet controls the vibrations of a steel membrane in the earpiece. As the membrane vibrates it sends out sound waves

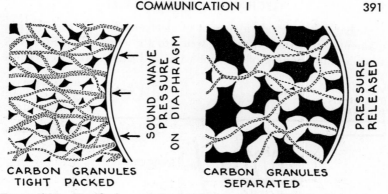

CARBON GRANULES
TIGHT PACKED

CARBON GRANULES
SEPARATED

Figure 5-36. Detail of a carbon-granule transmitter. The electric current (dotted lines) through the carbon granules varies as they are squeezed more or less tightly together by the diaphragm in front of your mouth.

to your ear. This simple arrangement can reproduce with surprising fidelity the complicated vibrations of the human voice.

2. AMPLIFIERS AND RECTIFIERS

A way had to be found to amplify the signals, in order to send messages over any great distance. The basic problem of amplification is an extremely important one. We need some way to make a small current control a large one. An analogy is provided by a single policeman controlling the heavy traffic at a busy intersection.

Morse used a relay for his purposes. A relay (Figure 5-37) is an electromagnetic switch which controls a second circuit. A feeble current on the incoming signal can pull the switch over and send out a signal from a very high-powered battery. With relays placed at suitable intervals along the line, telegraph messages were soon sent across the country. A simple relay cannot act fast enough to follow the vibrations of the human voice. Telephoning over long distances had to await the invention of the vacuum-tube amplifier.

The common radio tube is an example of the vacuum-tube amplifier. This was developed by De Forest in 1906 from an observation made by Edison in 1883. Edison had sealed an electrode into the side of an electric-light globe. When the electrode was charged positively a current of electrons flowed from the hot filament across the evacuated space to the electrode. Electrons were literally boiling off the hot wire, and this vapor of electrons

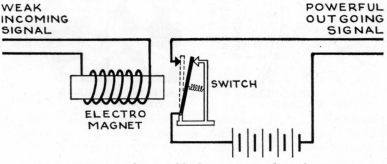

Figure 5-37. A relay suitable for use in a telegraph circuit.

was attracted by the oppositely charged electrode. When the electrode was charged negatively no current flowed to it from the filament.

The Edison effect was developed by Fleming into a vacuum-tube rectifier. The symbols inside the circle of Figure 5-38 represent the elements actually inside a highly evacuated glass tube. F stands for the filament which is heated by the battery. A variable resistance (not shown) may be used to control the temperature of the filament. P represents a metal plate which is sometimes a complete cylinder around the filament. We are going to consider the current along the wire C when a source of alternating current is connected to points A and B. When A is negative and B positive, electrons will flow from F to P and down through C. When A is positive and B negative, the current through C will stop, because electrons cannot boil off of the cold plate P. An alternating current attached

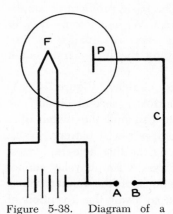

Figure 5-38. Diagram of a vacuum-tube rectifier.

to *A* and *B* will produce an intermittent direct (in one direction only) current through the wire *C*. A device which changes an alternating current into a direct current is called a rectifier.

De Forest had the inspiration to try putting a third element between the other two in this tube. He put a wire mesh, which he called a grid, between the filament and plate in an effort to control the current flowing to the plate. The symbols representing such a tube are shown in Figure 5-39. In operation, *F* is always negative and *P* positive. De Forest found that with *G* strongly negative the current to the plate was stopped. The current rose as *G* became less negative, and it was

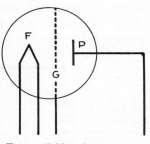

Figure 5-39. A vacuum-tube amplifier.

high with *G* slightly positive. A small variation in the voltage applied to *G* makes a considerable variation in the current flowing to *P*. It is this magnifying, or amplifying, effect of the grid voltage which makes it one of the most useful inventions ever made. Amplifications of a hundred thousand fold can be made in one tube. When the output (plate current) of one tube is used to operate the grid of a second tube, and this in turn feeds into a third tube, etc., the amplification achieved is fantastic.

The connections to a vacuum-tube amplifier are shown in Figure 5-40. Low-intensity signals come in to the step-up transformer *A*. The battery *B* (the *B* battery of a radio set) heats the filament *F*. The variations in voltage from the secondary of the transformer are led to the grid, *G*, where they control the current to the plate, *P*. The plate is kept at a high positive potential by the battery, *C* (the *C* battery of a radio set). The pulsating direct current from *P* passes through a step-up transformer, *D*, and high-intensity signals are sent out. The usual radio is operated on household alternating current and has no batteries. Vacuum-tube rectifiers take their place. Further details about the operation of a radio will be discussed in a later chapter.

A new type of rectifier and amplifier, called a transistor, was developed in 1948. A transistor exactly parallels the action of a vacuum tube and has many advantages over it. A semiconductor like germanium forms the heart of the transistor. When a fine wire is in contact with a crystal of germanium, electrons will flow much more readily from the wire to the germanium across the junction than in the other direction. This gives a rectifying action. To amplify a signal, a sandwich of three slices of germanium is made up as shown in Figure 5-41. As electrons flow across

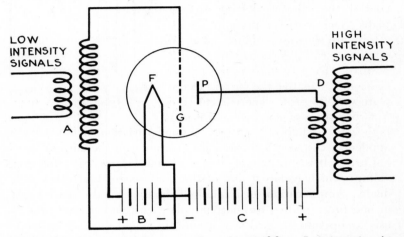

Figure 5-40. A circuit using a vacuum-tube amplifier. Low-intensity signals coming in at the left are amplified and sent out at the right.

the junction A from right to left, the current is modulated by the incoming signal. The modulated current controls the flow of electrons across junction B from right to left. These electrons come from battery C, and its output constitutes the outgoing signal that is amplified over the incoming signal some hundreds of times. Most of the amplification is due to the fact that the resistance to the flow of electrons from the germanium sheet to the wire at O is much greater than the resistance at E, where the electrons are flowing from the wire to the germanium.

Since a vacuum tube has a filament which has to be heated red hot, its power requirements are much greater than those of a transistor, and its useful life is much shorter. With the modern tendency to make apparatus as small as possible, the problem of dissipating heat from even a tiny vacuum tube has been a limiting factor in design.   A transistor can be made considerably smaller than a vacuum tube, and there is practically no heat loss to contend with.   These advantages, and the practically indefi-

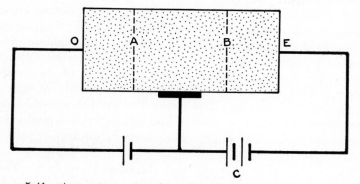

Figure 5-41.   A transistor.   Signals coming in from the left and amplified and sent out on the right.

nitely long useful life of a transistor, will revolutionize the building of long-distance telephone lines, electronic calculators, hearing aids, etc.   In a few years this tiny device will have found a useful place in nearly every home in our country.

3. RECORDERS

Edison also had a hand in developing the phonograph.   Basically, the phonograph consists of a lever, one end of which fits into a long groove and the other end is attached to a diaphragm. If the groove has the shape of one of the sound waves pictured in Figure 1-52 and it is drawn past the lever, the other end will vibrate the diaphragm so that it gives out a musical note.   Since the fundamental and all the overtones will be present, a reproduction of the original note will be obtained.   Now, reverse the process and start out with a straight groove cut in rather soft material.   Draw it past the lever as sound waves strike the diaphragm.   The vibrations of the diaphragm will make the lever vibrate back and forth so that it shapes the groove into a reproduction of the sound wave.

The playing and making of phonograph records are essentially as simple as the preceding description implies. You can hold the corner of a playing card on a rotating record and get a fair reproduction of the sound. This simple lever system has certain mechanical defects that spoil the quality of the tone. The more rapid vibrations of the overtones are lost. To obtain higher fidelity in recording a piezoelectric crystal is used. This crystal translates the vibrations of the diaphragm (microphone) into an electric current. After being amplified, this current controls the needle that is cutting a groove in the wax of the master record. Since the parts of an electrical system can be light in weight (low inertia) they can respond to the low-amplitude vibrations of the higher overtones, and much better reproduction can be obtained. The same system, a crystal pickup, is used to play the records.

We hear much of wire and tape recorders these days. They are used for recording interviews and radio programs and for teaching foreign languages. The same piece of wire or tape can be used indefinitely, the message being erased when it is no longer needed, or a full-length symphony can be recorded and stored on a small spool. The heart of these instruments is an electromagnet which varies the intensity of magnetization of a steel wire or a tape carrying a coating of magnetite. The electromagnet is actuated by the modulated current coming from a microphone. As the strip of wire or tape runs between the poles of the magnet it is more or less highly magnetized by the changing strength of the magnet.

To reproduce the message, the strip is passed through a coil in which it induces a varying current that corresponds to the original one. This current operates a loud-speaker either through a piezoelectric crystal or an electromagnet like the one used in a telephone earpiece.

SUMMARY

1. In a telegraph circuit the sending key is a switch controlling the current through an electromagnet at the receiving end. When the current is flowing a metal bar is drawn to the electromagnet, making an audible click.

2. In a telephone circuit the compressions and rarefactions of sound waves vary the resistance and, hence, the current flowing through a carbon-granule transmitter. The modulated current flows through an electromagnet and vibrates a steel diaphragm in the earpiece at the receiving end.

3. A relay consists of an electromagnet which operates a switch in a second circuit. In this way a weak current can control a strong one and messages can be amplified.

4. In the Edison effect electrons will boil off a heated filament placed in a vacuum.

5. A triode vacuum tube contains (a) a filament from which electrons evaporate when it is heated; (b) a plate charged positively, and to which the electrons from the filament flow; and (c) a grid placed between the filament and the plate, which controls the current to the plate by relatively small changes in voltage.

6. A diode containing only a filament and a plate can be used to rectify alternating current.

7. A triode is used to detect radio-frequency waves and to amplify feeble currents.

8. In making a phonograph record a needle cuts a sinuous groove in a wax disc. The needle is part of a lever arm that is actuated by the vibrations of sound waves. When the record is played the process is reversed. The moving groove actuates the needle, whereby the vibrations are relayed to a loud-speaker. In electrical recording and transcription a piezoelectric crystal is used in the circuit.

9. In making a wire or tape recording the variation in magnetization of a steel wire or a tape carrying magnetite is controlled by sound waves striking the microphone. When the wire or tape is run through a coil it induces a modulated current which, in turn, controls the vibration of a loud-speaker.

QUESTIONS AND EXERCISES

1. When a doorbell is being rung, where in the circuit could you observe a rapid sparking? Where could you put a condenser in the circuit to cut down the sparking?

2. What would be different about the telegraph circuit shown in Figure 5-33 if B were sending to A?

3. At what point might a piezoelectric crystal be used in a telephone circuit?

4. Using the correct symbols, sketch a vacuum-tube rectifier, including a variable resistance to control the filament current.

5. In what ways is a triode superior to a relay as an amplifier?

6. In a triode, which pole of the C battery is connected to the plate?

7. In England, a triode is called a valve. What part of the triode corresponds to the gate of a valve?

8. What would go wrong with a triode if you used a C battery that gave less volts than the B battery?

9. Look at a phonograph record with a strong magnifying glass or a microscope and notice the shape of the grooves.

10. Describe the electrical parts of a record player that uses a crystal pickup.

Communication II

1. RADIO

When an electron is at rest it repels other electrons and attracts positive charges, and so we say that it is surrounded by an electric field. When the electron moves it is surrounded by a magnetic as well as by an electric field. These combined fields are spoken of as an electromagnetic field. They can exert force at a distance.

Figure 5-42 shows a static machine, S, connected to a heavy

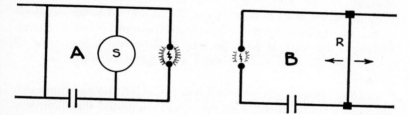

Figure 5-42. A primitive radio sender and detector. A static machine, S, sends sparks across the gap of A. With R in the correct position, a faint spark may be seen to jump across the gap of B.

wire rectangle, A, containing a narrow spark gap. On a separate insulated base is a similar heavy wire rectangle, B, with the movable rod, R, forming the side across from the spark gap. If the static machine is operated so that sparks jump across the gap of A, and the rod R is moved back and forth, a position will be found at which sparks jump across the gap at B in time with those at A.

This experiment is similar to one in which a stone is dropped near a cork floating on a still pond. The waves moving out from where the stone hit the water will make the cork bob up and down. By analogy, we say that the electromagnetic waves traveling out from the moving electrons of the spark at A make the electrons of B move back and forth across the gap. There is also a similarity to the experiment with the vibrating bars described in the chapter on sound (page 44). The second bar would pick up the energy of the sound wave only if it had the same natural frequency of vibration as the first bar (the two bars had to be tuned to the same note). By moving the rod R (Figure 5-42) back and forth we tuned the circuit B and found a position where A and B had the same period of electric vibration. From this type of experiment there developed the point of view that electromagnetic waves were generated at A and were detected at B.

With water and sound waves something tangible is vibrating; there is a medium to transmit the energy. With electromagnetic waves no medium can be found. The term aether (or ether) was invented to apply to the medium, but since there is absolutely no evidence to indicate its existence, we have reluctantly abandoned the idea. We have to imagine waves traveling through space with nothing there to vibrate. Or we can look at the matter somewhat differently and assume that the energy travels in the form of particles, like bullets, which also have all the properties of a wave motion, such as wavelength and frequency.

In 1865 James Clerk Maxwell had predicted the possible existence of electromagnetic waves and had suggested that light was an example of such vibrations. He said that light constituted only a small fraction of the many wavelengths possible. The experiment described in Figure 5-42 was performed in 1888 by Hertz. Following the lead of Maxwell's theory he found that these waves showed reflection, refraction, and interference. In 1896 Marconi succeeded in applying Hertz's technique to the problem of sending a message through space.

The inadequate details above merely touch some of the high spots leading to the development of radio communication. They do, however, suggest how completely dependent we are upon the interaction of the minds of many men from many countries for scientific progress. Contributions from the United States, England, France, Germany, Russia, and Italy were fitted together in a sequence that depended upon free exchange of ideas and upon freedom for the experimenters to work on the problems that seemed significant to them. At no point along the line was the driving force the idea of making a radio.

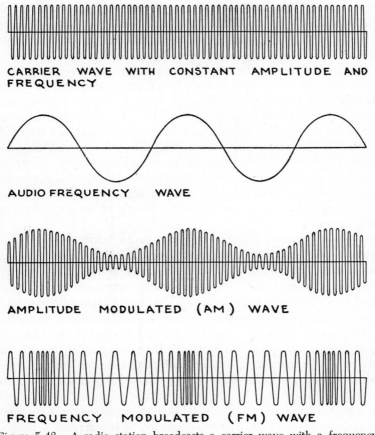

CARRIER   WAVE   WITH   CONSTANT   AMPLITUDE   AND FREQUENCY

AUDIO FREQUENCY   WAVE

AMPLITUDE   MODULATED   (AM)   WAVE

FREQUENCY   MODULATED   (FM)   WAVE

Figure 5-43. A radio station broadcasts a carrier wave with a frequency much too high to hear. The sound waves entering the microphone modulate this carrier wave either in amplitude (AM) or in frequency (FM).

A modern radio-sending station operates on a fixed frequency or carrier wave of very long wavelength and high frequency. This carrier wave is generated by a piezoelectric crystal which vibrates at about 550 to 1600 kilocycles per second. The ampli-

tude of the carrier wave is modulated by the sound wave striking the microphone so that an amplitude-modulated (AM) wave
is broadcast (Figure 5-43). The electrical characteristics of a
radio receiver are modified by tuning it to the characteristic
frequency of the sending station. Notice that the numbers on
the radio dial range from 550 to 1600. The amplitude-modulated
wave is detected and amplified by tubes like the one in Figure
5-40. The current from these tubes controls your loud-speaker.

Instead of having the sound waves that strike the microphone
modulate the amplitude of the carrier wave, they can be made
to modulate its frequency (Figure 5-43). This gives us frequency
modulation, or FM radio. One of the principal advantages of
FM over AM is that static is not detected and does not interfere
with FM reception. Another is that FM stations can transmit
more of the higher frequencies of the characteristic overtones
without interfering with each other. Two AM stations operating
on neighboring channels (nearly the same carrier frequency)
must cut out the higher overtones to avoid overlapping and
interference.

One of the surprising facts about radio transmission is that
signals will carry around the curve of the earth. Since the signals travel in straight lines like light, those going up into the air
must be refracted back to earth. In fact they must bounce back
and forth between the earth and the upper atmosphere several
times in traveling thousands of miles. The existence of such a
refracting layer in the atmosphere was predicted by Kennelly
and Heaviside, and it is named in their honor. Apparently, radiation from the sun splits the particles of the air into charged
ions that refract radio waves to give total internal reflection for
the frequencies used in AM broadcasting (Figure 5-44). Since
the higher-frequency waves used in FM broadcasting, television,
and radar are not refracted satisfactorily, their reception is limited
to a radius of a hundred miles or so from the sending station.

2. CATHODE-RAY OSCILLOGRAPH

In the Fleming diode rectifier (page 392) electrons boil off the
hot filament and travel to the positively charged plate. If the
plate is perforated there will be a beam of electrons streaming

through the hole and traveling in a straight line beyond it. This is a convenient way of obtaining the beam of electrons used in a cathode-ray oscilloscope. The beam next passes between two condenser plates that are in a vertical plane and then between two that are in a horizontal plane, and finally it strikes a fluorescent screen at the end of the tube (Figure 5-45). With no charge on either set of condensers, a single bright spot is observed on the screen. If a 60-cycle alternating current is applied to the

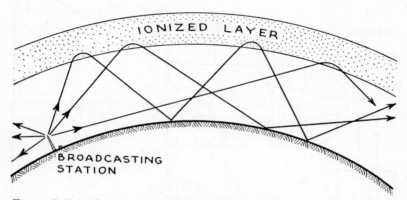

Figure 5-44. The Kennelly-Heaviside layer of ionized gases refracts AM radio waves so that they can be transmitted around the curving earth.

first set of condensers, the beam will sweep back and forth in a straight, horizontal line as it is attracted to first one and then the other of the two plates. The alternations of the current and the sweeping of the oscillograph beam back and forth might be compared to the swinging of a pendulum.

If the deflecting voltage on the condenser built up relatively slowly and then dropped rapidly we could compare the action to the motion of a pile driver. The luminous spot on the screen would still be describing a horizontal line, but it would travel slowly across the field in one direction and would then return very rapidly to the starting point. This type of motion is called scanning.

The second set of condenser plates, the ones in the horizontal plane, can deflect the beam in a vertical direction. With the beam scanning horizontally, an alternating voltage on the ver-

tical deflectors will make the spot snake its way across the field.
As the beam moves steadily from left to right, for instance, it is
deflected upward and then down below the center line so that
its path is like a sine-wave curve.

The cathode-ray oscillograph can be used to study sound
waves by leading the current from a microphone to the condensers, which deflect vertically. The variations in air pressure

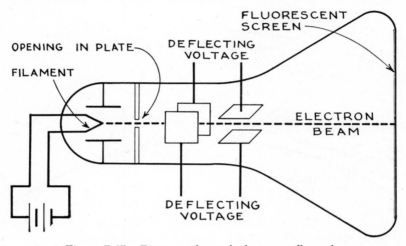

Figure 5-45. Diagram of a cathode-ray oscillograph.

of the sound are translated into variations in electric current,
which affect the path of the scanning beam so that we can see
and photograph them. The pictures showing the difference in
shape of the sound waves from different instruments were taken
this way.

Any signal that can be translated into an electric current can
be studied by this technique. In navigation by radar a short-
wavelength radio impulse is sent out from a directional antenna
that also serves as a detector. If the radio signal is reflected
from something, the echo returns to the antenna and is led to an
oscillograph. The original signal shows up as a peak, and the
echo appears beside it as a small "pip." The distance between
the two is a measure of how far away the reflecting object is.
Ships can avoid each other in a foggy harbor; airplanes can tell

how high above the ground they are; and a radar screen to detect hostile aircraft can be thrown around a continent.

We have yet to send a manned rocket to the moon, but we have shot a radar signal to the moon and recorded the echo. The short-wavelength, high-frequency radar waves penetrated the Kennelly-Heaviside layer, sped to the moon, bounced off its surface, and returned to earth in less than 3 seconds.

3. TELEVISION

Television combines several of the problems of movies and radio. A scene must be recorded, transmitted, and projected, and this sequence must be repeated 30 times a second to give the illusion of smooth motion. In the television "camera" (Figure 5-46) there is no film. The scene is focused on a screen which is a fine-grained honeycomb of photoelectric cells. Such a screen is comparable to the mosaic of rods and cones on the retina of the human eye (page 32). The variations in light intensity of the image build up variations in voltage on these cells. A scanning beam of electrons sweeps across the cells very much as your eye scans a page of this book. It moves steadily across, rapidly back and down a row, and across again until it has covered the whole screen. (The trouble with this analogy is that your eye does not move steadily; it proceeds by a series of jerky motions.) A complete scanning of the screen constitutes 1 picture, and 30 pictures a second are transmitted.

When the electron beam hits one of the photoelectric cells the voltage on the cell is neutralized, and it is this drop in voltage which is used to modulate the outgoing radio-frequency signal. The modulated signal is detected and amplified by the receiving set and used to control the intensity of its scanning beam. The scanning beam in the tube of the set travels from side to side, starting at the top and adding line after line until the picture is completed. A bright spot on the original image produces a high intensity of the scanning beam, and so there is a corresponding bright spot on the screen. The picture is actually drawn before your eyes, but it happens so fast that it appears to be instantaneous.

Since 525 horizontal lines are drawn for each picture and each line has 420 bright or dark spots, the picture is made up of over 200,000 elements. Electronic engineers have a reputation for

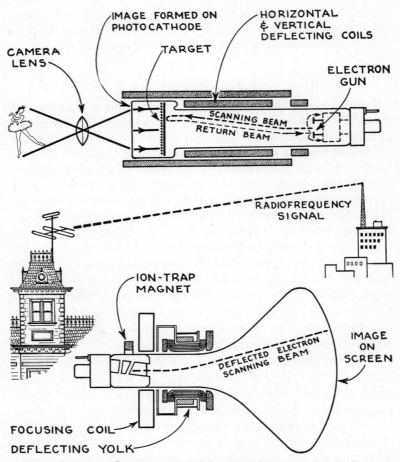

Figure 5-46. A television camera (above) and picture tube (below).

accomplishing the fabulous, but they still have room for considerable improvement in the quality of television pictures. Their headaches have been tripled by the attempts to perfect color television. Here each final picture is made up of three: one red, one green, and one blue, and they are fused together (color by addition).

SUMMARY

1. A moving electron generates an electric and a magnetic field (electromagnetic waves) that travels out from it through space with the speed of light.

2. Electromagnetic waves can be detected by a properly tuned receiver.

3. Electromagnetic waves show the usual properties of waves, such as wavelength, speed, reflection, refraction, and diffraction, but they do not require a medium for transmission.

4. Maxwell predicted electromagnetic waves and said that light was this kind of vibration.

5. Hertz was the first to demonstrate the existence of long-wavelength electromagnetic waves (radio waves).

6. Marconi developed the technique of sending and receiving radio waves to such a point that they were practical for communication.

7. Radio stations send out a carrier wave of fixed frequency and modulated amplitude (AM), or of fixed amplitude and modulated frequency (FM).

8. Radio waves are detected and amplified by triode vacuum tubes.

9. The Kennelly-Heaviside layer is a region of ionized gas molecules in the upper atmosphere that refracts AM frequency radio waves in such a way that they can be sent completely around the earth.

10. Since the higher frequencies used for FM, television, radar, etc., are not refracted by the Kennelly-Heaviside layer, their reception is limited to straight-line distances from the transmitting station.

11. In a cathode-ray oscillograph, a beam of electrons strikes a fluorescent screen after passing between two sets of condensers at right angles to each other.

12. By having the potential on one set of condensers build up slowly and break down rapidly, a luminous horizontal line is drawn in one direction across the screen. This process is called scanning.

13. Variations in the potential of the other set of condenser plates give the scanning beam a vertical motion, so that it follows a curved path across the screen. A study of the path reveals information about the current reaching the second set of condensers.

14. Sound waves and any other signal that can be translated into an electric current can be studied with a cathode-ray oscillograph.

15. In echo location by radar, the time for return of a reflected radio wave measures the distance to the reflecting object.

16. In television the image is recorded on a screen consisting of a mosaic of tiny photoelectric cells. They are scanned by a beam of electrons that neutralizes their charge. The drop in potential of each cell modulates the radio-frequency signal going out at the time. The modulated signal controls the intensity of a scanning beam in the receiving set.

17. Thirty times a second the whole scene is sent out and portrayed on the receiving screen. The completed picture is composed of 525 lines with 420 spots of varying brightness in each line.

QUESTIONS AND EXERCISES

1. How fast do radio waves travel?

2. What is the wavelength of a carrier wave with a frequency of 550 kilocycles per second?

3. Is the speed of AM radio waves in the Kennelly-Heaviside layer greater or less than in un-ionized air?

4. In a cathode-ray oscillograph tube, if the scanning voltage were placed on the horizontal pair of deflecting plates, what would appear on the screen?

5. Electromagnetic force acts at a distance without the need of a medium. What other force like this have we studied?

6. The following scientists were citizens of what countries: Maxwell, Hertz, Marconi, De Forest, Fleming?

7. Describe the motion of a scanning beam.

8. How long did it take the radar signal to travel from the earth to the moon and back?

9. How many lines are drawn by the scanning beam of a television tube each second?

10. In what way is the picture on a television screen similar to a colored magazine picture? Why is it a mistake to sit close to a large television screen?

Electricity and Your Car

1. LIGHTS, HORN, ETC.

Under the hood of a car there is a complete electric power plant. The services that use electricity include the lights, self-starter, horn, and ignition system, and possibly a radio, fan, and motors to raise and lower the top and the windows. When the car motor is running it operates a generator to supply the current for these devices, and there is a battery to furnish current when the car is not running.

In the battery a series of chemical reactions furnishes a current of electricity as described in Chapter 1, Part 5 of this unit. Although the particular reactions need not concern you here, you should know a few things about them. They are reversible; that is, after the materials have been pretty well used up (discharged) an electric current can be driven backward through the battery to regenerate the substances. This is called charging a battery. Since the density of the liquid in a fully charged battery is higher than that in a discharged one, the condition of a battery can be checked with a hydrometer. The liquid in a well-charged battery freezes at a much lower temperature than that in a discharged battery, and so it is important to keep track of this in cold weather. It is also important to keep track of the liquid level and replace any distilled water that evaporates. The battery furnishes current at a pressure of 6 volts, which is not very high, but it can supply it so fast (about 100 amp) that you can get a most uncomfortable spark by placing a metal tool across the two terminals.

The generator (Figure 5-47) is driven by the engine when it is running; it supplies all the current needed and recharges the battery. The battery is designed to operate for short periods, such as starting the car, and any long-term drain on it will wear it out rapidly.

The lights, horn, blowers, etc., of an automobile are not particularly different from those in use elsewhere. The parabolic reflector for the headlights was described on page 6. There are two filaments in the headlight bulbs. For country driving the lower, brighter one is used to send a horizontal beam far out

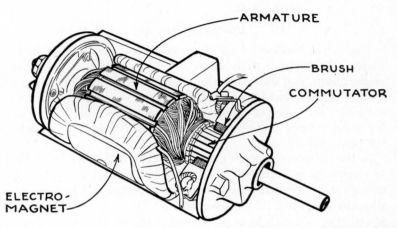

Figure 5-47.   An automobile generator.   (*From Electricity and Wheels, by General Motors Corp.*)

ahead, and for city driving and passing the upper filament sends a beam which strikes the road close to the car and avoids serious glare in the eyes of the approaching driver. The general use of Polaroid filters (page 91) would greatly improve the situation. Only one wire passes to each of the above-mentioned electrical devices, the frame of the car being used to return the electrons to the battery and generator.

The self-starter is a powerful electric motor which turns the engine over until it can operate on its own power. A motor strong enough to do this job properly would be almost as large as the engine itself, but since it operates for such a short time, a smaller motor can be overloaded temporarily without burning out. C. F. Kettering had used this line of reasoning in building an electrically operated cash register, and he fooled the scoffing

experts in the automobile industry by developing the first successful self-starter in 1912.

2. THE IGNITION SYSTEM

In the ignition system of a car sufficient voltage must be provided to make a spark jump across the gap of the spark plugs

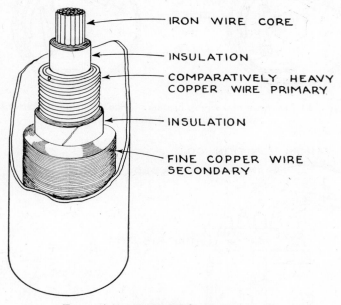

IRON WIRE CORE

INSULATION

COMPARATIVELY HEAVY
COPPER WIRE PRIMARY

INSULATION

FINE COPPER WIRE
SECONDARY

Figure 5-48.   Diagram of an ignition coil.

and this current must be directed to the right spark plug at the
right time.   The 6 volts from the battery must be stepped up to
about 10,000 volts at the spark plugs.   A transformer is the obvious solution to the problem, but a current interrupter of some
sort must be provided because the battery delivers a steady,
direct current.   The transformer used is called an ignition coil
(Figure 5-48).   This coil has a hundred or more windings of
comparatively thick copper wire for a primary, and many thousands of turns of fine wire on the secondary.   The current interrupter is called a circuit breaker, and one for a six-cylinder car

is illustrated in Figure 5-49. As the hexagon turns, its points push back the switch and stop the current (*B*). When a side comes across from the switch it closes and the current flows (*A*). Notice that there is a condenser in the circuit. It serves as a reser-

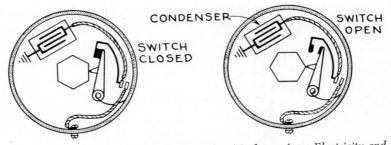

Figure 5-49.   Diagram of a circuit breaker. (*Redrawn from Electricity and Wheels, by General Motors Corp.*)

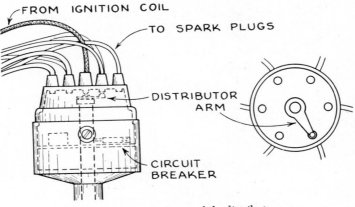

Figure 5-50. An automobile distributor.

voir for the current to surge into when the circuit is being broken. This not only cuts down on excessive sparking in the circuit breaker but it also provides a greater flow of current when the switch is closed. The current flows from the battery, through the primary of the ignition coil, through the circuit breaker, and back to the battery.

When a momentary current flows through the primary, a high-voltage current is induced into the secondary and it flows to the distributor (Figure 5-50). The distributor is easy to recognize under the hood because it is the center of the spiderweb of wires

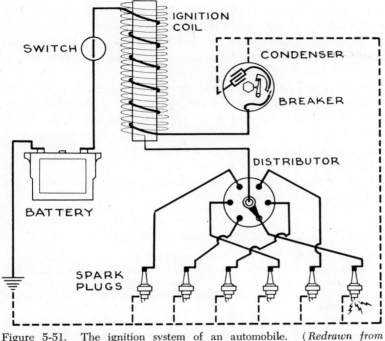

Figure 5-51. The ignition system of an automobile. (*Redrawn from Electricity and Wheels, by General Motors Corp.*)

leading to each spark plug. In it is a rotating arm which acts as a switch to send the current from the ignition coil to each of the spark plugs in turn. The distributor is mounted on top of the circuit breaker, and, since the same rod turns the hexagon of the circuit breaker and the arm of the distributor, they keep in perfect time. This whole system is put together as shown in Figure 5-51.

SUMMARY

1. Since the chemical reactions that furnish an electric current from a storage battery are reversible, a battery that has run down can be recharged.

2. The generator supplies all the current needed and also recharges the battery when the motor is running.

3. Kettering developed the self-starter by designing a small electric motor that could be overloaded for the short time necessary to get the engine started.

4. The ignition coil is a step-up transformer that changes the 6 volts from the battery into about 10,000 volts at the spark plugs.

5. The circuit breaker is a switch that interrupts the direct current from the battery to give the changing magnetic field necessary for the operation of a transformer.

6. The distributor is integrated with the circuit breaker so that the pulses of high-voltage current are directed to the proper spark plug at the right time.

QUESTIONS AND EXERCISES

1. Would the float in a hydrometer used to test a fully charged automobile battery float high in the liquid or sink low with only a little of the stem showing?

2. What is the purpose of the ignition coil? the circuit breaker? the distributor?

3. Why can very fine wire be used in the secondary of the ignition coil, whereas comparatively heavy wire is needed for the primary?

4. Look under the hood of a car and see how many of the parts of the ignition system you can recognize.

5. Current runs through the starting motor of a car at the rate of about 80 amp, and the generator produces it at about 7½ amp. If you take half a minute to start your car, how long will the engine have to run before the battery is recharged?

9

CHAPTER

Be Careful

Every year many people are killed through carelessness or ignorance of the dangers of electricity. We have so many potentially dangerous contacts with electrical devices every day that we all should know what precautions to take.

There is no simple rule about the number of volts that can be handled safely. Four dry cells connected in series will deliver 6 volts, and the shock from them would not hurt a kitten; but the difference in potential across the two terminals of an automobile battery is also 6 volts, and a shock from it can be an unpleasant experience. A spark at 100,000 volts from a static machine is a rude surprise but not dangerous, yet contact with the 120 volts of the usual home wiring system has been fatal to many a person.

As a general rule, avoid contact with any wire that might be carrying electricity. If you are repairing any electrical gadget be sure that its plug is pulled out, and turn off a lamp when you are replacing a burned-out bulb. It is well to have a neon test lamp handy to be sure whether a circuit is "live" or "dead." When a fuse blows out, something is wrong—probably an overloaded circuit or a short circuit—so find and fix the trouble before replacing the fuse. Never put a coin underneath a fuse. This is comparable to tying down the safety valve on a steam boiler.

Electrical devices are supposed to be insulated perfectly, but they rarely are. If your hands are dry you will seldom get a shock from a toaster or radio, etc., but it is not unusual to notice a warning tingling when your hands are wet. When you are really well connected (electrically) to the ground, as when your feet are wet, your hand is on a faucet, or you are in the bathtub, you should avoid touching any electric switch, bulb, radio, etc. You may get away with such foolish practices several times, but it takes only one good shock to kill you and several people are killed every year by just these kinds of careless actions.

An electric current through your muscles makes them contract, and if it flows through your heart muscle the muscle may tighten up and not be able to relax again. Lacking any other way of testing a wire in a crisis, you may touch it lightly with the back of your fingers. If you get a shock the finger muscles will contract and pull your hand away from the wire. The shock from a live wire touching the front of your fingers makes your hand contract around the wire and hold it with a grip that will not relax.

"Cause of the fire—defective wiring." This is the verdict all too frequently after a fire that has left families homeless and has even sacrificed lives. Frayed insulation or kinked extension cords will allow a small current to leak away. This current heats up a rug until it bursts into flame, and the rest of the story depends on luck and the efficiency of the fire department. Cords should be replaced at the first sign of wear. Plan for numerous wall outlets rather than for one or two that are stuffed with multiple plugs and many long extension cords. When a home is left unoccupied for any length of time it is wise to pull out all extension cords and disconnect all radios, refrigerators, etc.

We have replaced human slaves by electrons, and a little understanding and care will keep them in their proper place as servants.

Unit 6

▼

ATOMIC STRUCTURE

The Four Freedoms

One of the most active and interesting frontiers of modern science is the study of atomic structure. The work in this field illustrates the power of the scientific method as a tool, and it shows the close interplay between the practical demands of industry and theoretical developments in science. Many a theoretical problem has been held up until industry could provide the necessary tool; many an industrial need has prompted scientists to look into a neglected problem; and many an abstract scientific development has been the root from which a whole industry has developed.

The period between 1700 B.C. and A.D. 1700 was nearly barren of significant industrial and scientific achievements. Four developments during this time, however, made outstanding contributions to the freedom of mankind.

Gutenberg's invention of movable type in 1440 is the basis for our ability to communicate ideas to large numbers of people. Without printing, it would be impossible to have education on a broad scale. Before this invention the great mass of people were completely dependent upon a small group, the priests, for knowledge. When books were made cheap, men's minds were released from this slavery.

The invention of the telescope by Galileo in 1600 provided the information that released men's minds from the confining idea of an earth-centered universe. Through philosophy and literature this expanding world view gradually worked its way outward to the general population.

In spite of the intrepid Columbus and other explorers, any large-scale world trade and migration across oceans was held up by the inadequate clocks of those days. In order to determine a ship's longitude it was necessary to know the time with considerable accuracy (page 136). The development of accurate timepieces was a slowly unfolding achievement to which a vast number of craftsmen contributed. The first chronometer that was dependable enough for navigation was built by Harrison in 1714, and from then on world trade grew from a trickle into a torrent. The strong-minded individualist of the Old World no longer had to suffer the indifference or persecution of vested interests. He could escape the geographical slavery of Europe and prove himself in the New World.

The fourth development that had such far-reaching effects was the application of gunpowder to warfare. Up to the time of the Middle Ages warfare was a serious but nevertheless polite kind of game. It consisted of individual combat between men of equal social standing. The use of the longbow and the crossbow by the English yeomen was probably the first step in breaking this rule, but when balls could be shot from muskets and cannon it was impossible to observe the niceties of social distinction. Warfare became so expensive that feudal lords had to band together as a nation. The feudal system, with its virtual slavery of the individual, was given its deathblow.

And so these four freedoms: the freedom from intellectual slavery, the freedom from a concept of an earth-centered universe, the freedom to make a new life for oneself across the sea, and the freedom from personal slavery were achieved by Western civilization by about 1700.

CHAPTER

Alchemist + Balance = Chemist

1. BOYLE'S LAW

We are now going to trace briefly the sequence of ideas that led up to the point of view that there must be a limit to the extent to which matter can be subdivided. We call this the atomic theory of matter. The medieval scientists working with retort and crucible, medicine and metal, salts and philosopher's stone, were called alchemists. They busied themselves with attempts to turn lead into gold, to find the elixir of life, and to brew magic medicines. They developed a considerable body of information about the qualitative behavior of substances but made little or no progress in discovering quantitative relationships. Just as the quantitative measurements by Brahe led to Kepler's theory of the structure of the solar system, so the quantitative studies of the eighteenth century led to Dalton's atomic theory.

When warfare became big business it raised a host of industrial problems. The ingredients of gunpowder are charcoal, sulfur, and saltpeter. Charcoal was easy to make; sulfur was found near every volcano; but saltpeter was found only near manure piles, and these were ransacked from one end of the country to the other. A rapid increase in the use of iron for guns and cannons sent the mines deeper and deeper. Charcoal was used in making iron from iron ore, and the oak forests of England were rapidly disappearing before the onslaughts of the charcoal ovens. Queen Elizabeth put a stop to this, and first coal and then coke was tried as a substitute. The successful use of coke sent the soft-coal mines deeper into the earth. With increasing depth the mines had to be ventilated and pumped free from the water that seeped into them. This industrial need prompted an interest in the study of the action of pumps and the behavior of gases at different pressures. In 1660 Robert Boyle published his paper containing a description of the relationship of the volume of a gas at different pressures that we call Boyle's law (page 259). This law was a necessary forerunner to any quantitative study of gases.

2. THE CONSERVATION OF MASS

The idea that matter is indestructible, that it can be neither created nor destroyed, is fundamental to any quantitative study. Yet, the common experience of watching a heavy log burn down to a light pile of ashes seems to contradict the law of the conservation of mass. The great French chemist, Lavoisier (1743–1794), carried out a significant experiment involving the oxidation of tin. He placed a weighed quantity of tin in a large glass vessel and sealed it off. He then weighed the vessel, heated it for several hours until the tin had turned into tin oxide, and weighed it again. Next, he broke the glass seal, noticed that air rushed in, and reweighed the flask. Finally, he weighed the tin oxide that was formed. With letters to represent the weights actually recorded, his experiment can be outlined as follows:

1. Weight of tin $= a$
2. Weight of tin + air + flask before heating $= b$
3. During heating the tin changed to tin oxide
4. Weight of tin oxide + air + flask after heating $= b$
5. Flask opened and air rushed in
6. Weight of flask and contents after opening $= b + c$
7. Weight of tin oxide $= a + c$

Steps 2 and 4 show that there was no change in weight during the reaction. The weight of the air that rushed into the flask, c, was the same as the weight of the air that combined with the tin when it changed to tin oxide. From a bookkeeping point of view everything is accounted for. In this experiment Lavoisier not only made out a good case for the law of the conservation of mass but he also used a technique, the quantitative approach, that was absolutely essential for the developments that were to come.

3. ELEMENTS

Lavoisier also helped to make more clear our present-day meaning of the word element. For thousands of years mankind had been trying to show that the many different substances that we encounter around us were made up of varying combinations of a few simple units. A pile of bricks, mortar, and water can be combined into such diverse structures as a pavement, a wall, a bridge, a house, or a tower. Might it not be that stones, leaves, water, and air could be broken down into a few basic building materials?

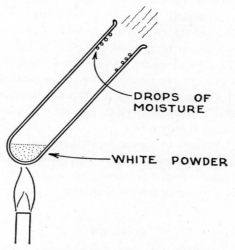

DROPS OF MOISTURE

WHITE POWDER

Figure 6-1.   Heating bluestone in a test tube breaks it up into a white powder and water.

By gently heating crystals of "blue stone," crystalline copper sulfate, you can observe moisture collecting near the top of the tube and the white powder that is left behind (Figure 6-1). If you collect enough of this moisture you can prove that it is water by measuring its boiling and freezing points. When the white powder has again cooled it will become blue once more when a few drops of water are placed on it. The products of the change brought about by heating are obviously simpler than the original crystalline material. Can these products be further simplified? Passing an electric current through water breaks it up into two gases, hydrogen and oxygen. As these can be recombined to produce water, water is complex.

In making lime we heat limestone. A gas, carbon dioxide, is

evolved, and lime is left behind. Burning coal in oxygen produces carbon dioxide, and burning the metal calcium in oxygen produces lime. Hence limestone, carbon dioxide, and lime are complex substances. They can be broken down into simpler parts, or they can be built up out of simpler parts. The word element refers to the relatively few basic substances that cannot be broken down or built up from other things. Since all the evidence was necessarily negative, it was extremely difficult to determine that a substance was an element. Lavoisier stated the problem in the above terms and compiled a list of substances that he thought were elements. In a later section of this unit we shall come to our current definition of an element and shall see that it is much easier to work with. You are familiar with many of the elements: hydrogen, oxygen, nitrogen, aluminum, copper, uranium, to mention only a few.

With the definition of element clarified and by using quantitative methods, the early nineteenth-century scientists soon accumulated some weight relationships which led them to the concept of the atomic structure of matter.

SUMMARY

1. The demands of industry turned the attention of scientists toward quantitative studies in chemistry.

2. The need for pumping out and ventilating mines led to the development of better pumps and to Boyle's law.

3. Lavoisier's experiments with the oxidation of tin helped confirm the law of the conservation of mass.

4. Lavoisier also contributed to the idea that an element is a basic form of matter that can be neither built up from nor broken down into something simpler.

QUESTIONS AND EXERCISES

1. State Boyle's law in words and symbols.
2. Was Lavoisier's experiment of any help in deciding whether tin is an element or a compound?
3. State the law of conservation of mass.
4. If Lavoisier had used an open flask instead of a sealed one dur-

ing his experiment, which one of the weights would have been different?

5. Does the fact that hydrogen will burn in oxygen to produce water prove that water is not an element?

6. Name five elements not mentioned in this chapter.

7. Name five substances that are compounds.

8. Suppose you pour vinegar over a substance in a test tube and observe bubbling and a gas given off. Does this prove that the substance is a compound?

9. How were limestone deposits formed?

10. If you have 100 cc of a liquid that you suspect is water, how can you identify it? (Do not taste it; it might be poisonous or contaminated.)

CHAPTER

Atoms, Molecules, and the Periodic Table

1. DALTON'S ATOMIC THEORY

In the material on atomic structure to be presented next only a few simple examples will be chosen from the thousands available. The sweeping generalizations made in the atomic theory are justified only because they are consistent with a great mass of evidence, of which this is just a small sample.

The two common oxides of carbon are carbon monoxide and carbon dioxide. In carbon monoxide 12 parts by weight of carbon are associated with 16 of oxygen. In carbon dioxide 12 parts of carbon are combined with 32 of oxygen. The ratio of the weights of oxygen which combine with the same weight of carbon is $16/32 = 1/2$. This is a ratio of small whole numbers. To illustrate this further, 32 grams of oxygen combine with 4 grams of hydrogen to form water and with 2 grams of hydrogen to form hydrogen peroxide. Here, again, the ratio of the weights of hydrogen that combine with the same weight of oxygen is $4/2 = 2/1$.

In methane (the main constituent of natural gas) we find 12 grams of carbon combined with 4 grams of hydrogen. We now have a three-cornered relationship. The same weight of oxygen (32 grams) that combines with 12 grams of carbon also combines with 4 grams of hydrogen, and these two elements combine with each other in exactly this proportion by weight. This is diagrammed below.

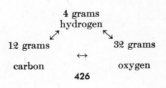

The above type of evidence was available by 1800 and could have led directly to the atomic theory; instead, it served the important role of confirming and selling the idea to the skeptics after it had been arrived at by a different and much less conclusive line of argument. John Dalton was trying to understand how one kind of gas could diffuse through another. He hit upon the explanation that each kind of gas was composed of particles that were alike in size for any one gas but different from all others. He drew pictures of these particles, which he called atoms, showing how similar ones could not interpenetrate but different types could. He realized that, if this explanation were true, the atoms of any one substance should have characteristic weights. He turned to the analytical results obtained by other chemists and found that they were consistent with this theory.

If each element is made up of atoms that are all alike in size and weight but are different from the atoms of any other element, then we should be able to prepare a table of the characteristic atomic weights of each of the elements. Dalton realized that these atoms that he was postulating must be extremely small and that it would be out of the question to weigh a single, isolated one. The important thing was to compare the weights of the different kinds. Since hydrogen was the lightest substance known (and still is), he placed its atomic weight as 1 and figured the rest of his atomic weights with hydrogen as a standard of comparison. For reasons of convenience we now use the atomic weight of oxygen as 16.000 as our standard of comparison. There were many pitfalls along the path, and it was 50 years before the scheme was put on a rational basis. But, with all its faults, Dalton's atomic theory gave science an acceleration and a direction for advance.

2. MOLECULES

Applying Dalton's theory to the data we first considered, we get information about the make-up of the molecules of carbon monoxide, carbon dioxide, water, hydrogen peroxide, and methane. A molecule is the smallest unit that contains more than 1 atom. If all carbon atoms have a weight of 12 units and the oxygen atoms a weight of 16, then carbon monoxide would have

1 atom of each element and carbon dioxide would have 1 atom of carbon and 2 of oxygen. Since 32 grams of oxygen combine with 4 grams of hydrogen to form water, we would expect that it contained 2 atoms of oxygen and 4 of hydrogen. Other lines of evidence show that the molecule is actually half this amount, with 1 atom of oxygen to 2 of hydrogen. Water is the familiar H two O, or H_2O, as it is written in a chemical formula. Hydrogen peroxide has 2 atoms of hydrogen to 2 of oxygen, and methane has 1 atom of carbon to 4 of hydrogen, as you would expect. An atom (the word means indivisible) is the smallest particle of an element, and a molecule is the smallest particle of a substance whose particles contain more than 1 atom. Some molecules contain only 2 or 3 atoms; others are made up of thousands. Molecules can be broken into smaller parts, but these parts no longer have the properties of the original substance. Breaking down a grain of sugar into individual molecules may be compared to tearing up a sheet of postage stamps into individual stamps. Any one stamp can be torn into pieces, but one of these pieces can no longer be used for postage on a letter.

3. MENDELEEF'S PERIODIC TABLE

With these fundamental concepts made clear, chemists busied themselves with discovering new elements, determining their atomic weights, and studying how they could combine to form molecules. Berzelius (1819) suggested that it would be convenient to designate the elements by one or two letters from their names, and so we have O for oxygen, C for carbon, Ca for calcium, etc. There is little need for us to use this chemical shorthand, but it will be convenient in looking at the periodic table and in a few radioactive changes to be considered later.

After fifty or sixty elements had been identified some striking similarities in the properties of several of them became apparent. It was possible to group a number of elements together in families. Just as lemons, oranges, and grapefruit, although different, are grouped together as citrus fruit, so chlorine, bromine, and iodine were grouped together as the family of halogens. After many hesitating attempts at over-all organization, Mendeleef, in 1871, showed that the elements could be arranged in a rectangular, calendar-like chart if placed in the order of their increasing atomic weights.

When the elements were arranged this way they showed a smooth change in properties, with a return at regular intervals to repeat the sequence of changes. Those elements that were similar he placed under each other. A modern form of his table is shown on the back cover. What this table points out is that the properties of the elements are a periodic function of their atomic weights. It is the chemist's most useful organizing principle because it enables him to predict the properties of an element from a general knowledge of how properties change from one part of the table to another.

We now consider Mendeleef a genius because he made some rash statements that turned out to be true. For several years after his table was published he was not taken seriously because his statements seemed so improbable. In the first place, several of the elements were put considerably out of their order according to their known atomic weights. Mendeleef said that the atomic weights had been determined incorrectly. He was so sure that his scheme was right that he felt anything inconsistent with it must be wrong. Another striking thing that Mendeleef did was to leave blank spaces in his table. In order to make the rows fit under each other properly he had to leave some places empty. Since his arrangement was supposed to show an orderly sequence of changes, the properties of the missing elements could be predicted from those on either side of the blank space. Mendeleef outlined in some detail what the missing elements would be like. When the first few of them were discovered and the predictions were found to be accurate, Mendeleef received the acceptance and praise that were due him.

SUMMARY

1. An analysis of the weight relationships of the elements present in compounds shows that: (a) two elements frequently can combine in more than one proportion; (b) if a ratio is made of any two of the different weights of one element which combine with the same weight of the other element, this ratio can be expressed in small whole numbers; (c) there are many examples

of an element combining with two other elements, and these two, in turn, combining with each other; (d) in several of the examples mentioned in (c) above, the weights of the two other elements which combine with the same weight of the first element are the weights by which these two other elements combine with each other.

2. Dalton assumed from several lines of evidence that an element is composed of very small, indivisible particles, which he called atoms. The atoms of any one element were supposed to have a characteristic size and weight.

3. Dalton prepared a preliminary table of atomic weights based on a comparison with hydrogen taken as having a weight of 1 unit.

4. If the smallest possible particle of a substance contains more than 1 atom it is called a molecule.

5. Berzelius developed a shorthand system of notation for referring to elements.

6. When the elements are arranged in the order of their increasing atomic weights there is a recurring pattern of similarity in their chemical and physical properties.

7. Mendeleef organized the elements into a table based on the above fact. This table is an outstanding example of the usefulness of an organizing principle.

QUESTIONS AND EXERCISES

1. In what countries did the following men live: Boyle, Lavoisier, Dalton, Berzelius, Mendeleef?

2. How do we at present explain the diffusion of one gas through another?

3. Is the smallest particle of limestone an atom or a molecule?

4. Give two examples that we have studied of molecules being broken down into simpler parts.

5. Find one of the examples in the periodic chart of the elements where a lighter element follows a heavier one. These examples will be explained in a later chapter.

6. What is the average of the values for the atomic weights of chlorine and iodine? How much does this differ from the atomic weight of bromine?

7. One of the blank spaces left by Mendeleef is now occupied by aluminum. He predicted its atomic weight by averaging the values of

the atomic weights of the elements immediately above and below it. Do this and see how close he came.

8. How many elements are now known?

9. Why is it that the values of atomic weights of elements are the same in the English-American system, where the pound is the unit of weight, as they are in the system in which the gram is the unit of weight?

10. The chemical formula for limestone is $CaCO_3$. How many atoms are there in this molecule?

4

Inside the Atom

1. CATHODE RAYS

During the first three-quarters of the nineteenth century the atomic theory was placed on a firm foundation. By 1875 it was generally accepted that atoms and molecules were the fundamental units of chemical change, and the actual spatial arrangement of the atoms was worked out for many molecules. Since no one ever had seen and probably no one ever will see any of these simpler molecules, the theory was a most impressive triumph. The non-scientist may well be disturbed by this situation. How can we be so sure of something that we cannot actually see? One place that we can get an answer to that question is in a modern police station. The criminologist is constantly putting together bits of evidence into a consistent picture that describes how a crime was committed and who did it. For example, the gun is identified by comparing the scratches on a test bullet and the fatal one. The victim's shirt is analyzed for gunpowder to determine from how far away the shot was fired. Fingerprints are identified. Analysis of the suspect's pocketknife shows traces of copper from cutting the telephone wires. A hair caught by a splinter of the window frame matches the suspect's. The cumulative evidence is overwhelming. The detective was not there at the time, but he can describe the crime in detail. The evidence for the theory of the atomic structure of matter is also overwhelming. It will undoubtedly be modified and improved, but that it will be completely discarded is most unlikely.

The last quarter of the nineteenth century saw the accumulation of evidence indicating that these basic particles called atoms were, in their turn, made up of smaller units. One of the major problems of the present century has been to work out the architecture of the atom. What are these more basic units, and how are they put together?

Using a discharge tube connected to a vacuum pump and an induction coil (a step-up transformer) (Figure 6-2), you can watch the change in the nature of the spark between the electrodes as the pressure is lowered. No spark passes at atmospheric pressure. As the pressure drops, a feeble spark shoots the length of the tube; soon the whole tube glows; and finally a series

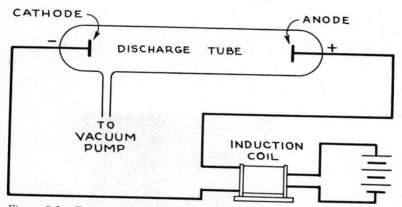

Figure 6-2. Diagram of vacuum discharge tube for studying cathode rays.

of luminous zones can be seen. The electrode through which electrons are entering the tube is called the cathode, and the positively charged electrode is called the anode. Investigations of this low-pressure discharge were made possible by H. Geissler, a German glass blower, who developed a technique for sealing metal wires through glass and who improved the vacuum pump about 1854. Edison's electric-light bulbs were also dependent on this technical advance. Other shapes of vacuum discharge tubes are shown in Figure 6-3. In part *A* of Figure 6-3 the cross casts a sharp shadow on the glass opposite the cathode. This phenomenon showed that something was coming off the cathode and traveling through the tube to the glass wall. For lack of a better name, this something was called a cathode ray.

William Crookes, an English physicist, made a thorough study of cathode rays about 1880. He showed that they could be fo-

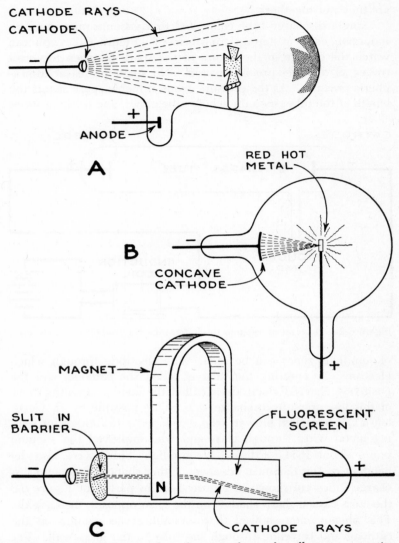

Figure 6-3.   Cathode-ray tubes of various forms that illustrate properties
of the rays.

cused on a piece of metal in the tube to heat it red hot (Figure 6-3B), that they made the glass of the tube and certain minerals in the tube fluoresce, that metal objects in their path cast sharp shadows, and that when passed between the poles of a magnet (Figure 6-3C) they were deflected in the same direction as a wire carrying a current of negative electricity. From these observations he concluded that cathode rays were a stream of negatively charged particles.

2. THE ELECTRON

Quantitative studies by J. J. Thomson in 1897, using a combination of electric and magnetic fields, demonstrated that all the negative charges obtained from cathode rays, by thermal means, and by the photoelectric effect, had the same ratio of charge (e) to mass (m). In 1911 Millikan perfected his oil-drop apparatus for measuring the elementary unit of charge, and it was determined that the mass of these negative particles was about 1/2000 of that of a hydrogen atom. A hydrogen atom weighs 1.673×10^{-24} gram and an electron 9.106×10^{-28} gram. Dividing the second by the first gives the ratio 1/1838.

In his oil-drop experiment Millikan used a microscope and a stop watch to measure the rate of fall, or rise, of a tiny oil drop between the two plates of a condenser. Since the drop was falling through air ionized by X-rays, it picked up a charge every now and then. If the sign of the charge was the same as that on the lower plate, the rate of fall was slowed down or the oil drop might even start to rise. After analyzing many hundreds of experiments, Millikan found that there was a definite, smallest amount by which the rate of fall of the drop changed. This meant that there was a definite, smallest unit of charge which the drop picked up. Sometimes the drop picked up two or three units of charge at a time, but it never picked up less than a whole one. This was our first proof that electricity comes in particles of a certain-size charge. Thomson had obtained an average value for the ratio of charge to mass, but Millikan could watch individual charges hopping on and off his oil drops. It was as though Gulliver had landed in a modern Lilliput where the inhabitants were so small that he could not see them. He could,

however, see their trains. Every time a train started up from a
station on its run he picked it up and weighed it and then put it
back again. He found that the difference in weights from one
station to the next was always some multiple of 0.1 milligram.
Sometimes the difference in weight was 0.3, sometimes 0.4, 0.1,
0.2, 0.5, etc., milligram. He concluded that there were passengers
getting on and off the train and that they weighed 0.1 milligram
each.

No matter what the means of obtaining them, no matter what
the residual gas in the cathode-ray tube, these negatively charged
particles were always the same and they were far lighter than
the lightest atom known. Here, then, was an even more basic
building unit, and it was called the electron.

3. PROTONS

It was natural that a search would be made for positively
charged particles in vacuum discharge tubes. Using a perfo-

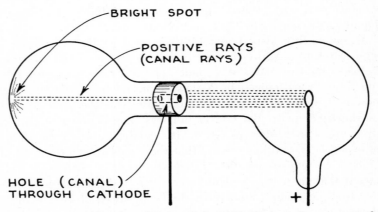

Figure 6-4. A tube that demonstrates positive rays. Some positively
charged particles strike the cathode, others pass through the hole and strike
the wall of the bulb on the left.

rated cathode (Figure 6-4) Goldstein observed these, and they
were called positive rays. They were found to have masses of
the order of magnitude of the atoms of the gases used in the

tubes. The lightest positively charged particle which exists for more than a small fraction of a second is the hydrogen ion, which is called a proton. We now have two of the basic units of atomic structure.

4. X-RAYS

Several scientists working with cathode-ray tubes had been bothered by the fact that packages of photographic film were

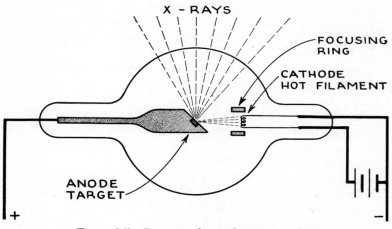

Figure 6-5. Diagram of a modern X-ray tube.

fogged after being left near the tubes. This was merely a nuisance until Roentgen, in 1895, looked into the reason for it. He discovered that it was not cathode rays penetrating the glass but a new type of radiation originating from the spot being struck by the cathode rays. This radiation had the remarkable ability of penetrating paper, wood, and even thin sheets of metal. Since it was not bent by electric or magnetic fields and could be made to take pictures, it was thought to be a type of light. To call attention to the unknown nature of these rays, Roentgen called them X-rays (Figure 6-5). They were soon used by doctors to help in setting bones and for studying internal disorders. Their discovery created a tremendous sensation, and one London shop even went so far as to advertise X-ray-proof underwear for modest Victorian women. In 1912 the diffraction spectrum of X-rays was successfully measured and their wavelengths determined to be of the order of magnitude of 0.1 to 100 AU.

SUMMARY

1. A spark will travel long distances through a gas that is at a very low pressure.

2. This spark consists of charged particles which travel in straight lines away from the electrodes. The particles leaving the cathode are called cathode rays, and those traveling in a direction from the anode toward the cathode are called positive rays.

3. Crookes showed that cathode rays traveled in straight lines, that they could make materials fluoresce, and that they were negatively charged.

4. Thomson showed that the average value of e/m was the same for negatively charged particles from several different sources. These particles were called electrons.

5. Millikan demonstrated that electricity was atomic in nature, that is, that there was a smallest unit of charge.

6. Using the value for e, the charge of an electron, its mass m is calculated to be 1/1838 of that of a hydrogen atom.

7. The lightest known stable, positively charged particle is a hydrogen ion. It is called a proton.

8. Roentgen discovered that when cathode rays strike a solid it becomes the source of a type of short-wavelength electromagnetic radiation.

9. He called this type of radiation X-rays and found that they were extremely penetrating.

QUESTIONS AND EXERCISES

1. Back of the discovery of the electron as a particle lies the work of Newton, Boyle, Volta, Oersted, Faraday, and Geissler, to mention only a few. Point out one relevant discovery made by each of these men.

2. What are some of the properties of cathode rays?

3. Why were cathode rays not thought to be a type of electromagnetic vibration like light?

4. What is the actual weight in grams of an oxygen atom?

5. How many oxygen atoms are there in 16 grams of oxygen? This number is known as Avogadro's number.

6. How does our first definition of "atom" stand up in the light of what was learned in this chapter?

7. What would be the effect of a magnetic field on positive rays?

8. What is the most convincing evidence that X-rays are a type of electromagnetic vibration?

9. Where do X-rays originate in a modern X-ray tube?

10. List five properties of X-rays.

5

Radioactivity

1. A PICTURE TAKEN ON A CLOUDY DAY

Roentgen had noticed that his X-rays originated from the fluorescent spot where the cathode rays struck the end of the tube. A French physicist, Becquerel, was interested in fluorescence and decided to see whether fluorescent minerals in general emitted X-rays. He wrapped a photographic plate with black paper, attached a crystal of fluorescent uranium salt to the outside of the package, and exposed it to sunlight. When he developed the plate it showed a black spot under the crystal. Further experiments showed that the radiation from the crystal could pass through thin sheets of metal. One day he put away some of these packages all made up for an experiment but not exposed because of cloudy weather. He developed them the next day, expecting to find only a faint image, but he discovered an unusually dark image. Apparently, exposure to sunlight had nothing to do with the results, and the effect was not connected with fluorescence. As so often happens, a false hypothesis, when followed through carefully, led to an important discovery.

2. QUANTITATIVE MEASUREMENTS AGAIN

A brilliant young scientist, Marie Curie, was in Paris at the time looking about for a subject for her thesis for the doctor's degree. She decided on a quantitative study of this new phenomenon discovered by Becquerel, and she soon named it radioactivity. After discovering that the intensity of the radiation was proportional to the amount of uranium present, she went on to investigate all the known elements for signs of radioactivity. Only one other element, thorium, showed any measurable amount. Then she tried a variety of minerals. Pitchblende, which is a complex mineral containing uranium, showed a greater activity than either pure uranium or thorium. Since she had already studied all known elements, she felt sure that pitchblende must contain a new one that was more highly radioactive than any so far studied. With the help of her husband, Pierre, who had investigated piezoelectricity, she worked 4 years under abominable conditions, breaking down a ton of pitchblende. They finally isolated two new radioactive elements, to which they gave the names polonium and radium. The following year, 1903, they shared the Nobel Prize in physics with Becquerel.

3. THE PROPERTIES OF RADIOACTIVITY

Mme. Curie in France and Ernest Rutherford in England were among the leaders of the scientists studying the nature of the radiation from radioactive elements. Their findings may be summarized as follows:

1. Elements emit radiation spontaneously. The rate is not affected by heat, light, pressure, chemical combination, or any other force brought to bear on the material.

2. Radium and some other radioactive elements glow in the dark.

3. Radioactive disintegration is accompanied by the evolution of heat. One gram of radium emits 132 calories per hour. This was a startling discovery which, at the time, seemed to be inconsistent with the law of the conservation of energy. Although the amount of energy from 1 gram of radium is not great, that which results from all the radioactive material in the earth's crust may well be enough to explain volcanic activity.

4. The radiation affects a photographic plate and brings about other chemical changes.

5. Among the chemical changes observed was the destruction of living tissue. Cancerous tissue is more susceptible to damage than normal tissue, but continued exposure to radiation will start a cancerous growth. Obtaining increasing amounts of radium for the treatment of cancer was one of the life-long projects of Mme. Curie. She and Pierre published their technique for isolating radium without patenting it or asking for any royalties.

6. When the radiation from radium is studied as indicated in Figure 6-6, it turns out that the beam is split into three parts by an electric field. One part is deflected slightly toward the negative electrode (alpha rays); a second part is deflected more strongly toward the positive electrode (beta rays); and a third part passes unbent through the field (gamma rays). These three parts were called rays because they were investigated by their

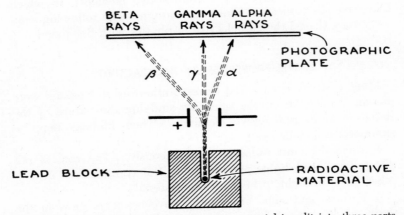

Figure 6-6. The radiation from radioactive material is split into three parts when it passes through an electric field.

action on a photographic plate. Later research showed that the alpha rays were positively charged helium ions, and so they are more properly called alpha particles. The beta rays turned out to be the same as electrons, and the gamma rays are a type of electromagnetic vibration with a wavelength like that of short-wave X-rays.

7. The radiation ionizes air. It knocks electrons out of the molecules of oxygen and nitrogen, leaving positively charged ions. These ions were first observed by their action in discharging an electroscope. Later, two instruments for observing the ionization of air were developed into powerful tools for studying radioactivity. They are the Wilson cloud chamber and the Geiger counter.

4. THE WILSON CLOUD CHAMBER

A Wilson cloud chamber is an artificial fog-making device (Figure 6-7). A small volume of air is trapped above water or alcohol that is dyed black. When the rubber bulb at the bottom is squeezed the water compresses the air. Releasing the bulb allows the air to expand rapidly. This quick expansion cools

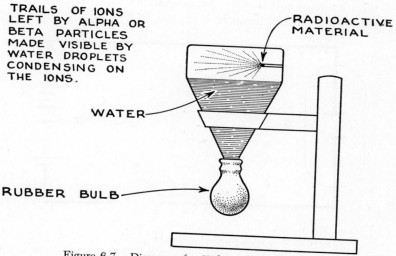

TRAILS OF IONS LEFT BY ALPHA OR BETA PARTICLES MADE VISIBLE BY WATER DROPLETS CONDENSING ON THE IONS.

RADIOACTIVE MATERIAL

WATER

RUBBER BULB

Figure 6-7. Diagram of a Wilson cloud chamber.

the air below the dew point, and a fog forms. After the apparatus has been worked a few times all the dust particles present are used up, and the fog has no nuclei on which to form. If, during an expansion, an alpha or beta particle dashes through the chamber, leaving in its wake a trail of ions, these serve as condensation nuclei. There will be a visible track of water droplets to betray the path of the radiation. Although we cannot see the actual particles, we can see and photograph their paths just as surely as we can see and photograph ski tracks across the snow.

When the cloud chamber is placed in a strong magnetic field the paths of charged particles are curved. From the appearance of the track and its radius of curvature the mass and charge of the ionizing particle can be determined. Much of the information that will be presented henceforth has been obtained from photographs of tracks in a Wilson cloud chamber.

5. THE GEIGER COUNTER

A Geiger counter (more precisely, a Geiger-Mueller counter) detects ionizing radiation by means of its electrical effects. The basic idea of such a counter is shown in Figure 6-8. In this

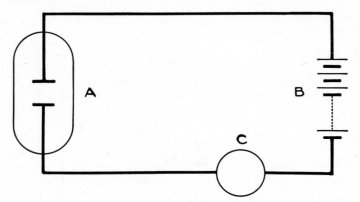

Figure 6-8. Diagram of a Geiger-Mueller counter.

figure, A is a glass tube containing two electrodes across which is applied a difference in voltage by battery B. C is a counter which flashes a light or makes an audible click when a pulse of current flows through it. When a low voltage is applied to the electrodes and an ionizing radiation forms an ion pair between them, the two ions will move in opposite directions and reach the electrodes. A single, very small pulse of current will flow. If the applied voltage is high enough, the ions, particularly the negative ion (electron), will be moving fast enough to start a cascade of ionization, and a single pair will result in a fairly large current flowing around the circuit. This is much easier to detect. Care must be taken to keep the applied voltage below that which will make a spark jump from one electrode to the other. A Geiger counter operates in the cascade voltage range (about

1000 volts). It has proved to be another invaluable tool in the field of radioactivity.

SUMMARY

1. Becquerel inadvertently discovered radioactivity in an attempt to show a connection between fluorescence and the production of X-rays.

2. Mme. Curie demonstrated that there were some minerals which had a more intense radioactivity than any known element. This fact indicated that the minerals contained an unknown and very active element.

3. Working on this theory, Pierre and Marie Curie isolated polonium and radium.

4. Radioactive elements show certain peculiarities of behavior, such as: (a) they emit radiation spontaneously; (b) heat is evolved during radioactive disintegration; (c) their radiation affects a photographic plate and brings about other chemical changes; (d) their radiation destroys living tissue, acting more rapidly on cancerous than on normal tissue; (e) their radiation consists of alpha particles, electrons, and gamma rays; and (f) their radiation ionizes air.

5. In a Wilson cloud chamber droplets of fog form on the ions produced by ionizing radiation, making the path of the radiation visible and subject to study.

6. When a cloud chamber is placed in a magnetic field the charge and mass of the radiation may be determined.

7. A Geiger-Mueller counter detects and counts ionizing radiation as it passes between the plates of a condenser.

QUESTIONS AND EXERCISES

1. Name four accidental scientific discoveries that we have studied so far.

2. Neither Marie Curie nor Ernest Rutherford was born in the country in which his or her scientific work was done. Where did each come from?

3. Show how an electroscope could be used to study radioactivity.

4. List some similarities and some differences between X-rays and the radiation from radium.

5. What is the meaning of a zigzag track in a Wilson cloud chamber?

6. Why are alpha-particle tracks straighter than electron tracks in a Wilson cloud chamber?

7. Are ions always formed in pairs (one positively charged and the other negatively charged) in a Geiger counter?

8. What is the advantage of applying 1000 volts instead of 100 volts across a Geiger counter?

9. Why must the window on a Geiger counter be very thin? It is so thin that it is extremely fragile, so treat it carefully.

10. If a Geiger counter is operated on 120 volts AC, what kind of a vacuum tube must be in the circuit?

The Solar System Atom

1. EXPLODING ATOMS

Let us now get back to atomic structure and see what the study of radioactivity contributed to it. From the next few paragraphs it will be obvious that the first effect was to spread confusion into a nice, orderly picture.

When an atom of radium explodes it expels an alpha particle and a gamma ray, and an atom of radon gas is left behind. The radon gas is radioactive in its turn (it is radon, not radium, that is ordinarily used in radium therapy). It expels an alpha particle and a gamma ray and turns into radium A. Radium A is also radioactive, and a series of changes follows that ends with inactive lead.

Each of these different radioactive elements has its own peculiar rate of decay. A given sample of radium is half gone at the end of 1600 years; this period is called its half life. The half life of radon is 4 days, and that of uranium is over 4 billion years. In a vast majority of disintegrations either an alpha or a beta particle is shot out of the atom during the disintegration. We have no way of predicting when a particular atom is going to explode. It is like trying to predict which kernel of corn in a pan is going to be the next one to pop.

This fascinating field soon attracted a large number of workers, and they discovered nearly thirty radioactive elements whose atomic weights ranged between the weights of lead and uranium, and which were related by some extremely perplexing changes. In reading the following there is no need to remember the names of the elements or the parenthetical numbers after them (their atomic weights), but the point can be made only by using specific instances. Thorium (232) → alpha particle + mesothorium (228) → beta particle + mesothorium II (228) → beta particle

+ radiothorium (228). Thorium and radiothorium are chemically the same element, yet they have different atomic weights; mesothorium I and II are chemically different elements, yet they have the same atomic weight. With the discovery of these bewildering relationships, the whole basis for the organization of the periodic table (the arrangement of the elements in the increasing order of their atomic weights) began to crumble. Several more examples of this same sort turned up, and confusion gave way to chaos. It was found that the series of disintegrations that started with uranium 238 ended with lead 206. The series starting with protoactinium 231 ended with lead 207, and that starting with thorium 232 ended with lead 208.

The English physicist Soddy stepped into the breach with a term to clarify this situation. He suggested that we apply the word isotope (meaning same place) to those forms of an element that had different atomic weights. Lead 206, 207, and 208 are all isotopes of the element lead. He further suggested that, since we know the length of time required for a given amount of lead 206 to accumulate from the disintegration of a sample of uranium, we could measure the amount present in a uranium ore and calculate how long it had been disintegrating. The resulting figure would give a measure of the age of the earth's crust. Several such measurements have been made, and the results average close to 3 billion years. This is considered to be the most accurate way to estimate the age of the earth.

2. ATOMIC NUMBER

In an X-ray tube the cathode rays are focused on a metal plate called the target (Figure 6-5). The X-rays are given off by the target. In 1913 Moseley measured the wavelength of the X-rays obtained when he used a number of different metals as targets. He found that each element had a characteristic wavelength and that the wavelengths decreased regularly as he went up through the periodic table. He could then put all the elements in a definite order depending on the characteristic wavelengths of their X-ray spectra. On the basis of hydrogen as number 1, each element could be given an atomic number. The atomic number of an element is a more fundamental property than its atomic

atomic weight of 228. That is why radiothorium is chemically like thorium but has a different atomic weight. We now have a clearer idea of what is meant by the word element. All the atoms of a given element have the same atomic number. The atomic weight of the element represents the average atomic weight of all the isotopes taken in the proportion in which they occur in nature.

Bohr's theory of the atom with its definite electrons revolving in definite orbits around the nucleus is a clear-cut, intellectually satisfying picture that is, unfortunately, a little too good to be true. One of the essential points about an acceptable scientific theory is that there be some way to test its validity. And one of the necessary difficulties with any such definite theory about the detailed structure of the atom is that we have no particles lighter than the electron to use to check it. If we try to locate the electrons by studying the scattering of other electrons in the same way that Rutherford studied the nucleus, we knock our quarry completely out of their orbits. It is like hunting rabbits with a cannon. We might kill some, but we would not know where along the path of the shell they had been when they were hit. So, strictly speaking, we are reduced to vague terms such as the probability distribution of electrons, etc. With this reservation, the Bohr atom is an extremely helpful model.

5. THE NEUTRON

Since the neutron was not discovered until several years later, Bohr suggested that in addition to protons in the nucleus there were proton-electron pairs. The probable existence of a neutral particle with the mass of a proton was forecasted several times, and in 1932 Chadwick showed that some very puzzling results obtained by Bothe and Becher and by Irene Joliot-Curie (Mme. and Pierre Curie's daughter) and F. Joliot could be explained by assuming that such a particle was formed in their experiments. Neutrons are very difficult to detect because of their lack of electric charge. Since they pass through gases without ionizing them, the usual cloud chambers and counters do not detect them. If a neutron is given off after the collision of two atomic nuclei, the fact can be deduced from a study of the recoil paths of the nuclei in a cloud chamber. Chadwick bombarded boron (B) with alpha particles (He) and obtained nitrogen (N) and a neutron (n). $_5B^{11} + _2He^4 \rightarrow _7N^{14} + _0n^1$.

The fine structure of the nucleus is only just beginning to emerge. At present it, too, seems to have a layer-like structure. This early interpretation is a natural extension of our picture of the outer structure of the atom, and it may be far from correct.

SUMMARY

1. Half life is the length of time required for half a given sample of a radioactive element to disintegrate.

2. The study of a number of radioactive-decay series revealed that two different elements could have the same atomic weight and that two different samples of the same element might have different atomic weights.

3. Soddy proposed the name isotope for those forms of the same element which have different atomic weights.

4. He also pointed out that we could analyze the disintegration products of uranium in natural ores and thus estimate the age of the earth's crust. By this method it is calculated to be about 3 billion years old.

5. Moseley discovered that the wavelength of X-rays depended upon the element used as a target material in the X-ray tube.

6. When the elements are arranged in the order of their characteristic X-ray spectra, this order turns out to be almost the same as that in the periodic table.

7. Numbering the elements in this order gives each its atomic number.

8. Rutherford studied the scattering of alpha particles and discovered that most of the space inside an atom is empty and that most of the mass of an atom is concentrated in a small, positively charged nucleus.

9. Chadwick demonstrated the existence of neutrons as electrically neutral particles with the mass of a proton.

10. Bohr developed the solar-system theory of the structure of the atom. A slightly modified outline of this theory includes the idea of a small nucleus containing the same number of protons

as the atomic number of the element. Also in the nucleus are neutrons. The sum of the number of protons and neutrons is the same as the atomic weight of the isotope being considered. Revolving in orbits outside the nucleus are the same number of electrons as the atomic number of the element.

11. Isotopes of the same element differ in the number of neutrons in the nucleus. The isotopes of an element are chemically and physically similar, but they are not identical in their behavior.

12. Since we have no experimental way of determining with precision both the position and the velocity of the electrons in their orbits, our picture of atomic structure is necessarily vague in this respect.

QUESTIONS AND EXERCISES

1. In a sample of radium weighing 1 gram how many atoms will disintegrate in 1 minute? Avogadro's number (Chapter 5, Problem 5) is the number of atoms in an atomic weight.

2. Describe the make-up of $_3Li^7$.

3. How many neutrons are in the isotope of oxygen $_8O^{18}$?

4. Using the proper symbols, write the series of changes from $_{90}Th^{232}$ to $_{90}Th^{228}$. Use $_{-1}e^0$ for the electron.

5. Which of the three fundamental particles discussed has the least effect on the chemical properties of an atom?

6. If atoms are largely empty space why do they not interpenetrate?

7. How much of 1 gram of radon would be left after 12 days?

8. How has the meaning of the word element changed through the years?

9. Of the characteristic X-rays from cobalt and nickel, which has the greater wavelength?

10. What percentage of the diameter of the solar system is the diameter of the sun? Compare this figure with that of the atom and its nucleus.

7

CHAPTER

$hf = E = mc^2$ and Some Consequences

1. AN INTELLECTUAL REVOLUTION

The years around 1900 were very disconcerting for the older physicists. A century of progress had developed a picture of a world made up of stable, dependable atoms and molecules which obeyed Newton's laws of motion. Light and other forms of energy were in a separate mental compartment and were satisfactorily wave-like in behavior. The laws of the conservation of mass and the conservation of energy were two separate, experimentally well-established pillars to build on.

The discovery of radioactivity showed that atoms were not immutable. They not only could be changed; they did change spontaneously. In 1900 Planck showed that light as it was being emitted or absorbed had to be thought of as occurring in particles, or quanta. His argument was similar to that of Millikan, who showed that electricity came in unit packages. Planck found that the energy (E) of a light quantum could be calculated from its frequency (f) by the equation $E = hf$, where h is a universal constant now called Planck's constant. Neither Planck nor anyone since has suggested an easy way to think of a wave as consisting of particles or of a particle which behaves like a wave.

Einstein, in 1905, derived the relationship that $E = mc^2$, where m is the mass of a particle and c is the velocity of light. He was saying what everyone had known for centuries, that neither energy nor mass is ever observed alone. They are always associated. A particle of a certain mass has a certain energy. But he went on to say that the terms mass and energy are just two ways of expressing the same thing. Only the mass is apparent in an atom at rest. Only the energy is apparent in a quantum of light (a photon). One thing that the above equation shows is the amount of energy that could be obtained if an atom at rest were changed completely into energy. This law developed by Einstein does not contradict either the law of the conservation of mass or the law of the conservation of energy. It links them together into a single, more general statement.

Consequently, the decade from 1895 to 1905 saw the introduction of some most upsetting ideas. The transmutation of one element into another, which had been the will-o'-the-wisp of the medieval alchemist, was found to occur spontaneously; an intellectual hyphen was added to give the new words "wave-particle" and "mass-energy." Needless to say, these revolutionary ideas were considered by many to be subversive at the time, and they were not accepted without a struggle.

2. THE ELECTRON MICROSCOPE

In 1923 de Broglie calculated what the wavelength of an electron would be if it did show wave-like behavior. The experiments suggested by this calculation were carried out in 1927 in two different laboratories, and the theory was confirmed. By the use of thin sheets of crystalline metal for a diffraction grating, the wavelength of a beam of electrons was measured. The wavelength turned out to be 1.65 AU, and this measurement immediately suggested a new type of microscope.

By merely examining the appearance of the ocean waves that pass by a rowboat you might not realize that the boat was there. But a large ocean liner disturbs the waves passing it enough to cast a shadow. In order to be seen, an object must be larger than the wavelength of light used to examine it. Since violet light has a wavelength of about 4000 AU, we cannot see objects smaller than about 10,000 AU (1 micron) with a light microscope. Tiny ripples on a pond would be distorted by the rowboat mentioned above, and, correspondingly, objects only 100 AU or so across should be visible when viewed by a beam of electrons. Furthermore, an electromagnetic field will act like a lens for a stream of electrons; it will focus them. In a short time after 1927 an electron microscope with all its parts analogous to a light microscope was developed (Figure 6-9). A picture of one is shown in Figure 6-10, and Figure 6-11 shows a picture of a bacterium which would be no larger than a tiny dot under a

light microscope. In industry and in medical research the electron microscope has been a most valuable tool. You may well
ask why gamma rays or short X-rays are not used in a microscope

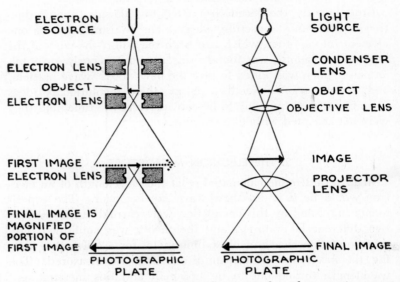

ELECTRON SOURCE

LIGHT SOURCE

ELECTRON LENS

CONDENSER LENS

OBJECT →

OBJECT

ELECTRON LENS

OBJECTIVE LENS

FIRST IMAGE
ELECTRON LENS

IMAGE

PROJECTOR LENS

FINAL IMAGE IS
MAGNIFIED
PORTION OF
FIRST IMAGE

FINAL IMAGE

PHOTOGRAPHIC PLATE

PHOTOGRAPHIC PLATE

Figure 6-9. A comparison of the optical systems of an electron microscope
and a light microscope.

since they have the same wavelength as electrons. They would
be used if we could find a satisfactory way to focus them. Ordinary lenses do not work. Electrons, on the other hand, are easily
focused by electromagnetic fields.

3. ADDITIONAL SUBATOMIC PARTICLES

In addition to the proton, neutron, and electron, other subatomic particles have been discovered. Since they have yet to
be fitted into our picture of atomic structure they will receive
only scant mention here, but you may hear more about them in
science articles in the future. In 1932 Anderson obtained a
cloud-chamber picture of a positron. This is a particle with the
mass of an electron and a single positive charge. In confirmation
of Einstein's theory of the equivalence of energy and mass, pic-

tures have been obtained (Figure 6-12) showing the energy of a cosmic ray turning into an electron and a positron. As may be

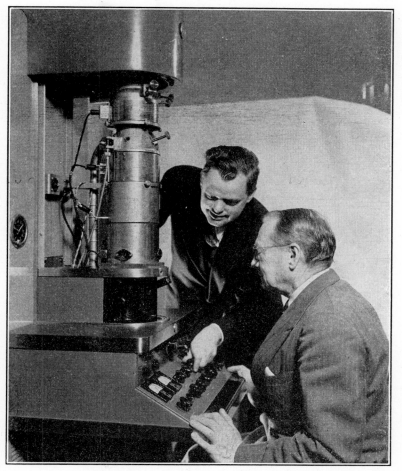

Figure 6-10. The RCA electron microscope shown with its inventors, Dr. V. K. Zworykin and Dr. James Hillier. (*Radio Corp. of America.*)

seen, the paths curve in opposite directions in the magnetic field of the cloud chamber. In 1935 Yukawa postulated the existence of a particle intermediate in mass between an electron and a proton. It was given the name meson, and there is good evidence for several kinds of mesons: positive, negative, and neutral ones; and ones with a mass about 150 times that of an electron and others about 300 times as heavy as an electron.

Figure 6-11. An electron microscope photograph of influenza virus particles (the big spheres) at a magnification of about 60,000 diameters. (*Radio Corp. of America and R. C. Williams and R. W. Wyckoff.*)

Information about another subatomic particle, the neutrino, has appeared in print since 1931, but it has yet to be detected. It is presumed to have no electric charge and a mass only a small percentage of that of an electron. Its main value is as a bookkeeping factor to be used in energy calculations.

SUMMARY

1. Planck demonstrated the particle-like nature of light and developed the relationship $E = hf$.

2. Einstein derived the equation $E = mc^2$, relating mass and energy.

3. Using the above relationships, de Broglie calculated that electrons should have a wavelength of the order of magnitude of 1 AU.

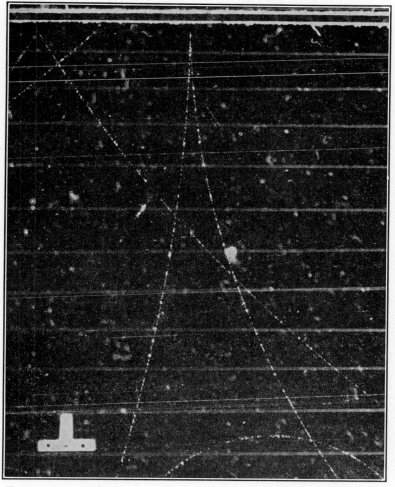

Figure 6-12. A cloud-chamber photograph, showing the production of an electron-positron pair. At the top center of the picture a cosmic ray (not visible) struck the lead plate and turned into an electron and a positron which shot off with opposite curvatures in the magnetic field of the cloud chamber. (*Dr. W. M. Powell, Radiation Laboratory, University of California.*)

4. An electron microscope was constructed using electromagnetic fields to focus the beam of electrons. This instrument has proved very useful for photographing large molecules, viruses, etc.

5. Some of the subatomic particles that have been studied but that are not included in our picture of atomic structure are: the positron, with a single positive charge and the mass of an electron; the neutrino, with no charge and a mass much less than that of an electron; and several kinds of mesons with positive, negative, or zero charges, and masses ranging between those of an electron and a proton.

8

CHAPTER

Atomic Energy

1. ARTIFICIAL RADIOACTIVITY

Using Einstein's equation relating mass and energy, $E = mc^2$, scientists and science-fiction writers did some figuring and came up with rather astonishing claims. A pound of coal turned completely into energy would supply as much energy as 1,500,000 tons of coal burned in the usual way. If the energy given off during natural radioactive changes came from a loss in mass, it could be shown that only a minute fraction of the total mass was being turned into energy. Would it be possible to prepare artificially radioactive substances and thus increase the energy available?

The first step in this direction was taken by the Joliots in 1934. They bombarded boron with alpha particles and obtained a radioactive isotope of nitrogen and a neutron: $_5B^{10} + _2He^4 \rightarrow _7N^{13} + _0n^1$. The nitrogen was separated and identified and found to be radioactive, decaying into carbon and a positron $_7N^{13} \rightarrow _6C^{13} + e^+$. On the basis of this development many new artificially radioactive elements were prepared by bombardment. This technique, however, does not bring us any nearer the goal of getting useful energy from the nucleus. In the bombardment with alpha particles the percentage of successful hits is extremely small. Much more energy is consumed in getting the products than is obtained from them.

2. THE CYCLOTRON AND OTHER ACCELERATORS

This inefficiency from an energy point of view is particularly true of the cyclotrons, synchrotrons, betatrons, bevatrons, etc., that are sprouting up in the physics departments of universities all over the country. All of them are glorified versions of the vacuum discharge tube in that they accelerate positive or negative particles in an evacuated space. They use electric and magnetic fields to accelerate and control the stream of particles. To express the energy which the accelerated particles attain in these atom smashers, the term mev (million electron-volts) is used. One mev is the energy that an electron has after being accel-

Figure 6-13. Cyclotron at the Radiation Laboratory, University of California. The chamber in which the particles are accelerated is in the middle of the picture, immediately above the stairs in the foreground. (*Radiation Laboratory, University of California.*)

erated from rest by a potential difference of 1 million volts. The bevatron is so named because it accelerates particles so that they have an energy of more than a billion electron-volts.

The cyclotron, invented by Lawrence in 1931, gives a positively charged particle a series of small pushes that builds up its speed to a high value. The acceleration is accomplished in a relatively small area by using a vertical magnetic field to keep the particles moving in a circular path between pushes (Figure 6-13). Remember that a charged particle is deflected at right angles to the direction of a magnetic field. The cyclotron has been called an atomic merry-go-round, but it may be compared more aptly to a discus thrower. The particles spiral outward from the center and are finally thrown free of the machine to travel in a straight path to the target. The energy used to operate the cyclotron and the other machines is many thousands of times greater than that obtainable from the radioactive products. These are quite impractical as sources of energy, but they are extremely valuable as research tools for studying atomic nuclei.

3. NUCLEAR FISSION

All the radioactive disintegrations that we have encountered so far involved the loss of a small particle (electron, positron, or alpha particle) and energy in the form of gamma rays, and the remaining atom always had an atomic number within two units of the starting material. In 1939 two German scientists, Meitner and Hahn, observed a peculiar kind of nuclear disintegration. When an isotope of uranium, $_{92}U^{235}$, was bombarded with neutrons, elements with an atomic number of around 45, several neutrons, and an unusually large amount of energy were obtained. This was something entirely different from previous experience. The nucleus was being split wide open; a larger amount of energy than usual was being liberated; and several particles (neutrons) like the one that started the process were resulting from it. This new type of disintegration is called a fission reaction, a cleavage of the nucleus (Figure 6-14).

Uranium 235 is a relatively rare isotope, constituting less than 1% of natural uranium, which is mostly uranium 238. If a small amount of pure uranium 235 is prepared and a neutron strikes it to produce a single fission, the chance that the resulting neutrons will, in turn, make any effective hits is small. With small amounts of fissionable material the reaction fails. As more and more uranium 235 is piled together, the chance for the fission reaction to spread from the first atom to the next and then to successive ones increases. Finally, a critical size will be accumulated, the neutrons from the first fission will break up more than one additional atom, and the reaction will spread like wildfire by geometrical progression through the whole mass (Figure 6-15). This spreading of the fission is called a chain reaction, and it takes place only after the critical size has been exceeded.

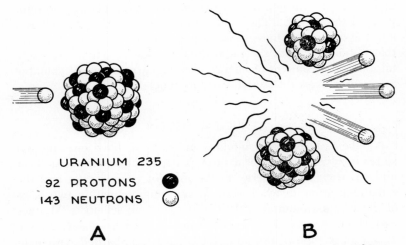

URANIUM 235

92 PROTONS ⚫

143 NEUTRONS ⚪

A   **B**

Figure 6-14.   Details of a single fission reaction.   A neutron is striking a
uranium 235 nucleus at *A*.   The fission reaction at *B* produces two medium-
sized nuclei, several neutrons, and much energy.

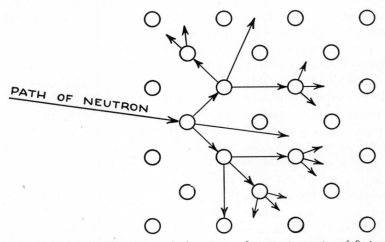

PATH OF NEUTRON

Figure 6-15.   A chain reaction which consists of a growing series of fission
reactions.

Since there are sufficient stray neutrons around, it takes place inevitably when the critical size is exceeded.

The concept of critical size and chain reaction may be illustrated by the imaginary experiment of firing a bullet into a pile of shotgun shells. If one shell is hit properly it will explode and send out shot which, in their turn, are capable of exploding other shells, and so on. With a small pile of shells, the explosion from a successful hit would probably not set off even one more. As more and more shells are added to the pile the chain of explosions would lengthen. There would hardly be any direction that a shot could travel without exploding another shell. Below the critical size the chain dies out; above it, it grows.

It took scientists all over the world only a short time to appreciate the significance of this discovery by Meitner and Hahn. With a small expenditure of energy a tremendous amount could be realized. Calculations showed that only about 0.1% of the mass of the uranium 235 was being converted into energy, but even this amount is enough so that the material in one atom bomb (about 20 pounds) releases energy equivalent to 20,000 tons of TNT. Atomic energy (more properly, nuclear energy) for constructive and destructive purposes was a distinct possibility.

A word might well be included here about the so-called secret of the atom bomb that the United States was supposed to possess for several years. Once scientists knew that such a thing as a fission reaction could occur, the atom bomb was almost inevitable. The reason we got it first was that we had the necessary technical skills to see the job done promptly. Any one of several properly trained groups of scientists throughout the world could have accomplished the task. Because of the unnecessary emphasis on keeping a non-existent secret, the progress of science has been seriously impeded. By having our own men keep information from each other we have hampered our own development.

4. THE SEPARATION OF ISOTOPES

The first step in this problem of releasing atomic energy on a large scale was the separation of uranium 235 and 238. The separation of isotopes is a tedious business. They are so nearly alike in all their properties that their separation is a long and costly process. Separation of the isotopes of hydrogen with masses 1 and 2 is the simplest. Ordinary hydrogen consists mostly of $_1H^1$, but it also contains a small amount of $_1H^2$ (sometimes called deuterium or heavy hydrogen). Prolonged electrolysis of water leaves a residue rich in so-called heavy water, which contains oxygen combined with deuterium. This is the usual

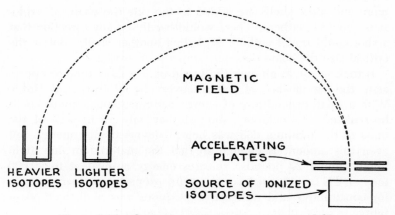

Figure 6-16. Separating isotopes in a magnetic field.

process for isolating it. If a mixture of isotopes is ionized and shot through a uniform magnetic field, the stream will be bent in circular paths with the heavier isotopes following a wider arc outside the lighter ones (Figure 6-16). From Newton's second law (page 116), $a = f/m$, the acceleration (rate of change in direction in this example) will be inversely proportional to the mass for a constant force, and so the heavier isotopes will not change their direction so rapidly as the lighter ones. This method was very successful at Oak Ridge in separating uranium 235 and 238. In passing through the fine pores of some substance like unglazed porcelain the lighter isotopes of a gas will stream ahead of the heavier ones. This gaseous diffusion process must be repeated hundreds and sometimes thousands of times to achieve a satisfactory separation, but it works well enough to be practical. There are other techniques for separating isotopes, but their usefulness is limited and we do not have space to consider them here.

5. EXTENDING THE PERIODIC TABLE

Fissionable isotopes are rare, and the possibilities of any large-scale use of atomic energy were severely limited until Seaborg discovered the reaction by which plutonium is produced from uranium 238. This abundant isotope of uranium can capture a neutron and turn into a completely new element, neptunium (Np). Neptunium is radioactive and spontaneously turns into plutonium (Pu).

$$_{92}U^{238} + {}_{0}n^{1} \rightarrow {}_{93}Np^{239} + e^{-}$$

$$_{93}Np^{239} \rightarrow {}_{94}Pu^{239} + e^{-}$$

Since plutonium is fissionable, both the isotopes of uranium can be used to liberate atomic energy. The Hanford, Washington, plant of the Atomic Energy Commission is producing plutonium. After his success in making these two new transuranium elements, Seaborg and his co-workers made the next four. Their names and atomic numbers are: americium (95), curium (96), berkelium (97), and californium (98). One could hazard a guess that Seaborg, after noticing that there were no planets beyond Pluto, came back to earth and remembered that he was working at the state university at Berkeley, California. There is every reason to expect that elements beyond number 98 will be discovered as time goes on. Seaborg and McMillan shared the Nobel Prize in 1951 for this work.

SUMMARY

1. The Joliots prepared the first artificially radioactive element.

2. The cyclotron is only one of a number of particle accelerators. In it a magnetic field keeps positively charged ions circling around while a rapidly oscillating electric field keeps accelerating them until they reach a very high velocity. The beams from these accelerators are valuable for making artificially radioactive elements and for studying atomic structure.

3. Meitner and Hahn first observed nuclear fission.

4. The characteristics of a fission reaction are that a nucleus breaks into two nearly equal parts and both a number of neutrons and a large amount of energy are released.

5. In a chain reaction the neutrons released from the fission of one nucleus bring about the fission of at least one more, which, in its turn, releases neutrons which start further fissions, etc.

6. A chain reaction will die out, maintain itself at a steady rate, or spread with increasing rate depending on the average of the number of new fissions that result from a previous one. If this ratio averages less than 1, the chain dies out; if it is greater than 1, it grows.

7. Critical size is the size of the pile of fissionable material that will keep the chain reaction barely self-sustaining.

8. In the fission of uranium 235 only about 0.1% of the mass involved is converted into energy.

9. Some of the methods used for separating isotopes are: (a) the prolonged electrolysis of water concentrates deuterium in the residue; (b) a beam of charged particles is passed through a magnetic field that separates the particles according to their masses; and (c) repeated diffusion through porous membranes separates a gas into lighter and heavier fractions.

10. Seaborg discovered that the non-fissionable isotope uranium 238 could be turned into a new fissionable element, plutonium.

11. Artificially produced elements have been added to the periodic table. These elements and their atomic numbers are: neptunium (93), plutonium (94), americium (95), curium (96), berkelium (97), and californium (98).

QUESTIONS AND EXERCISES

1. When atomic energy is the source of power a tremendous saving is made in the space occupied by the fuel. Name some situations where such a saving would be particularly useful.

2. In what countries did the following teams of scientists do their work: I. and F. Joliot, Meitner and Hahn, Seaborg and McMillan?

3. If a solid piece of metal is used as the target for the particles accelerated by the cyclotron, why are so few hits scored?

4. In what ways does a fission reaction differ from the usual radioactive disintegration?

5. How did the concepts of matter change around 1900?

6. Why is an electron microscope so important in research today?

7. What would determine the practical upper limit to the size of an atom bomb?

8. What would be one of the atoms formed in the fission of uranium?

9. How would the energy of a proton and an electron compare if both were traveling with the same velocity?

10. Compare the ratio of neutrons to protons in two or three of the elements near the middle of the periodic table with some elements having high atomic number. The result shows why a fission reaction is to be expected only with some of the higher ones.

CHAPTER

Putting Atomic Energy to Work

1. MAKING AND USING RADIOACTIVE ISOTOPES

Large quantities of uranium can be accumulated in a so-called pile if suitable neutron-absorbing material is present to keep the chain reaction from spreading (Figure 6-17). The production and absorption of neutrons can be balanced at any desired level. The energy given off can be used to generate power (Figure 6-18). Since the pile must be shielded with several feet of concrete to retain dangerous radiation, its usefulness is limited by its great size. This direct use of atomic energy for power is most promising for parts of the world where the cost of transporting fuel is high and for installations, such as in ocean vessels, where the usual fuel supply takes up much valuable cargo space.

Compared with protons and alpha particles, neutrons penetrate into atomic nuclei rather easily. The product of such a collision frequently is a radioactive isotope. In this way the atomic-energy piles are much more useful than the cyclotron. A sample of material to be treated is placed in the center of the pile, where it is exposed to a terrific bombardment from neutrons. After a suitable length of time it is removed, and the radioactive material is purified and used.

Radioactive isotopes are particularly useful in answering such questions as: In what particular form is an element best supplied as a fertilizer for plants? What is the sequence of compounds formed in photosynthesis? In what way does a particular vitamin or medicine do its job in the body? How far do mosquitoes range from their breeding places? What kind of oil is most effective in cutting down engine wear? Extremely small amounts of radioactivity can be detected by means of a Geiger counter, which can, if necessary, be used on a living plant or animal. Radioactive isotopes are proving to be at least as important a research tool as the microscope. They are usually referred to as

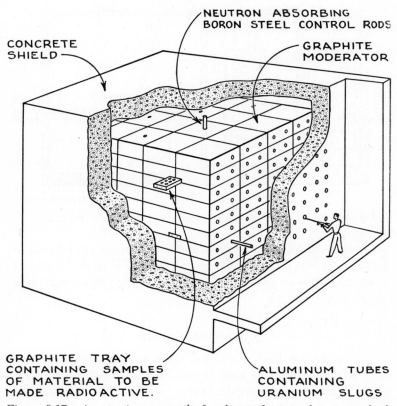

NEUTRON ABSORBING
BORON STEEL CONTROL RODS

CONCRETE
SHIELD

GRAPHITE
MODERATOR

GRAPHITE TRAY
CONTAINING SAMPLES
OF MATERIAL TO BE
MADE RADIOACTIVE.

ALUMINUM TUBES
CONTAINING
URANIUM SLUGS

Figure 6-17. An atomic-energy pile for the production of power and of artificially radioactive isotopes.

tagged atoms in popular articles. The Atomic Energy Commission supervises the preparation and distribution of these isotopes for research purposes.

A particularly useful isotope of carbon is prepared by the reaction $_7N^{14} + _0n^1 \rightarrow _6C^{14} + _1H^1$. Carbon 14 is radioactive and

HEAT EXCHANGER   STEAM TURBINE

ELECTRIC
GENERATOR

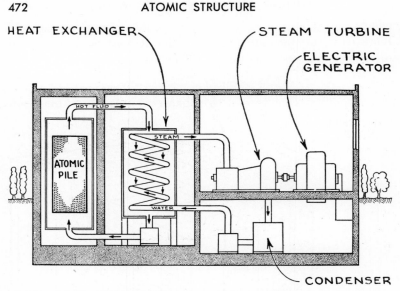

CONDENSER

Figure 6-18. The production of power from an atomic-energy pile.

has been used to study photosynthesis and many important biological reactions. Radioactive cobalt, which is made by the reaction $_{27}Co^{59} + _0n^1 \rightarrow _{27}Co^{60}$, has practically replaced radium in cancer therapy.

2. NUCLEAR FUSION

The energy released in a fission reaction comes from a loss in mass when elements of high atomic number break up into elements located near the middle of the periodic table. Calculations show that, if the nuclei of elements of low atomic number could be fused together to form heavier elements, there would also be a loss of mass and a release of energy. We have been using an approximate value of 1 for the mass of a proton and of a neutron. To show how energy can be obtained by a fusion reaction we shall have to use the most precise values we can get for these masses. A proton has a mass of 1.00778 units and a neutron one of 1.00897 units. If 2 of each of these went together to form a helium nucleus we would have the following balance sheet:

$$2 \text{ neutrons} = 2 \times 1.00897 = 2.01794$$
$$2 \text{ protons} = 2 \times 1.00778 = 2.01556$$

$$\text{total mass} = 4.03350$$
$$\text{actual mass of helium nucleus} = 4.00216$$

$$\text{mass lost} = 0.03134$$

The conversion of this mass into energy would release over 1×10^{12} calories, over a million million calories from the fusion reaction producing only 4 grams of helium.

The catch in this process is that 4 particles have to be brought together, and the positively charged ones would have to be traveling at a terrific speed to overcome their mutual repulsion. The speeds associated with several million degrees centigrade are needed to bring about nuclear fusion.

Calculations have been carried out on several fusion reactions to explore the possibilities of making a super atom bomb. Since the most promising of these involves the isotopes of hydrogen, either $_1H^2$ (deuterium) or $_1H^3$ (tritium), it is usually called the hydrogen, or H, bomb. A fission-reaction bomb would have to be used to give the high temperature required to get the fusion-reaction bomb started. The military advantage of the fusion bomb is that no critical size is involved. With the fission reaction bomb there is an upper limit to the amount of active material that can be used. The bomb can be made in two parts which are each less than the critical size and which are combined at the time of explosion, or it can be made of a porous structure that is compressed rapidly. Since it is mechanically impractical to try to bring more than two pieces together in the short time required for a bomb to explode, the total fissionable material involved would be less than twice the critical size. With a fusion-reaction bomb there is no theoretical upper limit to its size.

We speak of the "release" of atomic energy as though it were something that was being kept prisoner and we were setting it free. This process does indeed bear a resemblance to the familiar Arabian Nights story in which Sinbad broke the seal on a jar and out burst a jinnee ready to do his will. It seems that we, too, need the wisdom of Solomon to keep this power under control.

3. THE SUN AS A FURNACE

Geological evidence indicates that the sun has maintained its present high temperature at a remarkably even level for hundreds of millions of years. How can it be so prodigal with its energy for so long? A series of chemical reactions, such as combustion, can offer no satisfactory explanation. There is not enough material in the sun to last for more than a few years if such a process were going on. When radioactivity was discovered it was explored as a possible answer to the riddle of the sun, but it, too, is inadequate.

Hans Bethe examined a number of nuclear fusion reactions and in 1939 worked out a series that accounts for the known facts very satisfactorily. In this series of reactions the nucleus of a carbon atom acts as a landing field for 4 successive protons. After all 4 have gathered there they break off as a helium ion, leaving the carbon nucleus free to repeat the process. The net change is very much like that discussed on page 473. Four hydrogen atoms change into 1 helium atom with the release of energy.

The cycle of changes takes place in the following 6 steps: (atomic numbers are omitted):

1. $C^{12} + H^1 \rightarrow N^{13} +$ energy.
2. $N^{13} \rightarrow C^{13} + e^+$.
3. $C^{13} + H^1 \rightarrow N^{14} +$ energy.
4. $N^{14} + H^1 \rightarrow O^{15} +$ energy.
5. $O^{15} \rightarrow N^{15} + e^+$.
6. $N^{15} + H^1 \rightarrow C^{12} + He^4$.

In Figure 6-19 the cycle is summarized in a diagram. It shows the sun in the role of a furnace for which hydrogen is the fuel and helium the ashes. There is enough hydrogen in the sun to keep the process going for another 30 billion years. Hydrogen is the predominant element in all the stars, and this process is probably the major factor in keeping most of them hot.

It is to be hoped that all of us who understand the basic ideas of atomic energy will work for a world order in which its constructive possibilities can be realized. As you read in the preface to this book, the citizens of this country need a scientific background to help them make many of their political decisions. This book has made you acquainted with the terms, methods, and ideas of contemporary science. By the time you read this, new

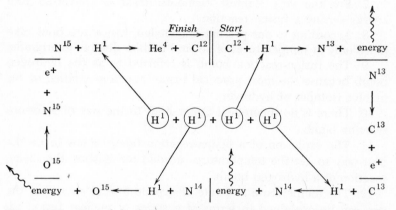

Figure 6-19.   One of the fusion-reaction cycles that supplies energy for the sun.

advances will have occurred, but you will be in a position to understand them and follow them as they are reported. If this book has been successful in its purpose, you will feel not only that you should but you will also want to keep informed about the field of science.

SUMMARY

1. By using neutron absorbers as a control, an atomic-energy pile can be balanced at any desired level of rate of fission.

2. Such a pile can be utilized for the direct production of power. Its usefulness is limited, however, by the thick shielding that is essential as a protection against the intense radiation coming from the pile.

3. The atomic-energy pile is a rich source of neutrons. Neu-

tron bombardment of elements placed in a well in the pile will turn them into radioactive isotopes.

4. A few radioactive isotopes are useful for replacing radium in cancer therapy.

5. A large number of radioactive isotopes have been very useful as research tools in science and in industry.

6. Nuclear fusion is the adding together of two or more light nuclei to form a heavier composite nucleus.

7. For the very lightest elements, mass is converted into energy during a fusion reaction.

8. According to our present knowledge, fusion reactions take place only at temperatures of several million degrees centigrade.

9. The fusion-reaction bomb is referred to as the hydrogen bomb because the most practical fusion reactions studied so far involve isotopes of hydrogen.

10. There is no theoretical upper limit to the size of a fusion-reaction bomb.

11. The explosion of a fission-reaction bomb seems to be the best way to get the temperatures needed for starting the fusion reaction of a hydrogen bomb.

12. The temperature and rate of expenditure of energy of the sun can be explained in terms of a series of nuclear fusion reactions, the net result of which is that 4 protons add successively to a carbon nucleus and then break off as an alpha particle. There is a loss of mass, which is transformed into energy.

13. An understanding of science is becoming an increasingly important part of the equipment of a good citizen.

QUESTIONS AND EXERCISES

1. What is the principal reason that neutrons can penetrate the atomic nucleus more easily than protons or electrons?

2. Devise an experiment using the appropriate radioactive element and a Geiger counter to solve one of the problems mentioned on page 470.

3. What equation is used to calculate the energy to be obtained from a loss in mass? Who developed it, and when?

4. From material presented in this and the previous chapter give a reasonable estimate of the critical mass for uranium 235.

5. What is the evidence indicating that the sun has maintained its

present high temperature at a remarkably even level for hundreds of millions of years?

6. What practical applications of atomic energy have you heard mentioned that are obviously absurd?

7. What elements are formed during the cycle of changes which is assumed to account for the energy of the sun?

8. As this is being written the first practical atomic power plant is being designed and built. What is this power plant to be used for?

9. What group controls the production and use of fissionable material in the United States?

10. What sort of an international agreement for the control of atomic energy would give you a sense of security? The Baruch Report will give you some ideas on this subject.

Index